MillionsFed

PROVEN SUCCESSES IN AGRICULTURAL DEVELOPMENT

Edited by David J. Spielman and Rajul Pandya-Lorch

INTERNATIONAL FOOD
POLICY RESEARCH INSTITUTE
sustainable solutions for ending hunger and poverty

Supported by the CGIAR

20 20 ᵐ
VISION

International Food Policy Research Institute
2033 K Street, NW
Washington, DC 20006-1002 USA
T.: +1-202-862-5600
F.: +1-202-467-4439
E.: ifpri@cgiar.org
www.ifpri.org

DOI: http://dx.doi.org/10.2499/9780896296619BK

Library of Congress Cataloging-in-Publication Data

Millions fed : proven successes in agricultural development /
[edited by] David J. Spielman and Rajul Pandya-Lorch.
    p. cm.
  Includes bibliographical references.
  ISBN 978-0-89629-661-9 (alk. paper)
1. Agricultural development projects--Developing countries.
2. Agriculture and state--Developing countries.
I. Spielman, David J. II. Pandya-Lorch, Rajul.
  HD1417M55 2009
  338.1'8091724--dc22

                  2009044452

ISBN: 10-digit: 0-89629-661-X
          13-digit: 978-0-89629-661-9

Contents

Annexes

Tables

Figures

Boxes

Acknowledgments

We gratefully acknowledge the support of The Bill & Melinda Gates Foundation for this project. We warmly thank the members of the Millions Fed Advisory Committee and the authors of the Millions Fed case studies for their valuable contributions and insights. The initiative by all who submitted or nominated examples of success is greatly valued—there may be many more successes in the making.

We are indebted to our colleagues on the Millions Fed Project Team—Klaus von Grebmer, Kenda Cunningham, and Sivan Yosef—for their tremendous dedication and enthusiastic involvement throughout the project. We extend our appreciation to Joachim von Braun for his guidance and support; to Heidi Fritschel for superb writing support; to Melanie Allen, Luz Marina Alvare, Evelyn Banda, Mulugeta Bayeh, Stevon-Christophe Burrell , Shirong Gao, Corinne Garber, Michael Go, Lucy McCoy, Carmen Ruiz, Gwendolyn Stansbury, Ashley St. Thomas, Joan Stephens, John Whitehead, and Margo Young for their extraordinary efforts to bring this book and other project products to fruition; and to Djhoanna Cruz, Vickie Lee, and Etenesh Yitna for their strong administrative and logistics support.

We also appreciate the advice and encouragement provided by Derek Byerlee, Steve Haggblade, Ellen McCullough, Willis Oluoch-Kosura, Prabhu Pingali, and Monty Yudelman as well as by our colleagues Kwadwo Asenso-Okyere, Lucy Bassett, Sam Benin, José Falck-Zepeda, Daniel Gilligan, Ruth Vargas Hill, Daniela Horna, Dawit Kelemework, Ruth Meinzen-Dick, Siwa Msangi, Gerald Nelson, Ephraim Nkonya, Lauren Pandolfelli, Agnes Quisumbing, Claudia Ringler, Mark Rosegrant, Tim Sulser, and John Ulimwengu.

Finally, we extend our appreciation to IFPRI's Publications Review Committee and the many anonymous scholars and experts who undertook thorough peer reviews of the research prepared in and underlying this book and provided thoughtful comments on our work.

Learning from Success

The world needs to greatly accelerate its progress in reducing poverty and hunger. At present, one in six people worldwide suffers from hunger and malnutrition—a tragically high proportion—and many more cannot afford a healthy diet. And as progress is being made, more challenges are on the way: the world's population is projected to grow to 9 billion by 2050, climate change is raising risks for farmers, environmental degradation is contributing to poor soils and scarce water, and we still face the same problems that led to devastating volatility in food prices in 2008.

It is also important to remember that the world has already achieved great successes in agricultural development that have fed billions. After all, although a grim Malthusian world once seemed inevitable, some 5 billion people now have enough food to lead a healthy and productive life and the proportion of people who are hungry is falling. The experiences of success that led to this achievement may offer valuable lessons about how to put agriculture to work to solve hunger and malnutrition. Until now, however, relatively little evidence has been available on where, why, and how these interventions succeeded.

To identify and examine successes in agricultural development and draw out the lessons they offer, The Bill & Melinda Gates Foundation (BMGF) called upon the International Food Policy Research Institute (IFPRI) to assess the evidence on what works in agriculture—what sorts of policies, programs, and investments in agricultural development have actually reduced hunger and poverty. This project follows on another recent project supported by BMGF and led by the Center for Global Development called "Millions Saved: Proven Successes in Global Health."

The case studies of success were chosen through a rigorous process that included an open call for nominations, a wide-ranging literature review, and expert consultations. More than 250 candidate case studies were winnowed down using a comprehensive set of criteria that took into account such issues as scale, impact, and sustainability. A committee of recognized international experts provided valuable insights and advice to this process. Ultimately, a total of 20 proven successes were identified.

The project leaders commissioned research studies on these successes, each one based on a synthesis of peer-reviewed literature, along with other relevant knowledge, that documents an intervention's impact on hunger and malnutrition and the pathways to food security. Each study brings the evidence together, examines the rigor with which the evidence was generated, and assesses the pros and cons of each success. All these studies were in turn reviewed by scholars and experts commissioned by Millions Fed project leaders. In addition, the individual studies and the book as a whole were subjected to rigorous peer review by IFPRI's independent Publications Review Committee. The detailed studies, listed in Annex F, are available at www.ifpri.org/millionsfed. This book captures the highlights of these detailed studies.

The successes presented in this book range from interventions that enhance productivity to those that combat diseases and pests, conserve natural resources, expand market opportunities, improve human nutrition, and improve the policy environment. While each success is distinct from the others, a common thread running through many of these success stories is the confluence of science, policy, and leadership.

Until hunger and malnutrition are eradicated, success cannot be truly claimed. Our hope is that this effort will direct more attention to sound agricultural development investments that cut hunger and to facilitate the scaling up and replication of successes.

Joachim von Braun
Director General, IFPRI

Prabhu Pingali
Deputy Director, BMGF

Mother and child farming together, Kenya

Fifty Years of Progress

David J. Spielman and Rajul Pandya-Lorch

In the late 1950s around a billion people—about one-third of the world's population—were estimated to go hungry every day. Famines were threatening millions, in Asia and Africa in particular, and prospects for feeding the world's booming population looked bleak. In response to this alarming picture, scientists, policymakers, farmers, and concerned individuals initiated a concerted push to boost agricultural production and productivity in developing countries. Developing and industrialized countries, together with development agencies and civil society organizations, pursued a range of interventions in agriculture: they applied modern science to crop and livestock production, constructed irrigation systems, developed new cultivation practices to conserve natural resources, introduced policies to encourage farmers to grow and sell more food, and launched many other programs in agricultural development.

The result? About a billion people now go hungry every day.[1]

This result may look like failure, and in one sense it is. The fact that 1 billion people remain hungry and malnourished is a tragedy on a grand scale. Looked at another way, however, the present situation reflects astounding success. While the absolute number of people who are hungry has remained the same, the relative figure—the proportion of the world's population that has remained hungry—has declined dramatically. In the mid-1960s, when the global population was about 3.3 billion, only about 2 billion people were getting enough to eat. Today's population has burgeoned to more than 6 billion—and some 5 billion people now have enough food to live a healthy and productive life.

Clearly, progress has been made. China and India, once viewed as dire cases, have experienced agricultural booms. China slashed the number of hungry people from 303 million in 1979–81 to 122 million in 2003–05, singlehandedly making a significant dent in world hunger because of its sheer size. In the face of rapid population growth, India also cut the number of people suffering from chronic hunger from 262 million in 1979–81 to 231 million in 2003–05.[2] Efforts to increase the global availability of food have led to enormous gains in agricultural productivity and food production, with yields of many staple crops multiplying severalfold. Great strides also have been made in improving the quality of food so that it contributes to good nutrition, and in improving the ability of the most vulnerable groups— most significantly, women and children—to access food needed for survival.

Importantly, these efforts have done more than just feed millions. The interventions of the past half century have also demonstrated that agriculture can be a key driver of growth and development for many of the world's poorest countries. Where scholars and leaders once viewed the agricultural sector with disdain—as a drag on their attempts to promote growth and modernization—they now recognize that agriculture can be a leader in the process of economic and social development.[3]

Yet the 1 billion hungry remain. In fact, progress in overcoming hunger has reversed in the face of the recent food price crisis and global economic downturn. In Latin America and the Caribbean, 45 million people still go hungry. In Sub-Saharan Africa, the number of chronically hungry people has almost doubled, from 125 million in 1979–81 to 212 million in 2003–05. In South Asia, while the declines in hunger are commendable, the sheer size of the population that remains hungry—314 million—is overwhelming.[4] In short, more remains to be done.

While the causes of chronic hunger and persistent malnutrition are complex, the experiences of the past 50 years show that the solutions are by no means beyond our reach. But what do we really know about what works in agricultural development, and where, when, and why some interventions succeed? Which policies, programs, and investments in agricultural development can substantially reduce hunger and malnutrition? And which of these interventions can do so within a changing global landscape characterized by growing natural resource scarcities, climate change, global market volatility, and major health and demographic changes?

This book looks to identify and describe successes in agricultural development that have made substantial contributions to reducing hunger and malnutrition. It is not an exhaustive compilation of all successes that have occurred during the last 50 years. Rather, it is an in-depth analysis based on 20 case studies (see Annex F) that aims to give readers a better understanding of what worked and why (see box below and Annex B). By drawing key insights and lessons from past successes, this book intends to inform future policymaking and leverage future investments in ways that will contribute to overcoming hunger and malnutrition.

What Worked?

Successes in developing-country agriculture are extremely rich and diverse in nature, varying

Criteria for Selecting Successes

Successes were chosen from about 250 submissions received in response to a global call for nominations posted in late 2008, feedback from experts in the field of agricultural development, and information garnered from scholarly literature, project documents, websites, and other sources.

The first qualifying criterion was that the intervention must have been operational in at least one developing country. The second qualifying criterion was that the intervention must have engaged agriculture directly—that is, it must have operated on constraints that are specific to agriculture. Once these criteria were met, the potential success had to meet *five evaluative criteria*:

- Importance—the intervention should have tackled an important food-security problem by addressing the needs of a vulnerable group;

- Scale—the intervention should have operated at scale, measured in terms of whether the number of beneficiaries exceeded several hundred thousand individuals or whether the intervention was, at a minimum, national in coverage;

- Time and Duration—the intervention should have been (1) fully operational at scale long enough to generate significant reductions in hunger or improvements in food security and (2) implemented in the past 50 years;

- Proven Impact—the intervention should have been supported by documented and rigorous evidence of a clear and measurable impact on individual or household hunger or nutritional status; and

- Sustainability—the intervention should have been sustainable, whether in financial terms (cost-effectiveness) or in broader social, political, or environmental terms.

For complete details of the methodology used to identify and examine proven successes in agricultural development, see Annex B.

in time, space, and character (Annex A). Some successes have emerged for just a few short years to trigger long episodes of growth and development. Some have resulted from years of dogged persistence that yielded returns despite substantial risks, uncertainties, and doubts. Others were achieved because communities took action to ensure their own survival under difficult environmental conditions. Still others were inspired by leaders and organizations who marshaled the resources needed to contain the spread of crop and livestock diseases that know no boundaries.

The pathways to success are also extremely varied. Some cases demonstrate how an improved crop variety or cultivation practice contributed to improving food security by increasing crop output per hectare of land, lowering production costs, or reducing crop losses caused by pests, diseases, drought, or soil erosion. Others demonstrate how new agricultural technologies improved the sustainable use of scarce resources like fertile soil and water, or enhanced the nutritional quality of food that people both cultivate and consume. Still others illustrate how changes in incentives—whether public policies, commercial regulations, or socioeconomic norms—encouraged farmers to produce more food, pursue more sustainable cultivation practices, and participate more actively in the marketplace.

But these pathways to success are not simply about increasing the physical supply of food. Rather, they are about reductions in hunger that result not only from an improvement in the physical availability of food, but also from a change in an individual's ability to secure quality food.[5] This change may result from any number of situations: an improvement in an individual's ability to produce food within the farm household; an increase in income that provides a consumer with greater purchasing power in the market; or a shift in norms that reduces the impact of practices and behaviors that limit an individual's entitlement to food within the household, community, or society.

Here, we examine these pathways by looking at successes in six different areas:

1. intensifying staple food production;

2. integrating people and the environment;

3. expanding the role of markets;

4. diversifying out of major cereals;

Homestead food production, Bangladesh

5. reforming economy-wide policies; and

6. improving food quality and human nutrition.

Intensifying staple food production

A loose timeline of recent successes in agricultural development begins somewhere in the mid-20th century, when the menace of war, hunger, and disease loomed large for many developing countries that had just gained independence from colonial control or influence. Crisis—whether the result of human actions such as conflict, oppression, or complacency, or the result of natural causes such as drought or pests—was a key driver in these early successes in agriculture.

During the late-1940s and early-1950s, astute political leaders keenly recognized that hunger was a threat to long-term security, development, and prosperity. In India, for example, then Prime Minister Jawaharlal Nehru put agriculture at the forefront of the national agenda following independence in 1947 by allocating substantial attention and public resources to building rural roads, expanding irrigation systems, generating rural power, establishing state agricultural universities and research centers, constructing fertilizer plants, and promoting land reform. The real and perceived threat of famine ushered in an era in which policymakers' key priority was to increase the output (greater production) and yields (greater production from a given area of land) of staple foods.

3

© CIMMYT

Contrast of native (left) and inbred line (right) maize crops

One of the first major successes came from a global effort to fight wheat rusts—a plague that has been known to humanity for thousands of years but had never been effectively contained.[6] Wheat rusts are actually fungi that can rapidly decimate wheat as it matures in the field, and are thus a threat to food security in industrialized and developing countries alike. The late Nobel Prize Laureate Norman Borlaug, with the eventual backing of policymakers, scientists, and philanthropists, catalyzed a global effort to combat the scourge by bringing modern science to bear on the problem—by breeding rust-resistant wheat varieties in Mexico with the help of innovative research methods. As a result of this global effort, about 117 million hectares of land under wheat cultivation were protected from wheat rusts, directly ensuring the food security of 60 to 120 million rural households and many more millions of consumers. Importantly, it also secured a place for science and technology in developing-country agriculture and gave rise to a global agricultural research system, including the Consultative Group on International Agricultural Research, dedicated to finding scientific solutions to ending hunger and food insecurity.

The wheat rust success evolved into a much larger and more multidimensional series of successes that began in the 1960s and came to be known as the Green Revolution.[7] In Asia, this revolution started with the introduction of improved rice and wheat varieties for irrigated land that could be cultivated twice a year instead of once. The process continued into the 1990s as successes expanded to lesser-known staple crops such as millet and sorghum and more marginal areas dependent on rain rather than irrigation. The investments in science and technology—along with complementary investments in irrigation systems, road networks, fertilizer production, and food price stabilization policies—that underwrote the Green Revolution paid off handsomely. Farmers rapidly adopted the new farming practices and technologies to such a massive extent that between 1965 and 1990, cereal output and yields doubled, pulling India and other Asian countries back from the brink of famine. Between 1970 and 1990, an estimated 1 billion people benefited from the Green Revolution in terms of improved access to food, increased earnings from agriculture, or both. A recent estimate suggests that without a Green Revolution, about 30 million children would have died in the developing world between 1970 and 2000, with more than two-thirds of these children being in Asia alone.[8]

Successes in Sub-Saharan Africa were smaller in magnitude but no less important in addressing the persistent threat of hunger in the region. In East and Southern Africa, applications of modern science to improve maize led to growth in both maize output and yields among the region's primarily small-scale, resource-poor farmers.[9] Between 1965 and 1990, maize yields in Kenya, Malawi, Zambia, and Zimbabwe increased annually between 1 and 5 percent—rates that compare respectably with yield and production growth rates in countries such as the United States—while annual maize production increases ranged from 1.8 to 3.3 percent in these same countries.

In West Africa between 1971 and 1989, the application of modern science similarly helped contain the spread of a cassava mosaic virus (a disease) and mealybug (an insect). Both threats can generate major losses in cassava, a crop that is central to the sustenance and incomes of the region's poorest farmers, particularly in times of drought or crisis.[10] By breeding cassava varieties that were resistant to the mosaic disease and by introducing a parasitic wasp to destroy mealybug in countries such as Nigeria and Ghana, the potential damage posed by these two threats was effectively contained. The introduction of disease-resistant cassava varieties is estimated to have contributed to making an additional 1.4 million tons of *gari* (a granular, fermented cassava flour commonly used in cooking) available per year, enough to feed 29 million people in the region. Similarly, the mealybug control program is estimated to have reduced losses from infestations by an estimated 2.5 tons per hectare.

Integrating people and the environment

By the 1970s, concerns emerged about the equity and environmental implications of rapid agricultural development.[11] These new concerns encouraged a move away from a strictly yield-increasing outlook on food staple productivity to a more complex perspective on agriculture and rural development. Sustainable development issues came to the forefront of the development discourse, partly in response to issues accumulated during the Green Revolution such as the overuse of agricultural chemicals, the depletion of scarce water resources, and the neglect of farmers' input into policymaking. New policies, programs, and investments were specifically designed to integrate rural communities into decisionmaking processes about their own development as a way of addressing sustainability along with equity issues. The idea that

agricultural development could work if driven by direct community participation, environmentally sustainable cultivation practices, and supportive public policies gained a global following.

Experiences in Nepal that began in the 1970s illustrate this change in perspective. During this period, a series of prescient legislative reforms and innovative forestry programs contributed to a transformation of the country's strictly conservation-focused approach to its natural forests into a more broad-based strategy that encompassed forest use, enterprise development, and livelihoods improvement with direct benefits for the rural poor.[12] Partly as a result of these reforms and programs, an estimated one-third of Nepal's population is participating in community forestry activities and directly managing over one-fourth of Nepal's forest area as a means of improving household food security and livelihoods.

In Burkina Faso and Niger during the 1980s, the rediscovery of community-based knowledge in the form of traditional agricultural management practices helped to transform the Sahelian region's arid landscape into productive agricultural land.[13] In the wake of repeated droughts, farmers

© David Rose/PANOS

Anti-desertification programs: a farmer waters his plants

Planting trees along a diguette, a line of stones built to prevent runoff and soil erosion

began innovating on simple practices: protecting and managing indigenous trees and shrubs among crops to provide fodder and firewood, and to improve soil fertility; digging pits on barren, degraded land to concentrate organic manure and rainwater for planting; and constructing stone contour bunds to control rainfall and runoff and combat erosion. With technical support from charismatic community leaders and nongovernmental organizations, the dissemination of these practices helped Sahelian households to intensify and expand the cultivation of essential food staples such as sorghum and millet, and to earn more income from the sale of crop surpluses, fodder, firewood, fruit and other products. In Burkina Faso's Central Plateau, the rehabilitation of between 200,000 and 300,000 hectares of land translated into roughly 80,000 tons of additional food per year, or enough to sustain about a half million people in the region. In southern Niger, similar efforts are estimated to have transformed approximately 5 million hectares of land, improving food security for at least 2.5 million people.

In Argentina, large-scale farmers adopted a different set of resource-conserving cultivation techniques, resulting in a significant increase in the global production of soybean in particular.[14] During the 1980s, farmers, researchers, extension workers, and private companies worked together to promote zero-tillage cultivation—a crop management technique in which farmers essentially plant seeds in unplowed fields to maximize the

gains from intensive double cropping and to lower production costs, with the added benefits of reducing land degradation, conserving soil fertility, and economizing on scarce water resources. By 2008, the area of land under zero tillage reached nearly 22 million hectares. The use of zero tillage, along with the introduction of herbicide-resistant soybean varieties and other factors, improved soil fertility by reversing decades of erosion, created an estimated 200,000 new agricultural jobs, and provided the international market with new supplies of soybeans that contributed to keeping global food prices low.

During roughly the same period in the 1980s, small-scale farmers in the Indo-Gangetic Plains—a vast region that encompasses parts of India, Nepal, Pakistan, and Bangladesh—began experimenting with similar zero-tillage techniques.[15] An estimated 620,000 wheat farmers have adopted some form of zero-tillage cultivation since these experiments began, accounting for about 1.8 million hectares of land in the region and generating average income gains of US$180–340 per household, particularly in the Indian states of Haryana and Punjab.

Expanding the role of markets

In spite of these successes, many developing countries still suffered from slow growth, general economic malaise, and persistent food insecurity through the 1980s. A shift to more market-driven development took hold in many countries during this period. In some countries, this shift came in the form of structural adjustment programs that sought to rein in public deficits, improve national balances of payments, liberalize markets, and encourage private investment in the economy.[16] In other countries, this shift occurred after the recognition that efficient supply chains played an important role in improving the production incentives for farmers, increasing incomes from farming, and improving food security. Market forces were expected to contribute to agricultural development, for example, by freeing up seed and fertilizer markets from state-owned monopolies, by removing price-setting policies in agricultural commodity markets to encourage more vibrant trading, and by closing the supply chain gaps that link farmers to markets through traders, processors, distributors, wholesalers, and retailers.

In Bangladesh, government moves to liberalize agricultural input markets in the 1980s led to an easing of restrictions on the importation and sale of irrigation equipment, such as low-lift power pumps and shallow tube wells.[17] These seemingly minor reforms stimulated the rapid growth of irrigated dry-season rice farming, which subsequently grew to account for 90 percent of the increase in rice production in Bangladesh between 1988 and 2007. And with this growth in rice production came a decline in the real rice prices facing food-insecure households, and ultimately, significant reductions in poverty in the country.

In China, policy reforms that promoted private investment in agriculture, along with breakthroughs in rice research, fostered the growth of a vibrant seed industry for hybrid rice.[18] Hybridization, first demonstrated in maize by scientists in the United States in 1918, is a process in which inbred parent lines of a crop are crossed to create seeds that are characterized by greater yield potential than either parent, an outcome known as "hybrid vigor." This vigor tends to decline with each generation of seed that is saved and replanted, so farmers need to purchase new seed each season to realize the full yield gains of these hybrids. In China, as in the United States and other industrialized countries, this character-istic of hybrid seed supported the rapid emergence of an entirely new industry—one that distributes good quality hybrid seed to farmers. Hybrid rice in China spread so quickly that between 1978 and 2008, it had grown to account for 63 percent of all land under rice cultivation. Importantly, its yield advantages helped China to feed an additional 60 million people per year during this period.

In India, similar policy reforms and scientific advances in the mid-1990s encouraged the growth of private investment in the marketing of improved seeds for pearl millet and sorghum, including hybrids.[19] These two crops are essential sources of sustenance and income for some 14 million poor households in India. Although together they account for just 10 percent of the total cropped area in India, they are cultivated in the country's arid and semiarid regions where nearly 60 percent of the rural population lives. The emergence of private seed companies, combined with good public research, has not only provided an estimated 6–9 million farmers with access to improved seeds that have increased yields by up to 85 percent in recent decades, but also served as the foundation of an important industry in India's growing economy.

Freshly milled rice

Farmers purchasing maize fertilizer

Reforms in Burkina Faso's cotton sector that began in 1992 brought together experiences from both market liberalization and cash crop development as drivers of success in agricultural development.[20] Saddled with a state-led cotton development strategy that was branded as inefficient, inequitable, and destabilizing to the national economy by the late 1980s, Burkina Faso pursued a reform path that combined efforts to strengthen the role of cotton farmers' groups before partially liberalizing input and output markets. Partly as a result of these reforms, and even despite consistently low world prices for cotton, Burkina Faso has emerged as the leading African exporter of cotton based on a threefold increase in production since the early-1990s. The cotton sector's growth has absorbed more than 200,000 new farmers who were either engaged in the cultivation of other crops or were return migrants from neighboring countries experiencing civil strife.

In Kenya, policy reforms in the early-1990s contributed to the rapid growth of private investment in fertilizer and maize marketing, the outcome of which has been a dramatic reduction in time, effort, and costs associated with purchasing fertilizer and selling surplus maize production.[21] The average distance that small farmers had to travel to purchase fertilizer decreased by half between 1997 and 2007, with similar decreases observed in the distances traveled to sell maize. The proportion of small-scale farmers using fertilizer on maize rose from 56 percent in 1996 to 70 percent in 2007, contributing to an increase in both yields and availability of this vitally important staple crop for Kenyan consumers.

Diversifying out of major cereals

The emphasis on markets also opened up new opportunities for cultivating and marketing non-staple crops—commodities such as legumes, fruits, and vegetables as well as dairy, livestock, and fish—as a means of increasing farm incomes and improving food security among the poor. Each success offers a different angle on how small-scale farmers, entrepreneurs, and policymakers responded to growth in market opportunities.

Across a range of Asian countries—Bangladesh, Bhutan, China, India, Nepal, Myanmar, Pakistan, Sri Lanka, and Thailand—the move away from food staples was exemplified by the diffusion of improved mungbean, a little-known pulse crop that is high in protein, iron, and other micronutrients, and particularly useful in maintaining soil fertility. Thanks to an international research program and active farmer participation in the research process, a wide range of mungbean varieties was released beginning in the mid-1980s with traits such as higher yields, shorter maturity times, and other qualities that targeted a variety of agroecological conditions in the region.[22] These improvements contributed to yield gains of 28 to 55 percent among an estimated 1.5 million farmers, and were key factors in the 35 percent increase in Asian mungbean production between 1985 and 2000.

Closely related to these successes are advances made in the area of livestock and fisheries—commodities that sometimes receive much less consideration relative to food staple and high-value crops but are of no less importance to millions of small-scale, resource-poor farmers and pastoralists, and to consumers who depend on milk, meat, and fish as key sources of sustenance and nutrition.

Global efforts to control and eradicate rinderpest—a livestock disease that, in its severest form, is capable of killing 95 percent or more of the animals it infects—reiterate the importance of livestock to rural livelihoods and food security.[23] Concerted global, regional, and national efforts in recent decades to control the spread of rinderpest through cattle vaccination, quarantine measures, and disease surveillance have played an important role in securing the livelihoods of small-scale farmers who keep livestock, as well as pastoralists whose livelihoods depend primarily on the health of their herds. Programs operating in Asia and

Africa have helped to avoid potentially massive financial losses in terms of milk, meat, animal traction and, for many pastoralists, their main livelihood assets, and have brought rinderpest to the edge of eradication, the first time an infectious disease has been eradicated since smallpox in humans.

In India, Operation Flood, an innovative national program that ran from 1970 to 1996, helped create a national dairy industry that integrated small-scale farmers—many of them women—with village-level dairy cooperatives, commercial dairy processors and distributors, and new technologies to modernize the industry.[24] With the backing of a supportive policy environment that ensured the dairy industry's steady growth and development, India went from being a net importer of dairy products to a major player in the global dairy market. Between 1970 and 2001, dairy production in India increased at the respectable rate of about 4.5 percent per year, with estimates during 2007–08 indicating that dairy production has exceeded 100 million tons per year. As a result, millions of consumers now have better access to milk and other dairy products, while India has become a top global producer of buffalo and goat milk, the sixth largest producer of cow milk, and an exporter of milk powder.

In the Philippines, the Genetic Improvement of Farmed Tilapia (GIFT) project that ran from 1988 to 1997 played an important part in enhancing the role of fish as a source of income and protein for many farmers and consumers.[25] By breeding a tilapia strain that originated in Africa, the project developed a new strain that is faster growing and more resistant to environmental stresses than other strains. These improvements significantly boosted fish yields and output, thus increasing the availability of fish for consumers, reducing market prices, and providing a cheaper source of protein for the country's poor.

Reforming economy-wide policies

As the emphasis of agricultural development evolved and diversified over recent decades, the role of the agricultural sector in the wider economy has similarly changed. Economic policy reforms in recent decades have contributed significantly to changing the traditional urban biases that historically discriminated against farmers and, ultimately, against the poor.[26] In some cases,

Women in a village-level dairy cooperative, India

trade and fiscal policy reforms have changed how both trade and aid are leveraged for development, transforming dependencies on food aid into more effective, long-term opportunities for development financing. In other cases, monetary policy reforms have reduced the distorting effects of exchange rates and lending policies on the agricultural sector, allowing for more rapid growth and development.

The most dramatic case in point comes from China. Between 1978 and 1984, China undertook a series of policy reforms that transformed the country's food and agricultural sector and reduced hunger on a scale unrivaled in history.[27] The reforms effectively reintroduced household farming after more than 30 years of collective agriculture. This new approach to agriculture—the Household Responsibility System—gave farmers the incentive to sell their surplus farm production at a market. By returning more than 95 percent of China's farmland to some 160 million farm households, the reforms directly contributed to an increase in rural incomes by 137 percent, a reduction in rural poverty by 22 percent, and an increase in grain production by 34 percent. Gains in on-farm efficiency also led to a substantial increase in the rural labor force available for non-agricultural employment, a shift that fueled a rapid process of industrial growth in rural China, and more broadly, China's remarkable march to industrialization during the past three decades.

In Vietnam, a series of similar reforms between 1987 and 1993 fundamentally shifted the country's economy to a greater market orientation, immediately transforming the agricultural sector.[28] During the period 1989–92, the agricultural sector emerged from its stagnation and grew at a rate of 3.8 per year, while the country shifted from being a net food importing country to the world's third largest exporter of rice in 1989. Within a decade, more than 10 million households—representing about 87 percent of peasant households—had received land use certificates for about 78 percent of Vietnam's agricultural land. These reforms, together with other market liberalization policies, encouraged farmers to produce food staples, livestock, and high-value crops far more productively, and for substantially greater market gain, than in previous eras. The reforms contributed substantially to Vietnam's dramatic reductions in poverty and contributed to both economic growth and industrialization.

Improving food quality and human nutrition

While massive gains in improving the availability of and access to food were achieved in China, India, and many other developing countries as a result of these successes, far less has been achieved in improving the quality of food. Scholars have argued that the decades-old effort to raise people's incomes to boost their calorie consumption and protein intake should be refocused to include improvements in people's micronutrient intake and dietary diversity.[29] With this shift comes the recognition that the pathways through which agricultural development affects hunger and food security are more complex than previously understood.

Taking aim at this challenge is an innovative program in Bangladesh that promotes home

Nutrition education class, Bangladesh

gardening, small livestock production, and nutrition education.[30] Helen Keller International, a nongovernmental organization, worked in partnership with more than 70 local organizations and the Government of Bangladesh to encourage food-insecure households to grow their own micronutrient-rich foods for both home consumption and the market. These homestead food production programs have reached an estimated 5 million individuals and contributed to combating micronutrient deficiencies that can be major causes of diseases such as night blindness, particularly among women and children.

Caveats

Five decades of investment in agricultural development have contributed significantly to feeding billions of people. Early interventions were critical to improving the availability of food by bringing modern science, rural infrastructure, public policy, and international collaboration to bear on the challenge of enhancing yields and output to feed millions. Many later interventions sought to integrate community participation and environmental sustainability into agricultural development, with important repercussions for the use of local knowledge resources and natural resources in combating hunger. Other interventions worked to strengthen the role of markets and agricultural incomes by encouraging the commercialization of small-scale farmers' production, improving supply chain efficiencies, and loosening the state regulation of both input and commodity markets. Still other interventions have focused

Smallholder production of animal source foods

on addressing the nutritional aspects of hunger, particularly the issues of micronutrient deficiency, dietary diversity, and food quality. But a few caveats are in order.

First, successes are rarely a progression of standalone events; rather, many are closely related in scope and intertwined over time. In China, the impact of the Household Responsibility System (1978–84) on rural food security was partly driven by the introduction of hybrid rice and other agricultural technologies. In Kenya, early successes in breeding improved maize provided the productivity gains needed to leverage subsequent liberalization of both fertilizer and maize markets. In the Indo-Gangetic Plains, the promotion of zero-tillage cultivation techniques is partly an attempt to reduce the dependence on chemical inputs that were heavily promoted during Asia's Green Revolution in previous decades. In short, the interrelatedness of these episodes of success demonstrates how interventions in agricultural development are solidly couched in what comes before.

Second, successes have not occurred or accumulated at a consistent pace over the past five decades. Instead, the historical record has been peppered with starts and stops. In Malawi, Zambia, and Zimbabwe, for example, the gains that came with the dissemination of improved maize (1965–90) came to a halt in the 1990s due to unsustainable fiscal burdens, erratic reforms, and bad weather. The benefits of community forestry in Nepal from 1978 to the present have similarly been disrupted by civil strife and political crises in the country. And the global effort to combat wheat rusts has been renewed by the emergence of UG99, a rust race that can overcome the resistance conferred by breeders during the last 50 years.

Finally, many successes that are important to reducing hunger and malnutrition exist beyond the ones presented in detail here. Some are briefly mentioned in the chapters that follow: the spread of community forestry programs in Cameroon, India, Mexico and Tanzania; the development of Brazil's Cerrado region; the diffusion of insect-resistant cotton in China and India; and the introduction of pro-poor regulatory reforms in Kenya's dairy industry. Others have not accumulated sufficient evidence to prove impact, but may intuitively be successes. Still others may be smaller in size and scale, or have yet to capture the world's attention, but are no less important.

Why Did It Work?

These successes in agricultural development provide valuable insights for the future—insights that are important to those directly involved in policy, programs, and investments in agriculture. They include policymakers designing progressive legislation, donors investing in projects and programs, nongovernmental organizations working with vulnerable farm communities, scholars studying growth and development, scientists breeding new crops in labs and fields, farmers' associations promoting their members' voices and interests, and people wanting to help ensure that agricultural development translates into reduced hunger. In all, eight key elements emerge from these successes.

Science and technology

Sustained investment in agricultural research and development is vital to developing-country agriculture. The application of science and technology to agricultural development—whether by developing advanced techniques for crop breeding or updating farmers' traditional soil and water management practices—is a common determinant of success. The critical role of long-term public investment in science and technology plays out across the entire developing world, from Asia to Latin America and Sub-Saharan Africa, and a range of successes from major food crops such as rice, wheat, and maize, to lesser-known crops such as millet, sorghum, cassava, and mungbean, and to livestock and fisheries.

These successes also demonstrate just how difficult it is to sustain public investment in

Lab technician studying the genetics of a rice strain

Cassava, a traditional food crop, is sold at a local food market

and improving irrigation systems in India and Pakistan, to providing extension and education services on zero-tillage cultivation techniques for Argentinean farmers. Conversely, the absence of sustained investments in infrastructure, supportive policies, and robust markets after 1993 in many East and Southern African countries stalled the gains in agricultural productivity growth and hunger reduction that had been achieved with the introduction of improved maize in the region. Clearly, sustained public investment can pay high dividends in terms of addressing chronic hunger and persistent malnutrition.

Private incentives

But even with sustained public investment in science, technology, and complementary investment areas, little can be achieved without the right incentives. By putting policies in place that encourage farmers, entrepreneurs, and companies to invest in agriculture, and by ensuring that markets provide accurate and timely price signals to these private sector actors, the likelihood of success in agricultural development increases.

China demonstrated this with the return to household farming, where a change in incentives encouraged farmers to invest in their land's productivity and grow more food. Kenya demonstrated something similar by loosening state control over fertilizer and maize markets, dramatically reducing the smallholder's costs of purchasing inputs and marketing surplus production. And, as Burkina Faso demonstrated by strengthening the role of farmers' organizations as cotton sector reforms heightened the competitiveness of the cotton sector, private incentives work best when market participants can respond effectively to these incentives, collectively or individually.

Cooperation and collaboration

Many successes are built around the notion of cooperation and collaboration. Partnerships among diverse actors in the agricultural sector—research institutes, community-based organizations, private companies, government agencies, and international bodies—are evident in almost all successes. But collaborative interventions are a tricky business and require know-how in effectively managing public and private resources, orchestrating foreign assistance and

agricultural science and technology in the face of competing demands for public resources. Often, policymakers and donors are put off by the long lead times in developing new technologies for small-scale farmers, or by the unending need to continuously develop new technologies in an effort to stay ahead of co-evolving pests and diseases, changes in market preferences, and new environmental stresses such as global climate change. Nonetheless, sustained significant public investment is vital to assuring and maintaining successes in agricultural development that address chronic hunger and persistent malnutrition.

Complementary investments

Still, science and technology are not enough: hunger and malnutrition are complex phenomena and there are no silver bullets in the struggle against them. To improve the chances that science and technology will make a real contribution to improving food security, sustained public investment in the hardware and software of agricultural development is also critical. This includes public investment in irrigation schemes, rural road networks, rural education, market infrastructure, and regulatory systems. All of these are areas that the private sector tends not to invest in directly because they seemingly offer little opportunity for profit, despite their value to society as a whole. Long-term public investment in the building blocks of agricultural development is a necessary condition for success, and is evident in each and every success case—from building community resources, and managing relationships among sometimes disparate interest groups.

Still, partnerships underscore many successes in agricultural development. Examples of successful partnerships include the scientific collaborations that went into developing rust-resistant wheat strains and semi-dwarf rice and wheat varieties; the grassroots-level partnerships to improve forestry management in Nepal and land management in the Sahel; the global and regional cooperation that helped eradicate rinderpest; and the public–private partnerships that brought improved sorghum and millet hybrids to Indian farmers.

Timing and planning

Many successes result from good timing, whether by chance or design. In some cases, the time was simply right for the intervention—the technological, economic, social, and political elements were all in place. In other cases, the intervention was adjusted to ensure that the timing was right: gradual reforms were undertaken step-by-step, calculated measurements of the potential gains and losses were undertaken, and a strong degree of support was provided to those affected by the reforms.

Burkina Faso's experience with the development of its cotton sector has proceeded relatively smoothly partly because of its staged effort to strengthen farmers' organizations before liberalizing the cotton sector. China's experience with a return to household farming has generated such significant gains in food security partly because of the carefully sequenced introduction of localized experiments in land tenure rights to the country as a whole.

Experimentation and evolution

Often, successes emerge from localized experiments that allow participants to learn from their mistakes, adapt to changes in the landscape, evolve as the playing field becomes more complex, and pursue incremental, step-by-step approaches to scaling up. Creating space for local experimentation and innovation is a critical means of generating big bangs from incremental changes. For example, China's land tenure reforms began as a local experiment undertaken by administrators in just one poverty-ridden county, but evolved rapidly into a national-level reform program. The homestead food production program in

Bangladesh integrated a learning process into its activities to ensure that the intervention could be improved with the accumulation of new evidence from the sciences and new experiences at the grassroots level. By encouraging farmers to improve on their traditional soil and water management practices in the Sahel, or by involving farmers in the breeding of improved mungbean in Asia, long-term investments in agricultural development paid off handsomely.

Community involvement

Similarly, by vesting communities with a stake in ownership of a development process, grassroots participation contributes much to the long-term sustainability of a success. Involving communities and smaller groups in local consultations, policy deliberations, scientific research, and experimentation is all part of building from the bottom up to achieve success. Similarly, involving local practices, customs, and knowledge in an intervention are the seeds of big successes. The successes in community forestry in Nepal, intensification of dryland cultivation in the Sahel, and homestead food production in Bangladesh, among many others, are all testaments to the value of community involvement and engagement.

Leadership and dedication

Often, the solutions needed to address agricultural development challenges require dedicated individuals to make the difference—champions to push the issue to the forefront of the public's consciousness, demonstrate what can be done in the face of seemingly insurmountable challenges, or mobilize the political and financial capital to overcome inertia. Some of these individuals are well known, such as Norman Borlaug, who received the Nobel Prize for his contributions to agricultural development. Others may be less well known, such as Yacouba Sawadogo, a farmer from Gourga in Burkina Faso who contributed significantly to the spread of soil fertility management techniques in the barren fields of the Sahel. Still others—the unsung heroes whose efforts have fed millions—include the extension agents with good ideas about how to improve local crop production and marketing, the credit officers who disburse and collect on small loans to small farmers, or the community organizers who help their fellow farmers find new ways of combating crop pests and

Rice terraces carved out of the hills, China

diseases. These champions, both renowned and anonymous, are essential ingredients of success. Creating an environment that encourages leadership on such issues and rewards individuals based on their merit is important to creating success.

What Can We Learn?

Looking to the future, the changing realities of the global food and agriculture system, and the persistence of hunger in the developing world, indicate that more and more frequent successes are needed. Agriculture is increasingly driven by market demand forces, consumer preferences, regulatory scrutiny, and ethical considerations. Agriculture is far more commercial and far more globalized through domestic market growth, international trade, and global finance than ever before. Emerging information, communications, and biological technologies are providing new opportunities for farmers and consumers, while climate change is imposing new constraints on agricultural practices, rural livelihoods, and the resilience of agroecological systems. New demographic

concerns are emerging with the continuing HIV/AIDS pandemic, changing age structures in some developing countries, rapid urbanization and rural flight, and growing regional and global migration.

The tools needed to address these evolving realities have changed during the past five decades. But how can the successes of the past help inform and influence agricultural investments that will contribute to substantially reducing hunger in the future? A few reflections are offered here.

Success is not a substitute for strategy.
Individual successes of any size or scale must stimulate broader and more sustained processes of national and global success building. But these processes are feasible only if countries pursue good strategies, create supporting policies, and encourage appropriate levels of investment and experimentation needed to accumulate successes that eventually add up to a sustained success. Without these necessary conditions, successes will likely be scattered, occasional events—outcomes of an unexpected scientific breakthrough or a one-off policy correction. Rather than generating these

types of short-lived successes, decisionmakers should design and implement strategies that take a comprehensive approach to raising agricultural productivity, increasing incomes, and reducing poverty. Comprehensive strategies along these lines can encourage many intertwined successes in agriculture to emerge with a frequency that adds up to a national or regional success story, rather than a fleeting, intermittent, or serendipitous set of successes.

Success is a process. Agricultural development must address a range of ever-changing priorities and challenges—containing the transboundary movement of new diseases and pests, strengthening ecosystem resilience in the face of climate change, improving the governance of global trade in food and agricultural products, encouraging both public and private investment in developing-country agriculture, and articulating grassroots voices on global and local issues more effectively. As such, successes are generated and sustained through experiential processes. This means discovering by doing, learning from mistakes, and adapting to change. The importance of designing an intervention that allows for learning and adaptation can increase the likelihood of success.

Success is recognizable. Sometimes successes emerge only in retrospect, once a substantial amount of time has passed to allow for reflection. But for successes in agricultural development to be recognized as such, they need to be sufficiently supported by strong evidence (see box below).[31] Such evidence comes in many shapes and sizes, ranging from first-hand accounts of individual participants to large-scale impact evaluation studies that combine both quantitative and qualitative evidence at the highest levels of academic rigor. Regardless of the type and level of evidence, the key point is that successes in agricultural development—and failures too—need to be systematically documented, examined, and shared so that others can learn lessons, adapt them to different circumstances and contexts, and avoid similar pitfalls.

Success can be ambiguous. In many cases, it is immediately obvious that there is no such thing as an "unequivocal success." Many successes are often accompanied by some type of trade-off. Increases in food production may depend on the intensive use of harmful chemicals. Productivity gains may generate price collapses that hurt farmers but benefit consumers. Scarce public resources allocated to rural infrastructure may be funds that could be used for other investments.

Improving the Proof

Assessing the impact of investments in agricultural development has long captured the interest and attention of policymakers, donors, and practitioners as a means of proving the effectiveness of development. Impact assessments come in many different forms, use many different methods, and are conducted at different points of an intervention. But irrespective of the approach taken, impact assessments are meant to provide a systematic analysis of the significant or lasting changes in people's lives attributable to an intervention and in relation to the counterfactual, or what may have occurred had an intervention not been taken.

In the last decade, policymakers and donors have increasingly emphasized the use of impact assessments to ensure accountability for results and to search for evidence of what works in agricultural development. This trend has led to an increasing focus on a more formal, systematic, and rigorous approach to assessing, evaluating, estimating, and analyzing impacts of investments in this area. To this end, rigorous approaches based on a common framework, along with the requisite resources, are needed.

With the right tools and sufficient funding in place, subjecting as many development interventions as resources allow to rigorous impact assessments based on a common framework can help build a critical body of evidence on the impacts of development interventions. This body of evidence can then be synthesized to build a knowledge base on what works and what does not.

For further details, see Annex C.

Prepared by: Mywish K. Maredia

Pearl millet ready for harvest

In fact, many successes are characterized by a mix of pros and cons. The continued central role of the state in Burkina Faso's cotton sector is criticized because of the public resources required to sustain the system. Difficulties in extending the gains from community forestry in Nepal to under-represented social groups are cited as a source of concern for the policy's long-term outlook. And the excessive and inappropriate use of fertilizers and pesticides that damage waterways and natural ecosystems, irrigation practices that lead to salt buildup on good farmland, and water scarcities resulting from the overuse of water from major river basins and groundwater, are similarly noted as major shortcomings of the Green Revolution.

Unfortunately, this ambiguity may be one reason why agricultural development became such an unpopular topic among both governments and donors in the 1980s, along with other reasons such as fatigue over the extensive lag times needed to demonstrate impact, frustrations with moving large government bureaucracies into action, and tendencies among investors and entrepreneurs to steer clear of all but the most low-risk investments in the agricultural sector. As a result, public invest-ment and donor assistance declined precipitously during this period: agricultural research spending stagnated while rural infrastructure development came to a halt in many developing countries.[32]

But investments in agricultural development have generated sizable dividends for society, demonstrating that agriculture is not only an important means of reducing poverty, but also a worthwhile investment portfolio.[33] For example, the research that culminated in the development and release of disease-resistant, high-yielding cassava varieties in Nigeria during the 1970s is estimated to have achieved an annual economic rate of return of 55 percent over a 31-year period. Similar estimates of the returns on investments in research indicate similarly high figures: 19 to 66 percent for wheat rust resistance; 43 to 64 percent in the case of hybrid maize research in East and Southern Africa; 50 percent and higher in the case of the modern varieties introduced during Asia's Green Revolution; and 70 percent in the case of tilapia improvement in the Philippines.

Returns to agricultural development projects are also comparable. In Burkina Faso and Niger, projects designed to bring degraded or new land under cultivation yielded returns ranging from 20 to 147 percent depending on the location and natural resource management technique being applied. The global control and eradication of rinderpest is estimated to have generated returns ranging from 11 percent in Cote d'Ivoire to 118 percent in Burkina Faso, while Operation Flood in India generated an estimated return of 45 percent.

These pros and cons mean that success in agricultural development requires careful consid-eration of difficult trade-offs. While interventions that increase the availability, access, and quality of food are all desirable, the resources available to undertake these interventions are limited, suggest-ing the need to weigh the benefits against costs in terms of economic and financial gains, environ-mental impacts, and sociopolitical importance. But the repercussions of failing to invest in agricultural development are clear: continued and persistent hunger among the rural poor and food-insecure households. And the precipitous rise in global food prices and hunger in 2008 makes these repercus-sions even more visible and urgent.

Looking ahead

Decisions have to be made on where, when, and how to invest in agricultural development. Without the Green Revolution, millions of households in Asia would still be facing the threat of hunger and famine today. Without hybrid maize in East and Southern Africa, hybrid millet and sorghum in the arid and semiarid tropics of India, or improved cassava varieties in Ghana and Nigeria, food-insecure farm households and consumers would have far fewer opportunities—and less food and income—than they have today. Similarly, without policy changes that strengthened the market incentives facing Chinese farmers or that improved the availability of seed and fertilizer to Kenyan farmers, agriculture in these countries might have been far less productive, and far less sustainable as a livelihood, than it is today.

Progress in feeding the world's millions has slowed, while the challenge of feeding its future millions remains enormous and subject to new uncertainties in the global food and agricultural system. Rapid degradation of the world's natural resource base, changes in rainfall and moisture availability due to global climate change, and volatility associated with closely integrated international markets suggest that learning from successes in agricultural development is now more urgent than ever.

Ultimately, the essentials remain unchanged: increasing the production of, access to, and quality of food to end hunger and feed millions. All of the lessons learned here must be applied and adapted for the future, but with a greater sense of urgency and commitment. ■

NOTES

1. FAO (Food and Agriculture Organization of the United Nations). 2009. *More people than ever are victims of hunger*. Rome.

2. FAO (Food and Agriculture Organization of the United Nations). 2008. *The state of food insecurity in the world 2008*. Rome; FAO (Food and Agriculture Organization of the United Nations). 2002. *The state of food insecurity in the world 2002*. Rome.

3. de Janvry, A. 2009. Agriculture for development: New paradigm and options for success. Elmhirst lecture presented at the 27th Conference of the International Association of Agricultural Economists, August 16–22, Beijing.

4. FAO 2008.

5. Sen, A. 1981. *Poverty and famines: An essay on entitlement and deprivation*. New York: Oxford University Press; Dreze, J., and A. Sen. 1991. Hunger and public action. New York: Oxford University Press.

6. Dubin, H. J., and J. P. Brennan. 2009. *Combating stem and leaf rust of wheat: Historical perspective, impacts, and lessons learned*. IFPRI Discussion Paper. Washington, D.C.: International Food Policy Research Institute.

7. Hazell, P. B. R. 2009. *The Asian Green Revolution*. IFPRI Discussion Paper. Washington, D.C.: International Food Policy Research Institute.

8. Evenson, R. E, S. Msangi, T. B. Sulser, and M. W. Rosegrant. 2006. Green Revolution counterfactuals. Paper presented at the annual meeting of the American Agricultural Economics Association, July 23–26, Long Beach.

9. Smale, M., and T. Jayne. Forthcoming. Maize in eastern and southern Africa: "Seeds" of success in retrospect. In *Successes in African agriculture*, ed. S. Haggblade and P. Hazell. Washington, D.C.: International Food Policy Research Institute.

10. Nweke, F. 2009. *Controlling cassava mosaic virus and cassava mealybug in Sub-Saharan Africa*. IFPRI Discussion Paper. Washington, D.C.: International Food Policy Research Institute.

11. Staatz, J. M., and C. K. Eicher. 1998. Agricultural development ideas in historical perspective. In *International agricultural development*, ed. C. K. Eicher and J. M. Staatz. 3rd ed. Baltimore: Johns Hopkins University.

12. Ojha, H., L. Persha, and A. Chhatre. 2009. *Community forestry in Nepal: A policy innovation for local livelihoods*. IFPRI Discussion Paper. Washington, D.C.: International Food Policy Research Institute.

13. Reij, C., G. Tappan, and M. Smale. 2009. *Agroenvironmental transformation in the Sahel: Another kind of "Green Revolution."* IFPRI Discussion Paper. Washington, D.C.: International Food Policy Research Institute.

14. Trigo, E., E. Cap, V. Malach, and F. Villarreal. 2009. *The case of zero-tillage technology in Argentina*. IFPRI Discussion Paper. Washington, D.C.: International Food Policy Research Institute.

15. Erenstein, O. 2009. *Zero tillage in the rice-wheat systems of the Indo-Gangetic Plains: A review of impacts and sustainability implications*. IFPRI Discussion Paper. Washington, D.C.: International Food Policy Research Institute.

16. Staatz and Eicher 1998.

17. Hossain, M. 2009. *The impact of shallow tubewells and boro rice on food security in Bangladesh*. IFPRI Discussion Paper. Washington, D.C.: International Food Policy Research Institute.

18. Li, J., Y. Xin, and L. Yuan. 2009. *Hybrid rice technology development: Ensuring China's food security*. IFPRI Discussion Paper. Washington, D.C.: International Food Policy Research Institute.

19. Pray, C., and L. Nagarajan. 2009. *Pearl millet and sorghum improvement in India*. IFPRI Discussion Paper. Washington, D.C.: International Food Policy Research Institute.

20. Kaminski, J., D. Headey, and T. Bernard. 2009. *Institutional reform in the Burkinabè cotton sector and its impacts on incomes and food security: 1996–2006*. IFPRI Discussion Paper. Washington, D.C.: International Food Policy Research Institute.

21. Ariga, J., and T. S. Jayne. 2009. *Private sector responses to public investments and policy reforms: The case of fertilizer and maize market development in Kenya*. IFPRI Discussion Paper. Washington, D.C.: International Food Policy Research Institute.

NOTES continued

22. Shanmugasundaram, S., J. D. H. Keatinge, and J. d'Arros Hughes. 2009. *The mungbean transformation: Diversifying crops, defeating malnutrition.* IFPRI Discussion Paper. Washington, D.C.: International Food Policy Research Institute.

23. Roeder, P., and K. Rich. 2009. *The global effort to eradicate rinderpest.* IFPRI Discussion Paper. Washington, D.C.: International Food Policy Research Institute.

24. Cunningham, K. 2009. *Rural and urban linkages: Operation Flood's role in India's dairy development.* IFPRI Discussion Paper. Washington, D.C.: International Food Policy Research Institute.

25. Yosef, S. 2009. *Rich food for poor people: Genetically improved tilapia in the Philippines.* IFPRI Discussion Paper. Washington, D.C.: International Food Policy Research Institute.

26. Lipton, M. 1977. *Why poor people stay poor: Urban bias in world development.* Cambridge: Harvard University Press; Lipton, M. 1984. Urban bias revisited. *Journal of Development Studies* 20 (3): 139–166.

27. Bruce, J., and Z. Li. 2009. *"Crossing the river while feeling the rocks": Incremental land reform and its impact on rural welfare in China.* IFPRI Discussion Paper. Washington, D.C.: International Food Policy Research Institute.

28. Kirk, M., and N. D. A. Tuan. 2009. *Land-tenure policy reforms: Decollectivization and the Doi Moi system in Vietnam.* IFPRI Discussion Paper. Washington, D.C.: International Food Policy Research Institute.

29. Berti, P. R., J. Krasevec and S. FitzGerald. 2004. A review of the effectiveness of agriculture interventions in improving nutrition outcomes. *Public Health Nutrition* 7 (5): 599 –609; Allen, L. H. 2003. Interventions for micronutrient deficiency control in developing countries: Past, present, and future. *Journal of Nutrition* 133 (11S-II): 3875S –3878S; Bouis, H. 2000. Improving human nutrition through agriculture: The role of international agricultural research. *Food and Nutrition Bulletin* 21 (4): 550–566.

30. Iannotti, L., K. Cunningham, and M. Ruel. 2009. *Improving diet quality and micronutrient nutrition: Homestead food production in Bangladesh.* IFPRI Discussion Paper. Washington, D.C.: International Food Policy Research Institute.

31. Maredia, M. K. 2009. *Improving the proof: Evolution of and emerging trends in impact assessment methods and approaches in agricultural development.* IFPRI Discussion Paper. Washington, D.C.: International Food Policy Research Institute.

32. Beintema, N. M., and G. Stads. 2008. *Measuring agricultural research investments: A revised global picture.* Agricultural Science and Technology Indicators (ASTI) Initiative background note. Washington, D.C.: International Food Policy Research Institute; Pardey, P. G., N. M. Beintema, S. Dehmer, and S. Wood. 2006. *Agricultural research: A growing global divide?* IFPRI Food Policy Report. Washington, D.C.: International Food Policy Research Institute.

33. Fan, S., 2008. *Public expenditures, growth and rural poverty: Lessons from developing countries.* Baltimore: Johns Hopkins University Press; Alston, J. M., C. Chan-Kang, M. C. Marra, P. G. Pardey, and T. J. Wyatt. 2000. A meta-analysis of rates of return to agricultural R&D: Ex pede herculem? Washington, D.C.: International Food Policy Research Institute.

Chapter 2

© Yue Jin/USDA

Fighting a "Shifty Enemy"
The international collaboration to contain wheat rusts

H. J. Dubin and John P. Brennan

Wheat, one of the world's staple food crops, is under constant attack in farmers' fields from diseases, insects, and weeds. Rust diseases, which have plagued wheat since ancient times, are among the most destructive plant pathogens in the world, especially to cereals.

Rust was found on specimens of wheat from the Late Bronze Age, around 3300 BC, and ancient Romans described rust damage to their crops. In 19th century Prussia, the losses for all cereal crops from rust diseases were estimated to be almost one-third of the total value of the crops.[1] In India, estimated losses on occasion reached 50 percent or more, exceeding the losses from all other pests and diseases. Under epidemic conditions, they can cause crop losses of 60–100 percent, trigger famines, and even ruin whole economies.[2]

During the past 50 years, an international effort to identify and breed wheat varieties that not only have high yields, but also are resistant to rust, has helped protect and improve wheat yields and feed millions. The success of the effort depended on a remarkable network of national and international agricultural research centers, gene banks, and nursery programs, underpinned by a free and open worldwide system of exchanging information and plant genetic materials.

The Threat to Wheat

In 2003, wheat was consumed in 175 countries and met more than one-third of the minimum food requirements of the average adult. Wheat is a particularly important crop in many poor countries in terms of both production and consumption: in 2007, farmers in 76 developing countries produced wheat, while consumers in 52 developing countries consumed more than 50 kilograms per capita.[3]

Diseases are an ever-present threat to this essential crop, and rusts, a group of fungi species, are among the most virulent. Wheat is susceptible to three types of rust: stem (black) rust, leaf (brown) rust, and stripe (yellow) rust. Although infection may occur on any part of the plant that is above ground, cereal rusts generally attack the stem and leaves and thus reduce yields. Rust disease has many stages, but its most obvious one is indicated by rust-colored spots that contain millions of infectious propagules, or spores of the fungus, that aid in the dispersal of the disease. Rust pathogens can produce billions of wind-borne spores that are then carried thousands of miles, and they have an excellent ability to vary through mutation or sexual reproduction; in this way, they overcome any resistance that a wheat variety might have.

Although the frequency and severity of rust epidemics have been reduced with the widespread use of modern wheat varieties, losses can still be severe (see Table 2.1). Dozens of rust epidemics occurred in Africa and Asia between 1970 and 1995.[4] Notable ones include the Pakistan rust epidemic of 1977–78, which caused losses of more than 1 million metric tons; epidemics in India between 1970 and 1973, losses from which are valued at US$118–222 million; a wheat leaf rust epidemic in 1976–77 in a region of Mexico that was responsible for more than 70 percent of the

---

This chapter is based on Dubin, H. J., and J. P. Brennan. 2009. *Combating stem and leaf rust of wheat: Historical perspective, impacts, and lessons learned.* IFPRI Discussion Paper. Washington D.C.: International Food Policy Research Institute.

Table 2.1—Developing country losses due to wheat rust diseases

Rust type	Yield losses in susceptible varieties		Endemic areas as proportion of total wheat areas (%)	Number of recent epidemics (1970–85)	Hot spots (areas where disease is most severe)
	Average in endemic area (%)	Average in epidemic (%)			
Stem rust	40	Up to 100	50	7	Highlands of Kenya and Ethiopia; Parana State, Brazil; South India
Leaf rust	15–20	Up to 50	90	8	Mexico; India; Pakistan; Bangladesh; China
Stripe rust	40	Up to 100	33	18	Highlands of South America and East Africa; North Africa; Middle East; Indo-Gangetic Plains of India and Pakistan

Source: Adapted from Hanson, H., N. E. Borlaug, and R. G. Anderson. 1982. *Wheat in the Third World.* Boulder, Colo., U.S.A.: Westview Press; Saari, E.E., and J.M. Prescott. 1985. World distribution in relation to economic losses. In *The cereal rusts, vol. II, Diseases, distribution, epidemiology, and control*, ed. A.P. Roelfs and W.R. Bushnell. Orlando: Academic Press.

country's wheat crop; and a stem rust epidemic in one part of Ethiopia in 1993–94 that contributed to severe food shortages for more than 300,000 people.[5]

In Pursuit of Rust-Resistant Wheat

In the summer of 1950, a virulent type of stem rust known as race 15B began to spread in the wheat fields of Mexico and the United States. Concern immediately arose in the U.S. Department of Agriculture (USDA) and similar agencies in Canada, Mexico, and several other Latin American

Wheat infected with stem rust

© Yue Jin/USDA

countries. Representatives from these agencies held a conference in St. Paul, Minnesota, in November 1950 to address what they saw as a real threat to food security in the region.

Although countries had informally exchanged genetic materials for breeding wheat for years, during the St. Paul meeting participants decided to formalize the search for rust-resistant wheat varieties through an international nursery program—that is, they decided to collect a set of genetic materials from a variety of countries with the specific purpose of finding improved rust resistance.

Initially seven countries—Argentina, Chile, Canada, Colombia, Ecuador, Mexico, and the United States—participated in the new International Spring Wheat Rust Nursery (ISWRN) program.[6] Testing immediately got underway on a sizable scale: the ISWRN screened more than 1,000 wheat lines a year for rust resistance in each participating location, sharing germplasm (plant genetic material) and information freely with all interested parties. The spread of stem rust race 15B culminated in a wheat rust epidemic in North America in 1953–54, but thanks to the rust-resistant varieties identified by the ISWRN and distributed to farmers, the disease was brought under control by the mid-1950s.

A great deal of the wheat-breeding work that contained the epidemic took place through the Mexico-Rockefeller Foundation International Agriculture Program, a leading center of wheat

The Birth of the International Agricultural Research System

The Mexico-Rockefeller program was an international agricultural development program founded in 1943 to help Mexico increase food production. Under the leadership of Norman Borlaug, the wheat program began employing the principles of free and open exchange of information and germplasm to promote cooperation in agricultural research. By the late-1950s, the Mexico-Rockefeller wheat program had gathered about 50,000 nursery entries. In 1960, the Mexican-Rockefeller program was superseded by the Inter-American Food Crop Improvement Program and expanded to include potatoes. It became home to the International Spring Wheat Yield Nursery (ISWYN) in 1964. During the next few decades, wheat research programs in other countries included their wheat-breeding materials in the ISWYN. In this way, Mexico became an international center for information and exchange of spring wheat germplasm.

Also in the early-1960s, the Ford Foundation and the Rockefeller Foundation helped create the International Rice Research Institute (IRRI) in the Philippines. On a world tour in 1963, Mexican President Adolfo Lopez Mateos, impressed by what he saw in the Philippines, became convinced of the need for more such institutions. Many countries noted the success of wheat in Mexico, and Lopez Mateos told the Rockefeller Foundation that Mexico would support a wheat and maize institute similar to IRRI. Thus Mexico became the home of the International Maize and Wheat Improvement Center (known by its Spanish acronym, CIMMYT). The wheat gene bank at CIMMYT is now one of the largest wheat collections in the world. CIMMYT is now one of 15 research centers that together make up the Consultative Group on International Agricultural Research (CGIAR). The principle of free sharing of germplasm, which underpinned the success of the rust-resistance breeding work, became the hallmark of this international network of centers.

research (see box above) led by plant breeder Norman Borlaug. It was here that Borlaug and his team developed new breeding techniques that helped bring about rapid advances in wheat breeding.

In the mid-1940s, for example, Borlaug realized that Mexico's traditional wheat-growing highland areas could not produce enough wheat to make the country self-sufficient in wheat production. Scientists at the Mexico-Rockefeller program looked to areas of northern Mexico where irrigation systems were being used—such as the Yaqui Valley in the state of Sonora—to accelerate the breeding process with a system called shuttle breeding. They planted test crops in May in the highlands around Mexico City and harvested the wheat in October. Then in November they planted the crops in the Yaqui Valley and harvested the wheat in April. Despite the prevailing dogma of the time that said shuttle breeding could not work, the technique succeeded. By allowing scientists to grow two crops a year, shuttle breeding cut the time required to breed rust-resistant varieties in half, from 10–12 years to 5–6 years. With the use of shuttle breeding, promising varieties were made more rapidly available to wheat farmers than was

previously thought possible. As a result, when race 15B became epidemic in North America, it was conquered within a few short years, mitigating a true food crisis.

However, the story did not end here. Genetic resistance to wheat rust can take one of two main forms: race-specific resistance, which generally does not last long, and non-race-specific resistance, which is longer lasting or durable. Rust can overcome specific resistance in about 5–6 years, causing boom and bust cycles in wheat production.[7] This unpredictability accelerated the search for more long-lasting, non-race-specific resistance. Under the Mexico-Rockefeller program, researchers used materials from the United States, Kenya, and South America, where resistant varieties were known to exist. During the 1970s, scientists were able to release new varieties with non-race-specific resistance in Mexico that soon spread to other countries.

Rust resistance was only one of the characteristics that scientists were pursuing in their wheat-breeding efforts. Once plant scientists in the Mexico-Rockefeller program released the new rust-resistant varieties of wheat, they continued to look for ways to produce better yields. They found

Farmer harvests wheat, India

that with good soil fertility and irrigation, tall wheat varieties fell down under the weight of their heavy grains. Borlaug had heard about dwarf wheat being developed at Washington State University and the USDA using Japanese materials and thought it a good approach for the growing conditions in northern Mexico. In the 1960s, Borlaug and his team released new high-yielding, semi-dwarf wheat varieties that were short and sturdy enough to hold up their grains. Several varieties were sent to India and Pakistan, where they launched the Green Revolution (see Chapter 3). These modern, high-yielding, semi-dwarf varieties were the vehicle for delivering improved rust resistance to farmers, and they were widely and rapidly adopted. By 2002, nearly 95 percent of the developing world's wheat was planted with modern varieties.[8]

Worldwide Benefits for Wheat Farmers and Consumers

As wheat is one of the world's most significant crops—with total production in 2005 of 607 million metric tons—the benefits of wheat rust resistance have also been global in scale.[9]

About half of the world's population living in poverty is located in the large irrigated areas of South Asia alone; these irrigated areas have received the overwhelming proportion of the benefits of rust resistance.[10] Many of these farmers, as well as millions of others in developing countries, rely heavily on wheat for their livelihoods and nutrition. For them, the benefits of rust resistance include higher yields, more stable yields, and better grain quality.

Moreover, rust resistance inherently favors low-income and small-scale farmers, who are less able to use fungicides because they are unavailable or expensive in local markets. Indeed, evidence suggests that for every 1-percent increase in the productivity of wheat, the extent of poverty has been reduced by 0.5–1.0 percent.[11] The availability of effective rust-resistant wheat varieties in developing countries, especially those with food deficits, has also reduced the need for food aid imports.

One dimension of the benefits of modern semi-dwarf varieties incorporating rust resistance is the gain in per capita calorie consumption in developing countries, and the reduction in the percentage of malnourished children. Researchers estimate that calorie consumption per capita in developing countries increased by about 13–14 percent between 1960 and 2000. That improvement led to corresponding gains in health and life expectancy, reducing the share of malnourished children by about 7 percent, or more than 30 million children.[12] Researchers have also attributed a wheat price reduction of 35–66 percent to the increased production resulting from semi-dwarf varieties.[13] If rust resistance was responsible for 30 percent of the increase in global wheat production from semi-dwarf varieties, then it has made a significant impact on both nutrition and lower food prices.[14]

Several studies have tried to put a dollar figure on the benefits of wheat rust resistance, but it is difficult to untangle its impact from the impact of modern, semi-dwarf varieties of wheat and the Green Revolution. One study estimates that the value of leaf rust resistance to developing countries is equivalent to $0.92 billion a year in 2006 dollars.[15] Another study estimates that the additional worldwide production resulting from international wheat-breeding research is equivalent to $2.24–6.84 billion in 2006 dollars.[16] Thus, if rust resistance accounts for 30 percent of the value of all wheat varieties, then the benefits of all rust resistance would be $0.67–2.05 billion a year. Similarly, it is difficult to determine the cost of rust resistance for developing countries as distinct from the cost of the rest of their breeding activities; however, it is estimated that the total cost for rust resistance is $59–98 million in 2006 dollars.[17] Because rust resistance is essentially embedded within high-yielding wheat seeds, the direct cost to farmers has been low.

Lessons Learned

The effort to breed rust-resistant wheat offers a number of important lessons. First, germplasm and information were exchanged openly and freely, and this spirit of collaboration informed the development of the international nursery system. Without the free exchange of germplasm and information, and the nursery system as the vehicle, the worldwide incorporation and distribution of durable rust resistance would likely not have happened.

Second, the practice of testing wheat in multiple locations has broadened the gene pool of the wheat program. This approach began with shuttle breeding in Mexico and then expanded to testing in more than 100 sites around the world.

Third, the training and development of young scientists was an important component of the effort. An undertaking this large requires many well-trained, field-oriented scientists.

Fourth, regional programs and partnerships played an important role. International staff members lived in the relevant regions and frequently interacted with national staff members, who were consequently able to participate in selecting national and international germplasm.

Fifth, the wheat program kept a clear focus on food production, despite pressures to take on tangential activities.

Sixth, the long-lasting support of agricultural research in developing countries by the Rockefeller Foundation, which allowed many breeding programs to bear fruit, was another factor for success in wheat rust resistance. This long-term commitment was essential to achieving an impact in agricultural research and development.

Fighting New Rust Diseases with Less Funding

Because rust continually evolves to overcome existing genetic resistance, no form of resistance lasts forever. Today, a new threat from wheat rust looms. In 1998, William Wagoire, a scientist in Uganda, found that rust-resistant wheat in the country had become susceptible to a new race of stem rust. This new race, known as Ug99, has now become endemic in Kenya and Ethiopia. In 2005, an expert panel report declared Ug99 to be a threat to world wheat production because it was predicted to migrate to areas that produce 19

Farmers loading wheat onto bull-drawn cart, India

percent of the world's wheat.[18] Scientists are now testing new germplasm in many key areas, but the new race is mutating and spreading as feared. Wind currents or inadvertent transport may eventually carry Ug99 to North Africa, Europe, West Asia, China, Australia, and the Americas.

A large effort is needed to achieve resistance to Ug99, but official international development support for agriculture has fallen drastically since 1980. In addition, donor fatigue in funding agricultural research has shifted funds for agricultural development away from work on breeding and rust resistance. Many national agricultural research systems have also let their systems for producing and distributing seeds deteriorate.

Conclusion

The collaborative international effort that successfully developed rust resistance in wheat had a tremendous impact on world food supplies. It is estimated that modern rust-resistant wheat varieties account for about 30 percent of the increase in wheat production worldwide, with consequent benefits for food production, poverty reduction, and food security. These varieties now account for 95 percent of the wheat in developing countries.

This impressive achievement came about through a system of extensive research based on free and open exchange of information and genetic material that was followed by a system for delivering rust-resistant, high-yielding wheat varieties to farmers. The lessons of this experience are critical as the world faces new threats from Ug99 and other evolving diseases. ■

NOTES

1. Howard, A., and G. L. C. Howard. 1909. *Wheat in India: Its production, varieties, and improvement.* Calcutta, India: Thacker, Spink and Company.

2. Park, R. F., H. S. Bariana, and C. S. Wellings. 2007. Preface. *Australian Journal of Agricultural Research* 58: 469.

3. FAO (Food and Agricultural Organization of the United Nations). 2009. FAOSTAT statistical database. Rome.

4. Saari, E. E., and J. M. Prescott. 1985. World distribution in relation to economic losses. In *The cereal rusts.* Vol. 2, *Diseases, distribution, epidemiology, and control,* ed. A. P. Roelfs and W. R. Bushnell. Orlando: Academic Press.

5. Dubin, H. J., and E. Torres. 1981. Causes and consequences of the 1976–77 wheat leaf rust epidemic in Northwest Mexico. *Annual Review of Phytopathology* 19 (September): 41-49; Shank, R. 1994. *Wheat stem rust and drought effects on bale agricultural production and future prospects.* Addis Ababa: United Nations Emergencies Unit for Ethiopia; CIMMYT (International Maize and Wheat Improvement Center). 1989. Wheat development and research in Pakistan. Mexico City.

6. The international rust nursery program later had spring wheat and winter wheat screening nurseries, but this chapter focuses primarily on spring bread wheat, which is the major wheat type grown in the developing world.

7. Kilpatrick, R. A. 1975. *New wheat cultivars and longevity of rust resistance, 1971–75.* U. S. Agricultural Research Service, North-East Region (ARS-NE) 64. Beltsville: Agricultural Research Service, U.S. Department of Agriculture.

8. Lantican, M. A., H. J. Dubin, and M. L. Morris. 2005. *Impacts of international wheat breeding research in the developing world, 1988–2002.* Mexico City: International Maize and Wheat Improvement Center.

9. FAO 2009.

10. Dixon, J., L. Nalley, P. Kosina, R. La Rovere, J. Hellin, and P. Aquino. 2006. Adoption and economic impact of improved wheat varieties in the developing world. *Journal of Agricultural Science* 144 (October): 489–502; Byerlee, D., and P. Moya. 1993. *Impacts of international wheat breeding research in the developing world, 1966–90.* Mexico City: International Maize and Wheat Improvement Center.

11. World Bank. 2005. *Agricultural growth for the poor: An agenda for development.* Directions in Development series. Washington, D.C.

12. Evenson, R. E., and D. Gollin. 2003. Assessing the impact of the Green Revolution, 1960 to 2000. *Science* 300 (5620): 758–62.

13. Evenson and Gollin 2003.

14. Dubin, H. J., and J. P. Brennan. 2009. *Combating stem and leaf rust of wheat: Historical perspective, impacts, and lessons learned.* IFPRI Discussion Paper. Washington, D.C.: International Food Policy Research Institute.

15. Marasas, C. N., M. Smale, and R. P. Singh. 2004. *The economic impact in developing countries of leaf rust resistance breeding in CIMMYT-related spring bread wheat.* Economics Program Paper 04-01. Mexico City: International Maize and Wheat Improvement Center

16. Lantican, Dubin, and Morris 2005.

17. Dubin and Brennan 2009.

18. Expert Panel on the Stem Rust Outbreak in Eastern Africa. 2005. *Sounding the alarm on global stem rust: An assessment of Race Ug99 in Kenya and Ethiopia and the potential for impact on neighboring regions and beyond.* Mexico City: International Maize and Wheat Improvement Center.

Chapter 3

© IRRI

Transforming Agriculture
The Green Revolution in Asia

Peter B. R. Hazell

Asia in the mid-1960s was on the brink of disaster. Hunger and malnutrition were widespread after decades of neglected food production compounded by rapid population growth. Back-to-back droughts in India, combined with similar episodes of food insecurity in neighboring countries, drew attention to the region's potentially enormous food deficit. Western powers grew concerned that escalating hunger and poverty would lead to the spread of communism (or red revolution). The effort to increase food production that followed—the Green Revolution—is a crucial chapter in the story of agricultural development in the 20th century.

In response to repeated calls for action, the Rockefeller and Ford Foundations took the lead in creating an international agricultural research program to help adapt new agricultural technologies to conditions in developing countries. Work started with research on rice and wheat, two of the most important food crops for developing countries. The breeding of improved rice and wheat varieties, combined with the expanded use of fertilizers and other chemical inputs, irrigation, and public policies that were supportive of agriculture, led to dramatic yield increases in Asia beginning in the late-1960s.[1] Agricultural yields and output doubled over a period of only 25 years, from 1965 to 1990.

The Green Revolution spread rapidly across Asia, and the resultant increases in food production pulled the region back from the edge of famine. Within 25 years, the region was producing food surpluses. At the same time, the Green Revolution lifted many people out of poverty; made important contributions to economic growth; and saved large areas of forest, wetlands, and other fragile lands from conversion to cropping. This story focuses on the years 1965 to 1985, a defining period for the Green Revolution in Asia, one that dramatically changed the fortunes of billions of people.

A Package Deal

The Green Revolution was, at its most basic level, the introduction of a package consisting of modern inputs—improved seeds, fertilizers, and pesticides—that together dramatically increased crop production. Its implementation also depended, however, on strong public policies and investments in agricultural research and development, rural infrastructure such as irrigation and rural roads, credit provision to farmers, systems to supply the input packages, and price stabilization mechanisms.

Attempts have been made to assess separately the contributions of the different components of the Green Revolution package, but in practice it was the powerful interactions among these individual components that made the difference. Only with all of these components in place did farmers—particularly small farmers—have the right economic incentive to adopt the new packages.

Irrigation, fertilizer, and improved seeds

Asian countries had invested heavily in irrigation before the Green Revolution, and by 1970 around one quarter of the agricultural land was already

---

This chapter is based on Hazell, P. B. R. 2009. *The Asian Green Revolution*. IFPRI Discussion Paper. Washington, D.C.: International Food Policy Research Institute.

irrigated. India had 10.4 million hectares of canal-irrigated land in 1961 and 4.6 million hectares of tank-irrigated land.[2] But the Green Revolution era brought large additional investments across Asia, and, between 1967 and 1982, irrigated area grew by 2.1 percent a year (see Figure 3.1).

Like irrigation, fertilizer use across Asia was also growing before the Green Revolution. In 1970, Asian farmers applied an average of 23.9 kilograms of plant nutrients per hectare of farmland. The Green Revolution, however, bumped fertilizer use way up. From 1967 to 1982, average use grew by a remarkable 10.75 percent a year (see Figure 3.1).

Irrigation and fertilizer helped raise cereal yields, but their full impact was only realized after the development of high-yielding varieties. Scientists sought to develop cereal varieties that were more responsive to plant nutrients and had shorter and stiffer straw that would not fall over

under the weight of heavier heads of grain. They also wanted tropical rice varieties that could mature more quickly and grow at any time of the year, thereby permitting farmers to grow more crops each year on the same land. Varieties also needed to be resistant to major pests and diseases that flourish under intensive farming conditions and to retain desirable cooking and consumption traits.

Borrowing from rice-breeding work undertaken in China, Japan, and Taiwan, the fledgling International Rice Research Institute in the Philippines developed semi-dwarf varieties that met most of these requirements and that could be grown under a wide range of conditions. Similar achievements were made for wheat after Norman Borlaug (later awarded the Nobel Peace Prize for his work) crossed Japanese semi-dwarf varieties with Mexican wheat varieties at what is now known as the International Maize and Wheat Improvement Center in Mexico.

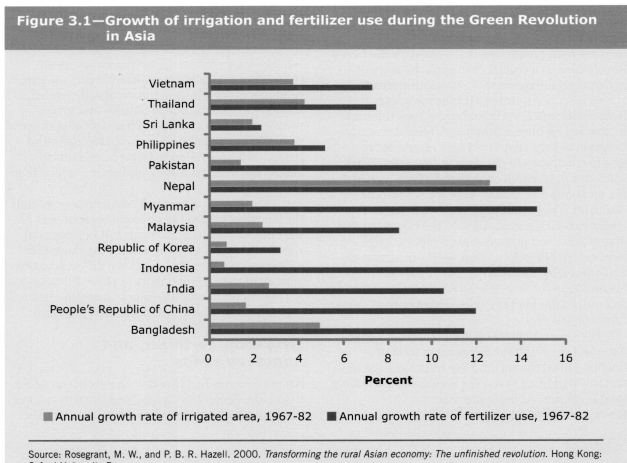

Figure 3.1—Growth of irrigation and fertilizer use during the Green Revolution in Asia

Annual growth rate of irrigated area, 1967-82   Annual growth rate of fertilizer use, 1967-82

Source: Rosegrant, M. W., and P. B. R. Hazell. 2000. *Transforming the rural Asian economy: The unfinished revolution.* Hong Kong: Oxford University Press.

These high-yielding varieties that powered the Green Revolution were not developed overnight. Rather, they were the product of a long and sustained research effort. Moreover, many of the initial varieties that were released had to be constantly improved and adapted to meet the challenges posed by continually evolving pests, changing environmental conditions, and local consumer preferences.

Nor were the high-yielding varieties limited to rice and wheat: high-yielding varieties have since been developed for a number of other major food crops important to developing countries, including sorghum, millet, maize, cassava, and beans.

The adoption of high-yielding varieties occurred quickly (see Figure 3.2), and by 1980 about 40 percent of the total cereal area in Asia was planted with modern varieties.[3] By 2000 this figure had increased to about 80 percent of the cropped area.

Public investment and policy support

The Green Revolution was more than a technology fix. It was also the result of a supportive economic and policy environment. Farmers were educated about the new technology. Systems for delivering inputs and credit were rapidly expanded to allow farmers to adopt and profit from the technologies. Processing, storage, trade, and marketing capacities were ramped up to handle the surge in production. Accomplishing these tasks was considered too large a challenge for the private sector on its own at the time, especially if small farmers were not to get left behind. So, to achieve these ends, governments across Asia actively intervened in launching and implementing the Green Revolution. Some—but not all—public interventions were market-mediated, and all were backed by substantial public investments in agricultural development.

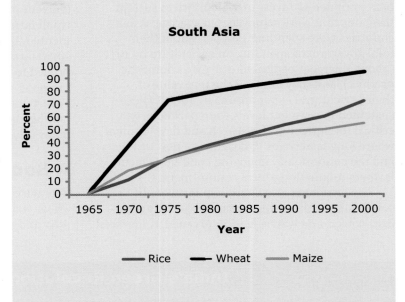

Figure 3.2—Share of harvested area under modern varieties, 1965–2000

South Asia

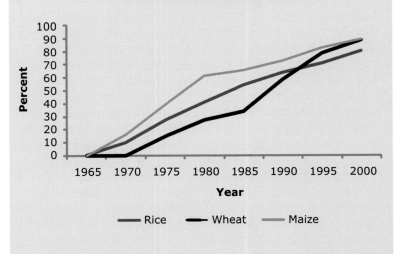

East and Southeast Asia

Source: Gollin, D., M. Morris, and D. Byerlee. 2005. Technology adoption in intensive post-Green Revolution systems. *American Journal of Agricultural Economics* 87 (5): 1310–16.

The high levels of public investment necessary to launch and sustain the Green Revolution were impressively met. Asian countries not only invested heavily to launch their Green Revolution, but continued to invest in agriculture to sustain the gains that were achieved. On average, Asian countries were spending 15.4 percent of their total government spending on agriculture by 1972 (about 7 percent of agricultural gross domestic product), and they doubled the real value of their agricultural expenditures by 1985.[4] These sustained investment levels were particularly critical for agricultural research and development, where long lead times in developing new products and the continuously changing conditions facing farmers require long-term commitment.

Governments also shored up farm credit systems, subsidized key inputs—especially fertilizer, power, and water—and intervened in markets to stabilize farmgate prices. Many governments used their interventions to ensure that small farms did not get left behind. Substantial evidence at the time showed that small farms were the most efficient producers in Asia, and land reform and small farm development programs were implemented to create and support large numbers of small farms. Small-farm-led agricultural growth proved to be not only more efficient, but also more pro poor, a win–win proposition for growth and poverty reduction. The approach taken in India (see box below) is indicative of what happened in many other Asian countries.

A Boom in Food Production

Average cereal yields grew impressively in Asia: wheat yields grew by 4.1 percent a year between 1967 and 1982 and rice yields by 2.5 percent (see

India's Green Revolution Agenda

Immediately after independence in 1947, the Indian government made agricultural development its top priority. Realizing that India would have to develop the physical and scientific infrastructure necessary to support modern agriculture, Prime Minister Jawaharlal Nehru and his government poured resources into the effort, allocating 31 percent of the country's budget to agriculture and irrigation. Massive irrigation projects, power plants, state agricultural universities, national agricultural research systems, and fertilizer plants sprang up across India. These steps were accompanied by land reform designed to create a more equitable distribution of land.

In the mid-1960s, drought and population growth made India more dependent on U.S. food aid, despite its own agricultural potential. Following a study by the Ford Foundation in the early-1960s, the Indian government set up the Intensive Agricultural District Program to invest heavily in agricultural extension and distribution of subsidized inputs. The government also established the Food Corporation of India, which bought excess production at a guaranteed price in order to provide stability to farmers. The government also took an active role in coordinating interventions from donors and development partners, who financed agricultural extension as well as research and development. All of this came on top of India's considerable existing infrastructure, including roads and irrigation systems—the Indian government coordinated interventions all along the market chain to enable the entire agricultural system to function.

As a result, most rural small-scale farmers could profitably obtain and use inputs such as high-yield seeds, fertilizers, irrigation, and credit. Despite the heavy government involvement in the production, dissemination, and adoption of these inputs, the private sector also had a key role. The dual private and public marketing system actually helped improve the efficient distribution of inputs to farmers. The success of India's Green Revolution arose from the combination of subsidized inputs, public investments in infrastructure (roads, power, and irrigation), research and extension, and, later, marketing policy interventions that assured farmers' access to market outlets at stable prices.

Early breakthroughs in productivity were concentrated in Punjab and Haryana in northwestern India, which became breadbaskets for the entire subcontinent. This agricultural growth cut poverty in the Punjab region significantly, partly because land distribution was relatively equal and the benefits of agricultural productivity improvements reached a large share of the population. In neighboring states like Bihar, where the land system was more feudal, poverty reduction was more limited and growth slowed down sooner.

Table 3.1). Higher yields and profitability also led farmers to increase the area of rice and wheat they grew at the expense of other crops. And with faster-growing varieties and irrigation, farmers grew more crops on their land each year. This change led to even faster growth in cereal production. All these gains were achieved with negligible growth in the total area planted to cereal—just 0.42 percent a year.

On average, total Asian cereal production grew by 3.6 percent a year between 1967 and 1982, with average annual growth rates of 5.4 percent, 3.3 percent, and 4.6 percent for wheat, rice, and maize, respectively (see Table 3.1). The growth rates were considerably higher in the breadbasket areas (such as Punjab and Haryana in India and Central Luzon in the Philippines) where the Green Revolution was launched.

Thanks to this rapid growth, cereal production in Asia virtually doubled between 1970 and 1995, from 313 to 650 million tons per year. Although the population increased by 60 percent, food production rose faster, with the result that cereal and calorie availability per person increased by nearly 30 percent and wheat and rice became cheaper.[5]

Nutrition Improves, Poverty Declines

By increasing the supply of food and reducing prices of food staples in Asia, the Green Revolution benefited poor people's nutrition. Higher yields typically led rural households in adopting regions to consume more calories and protein. One study, for example, found that over a 10-year period the spread of high-yielding rice in the North Arcot district of Tamil Nadu in southern India led farmers and landless workers to consume substantially more energy and protein.[6] About one-third of the calorie increase could be attributed to increased rice production.[7]

Some evidence shows, however, that other nutritionally rich foods like fruits and vegetables have become more expensive as the price of cereals has fallen. A study of Bangladesh showed that a downward trend in the price of rice over the periods of 1973 to 1975 and 1994 to 1996 was accompanied by upward trends in the real prices of other foods that are richer in micronutrients, making these less accessible to the poor.[8] As a result, micronutrient deficiencies are more common today than calorie and protein deficiencies.

Table 3.1—Annual growth rates in cereal production in Asia, 1967–82 (%)

Crop	Area	Yield	Production
Wheat	1.30	4.07	5.43
Maize	1.09	3.48	4.62
Rice	0.70	2.54	3.25
Other grains	-1.76	1.63	-0.15
All cereals	0.42	3.13	3.57

Source: Rosegrant, M. W., and P. B. R. Hazell. 2000. *Transforming the rural Asian economy: The unfinished revolution.* Hong Kong: Oxford University Press.

Although the primary goal of the investments underlying the Green Revolution was to increase food production, evidence suggests that it also helped slash poverty. Reliable poverty data are not available for the early Green Revolution period, but in 1975 nearly three out of every five Asians still lived on less than US$1 a day. This share declined to less than one in three by 1995.[9] The absolute number of poor people declined by 28 percent, from 1,149 million in 1975 to 824 million in 1995. These reductions in poverty would have been even more impressive if the total population had not grown by 60 percent over the same period.[10] The vast majority of the poor who were lifted out of poverty were rural and obtained at least part of their livelihood from agriculture and allied activities.

The relationship between the Green Revolution and poverty alleviation is complex, and there are a number of pathways through which the Green Revolution benefited the poor. By allowing poor farmers to increase their own production, it directly provided them with more food and nutrients and increased the output they could sell to raise farm income. Small farmers and landless laborers gained additional agricultural employment opportunities and higher wages within adopting regions. The Green Revolution also benefited the poor in less direct ways. Soaring agricultural growth in the Green Revolution regions created jobs for migrant workers from other regions. It also indirectly stimulated growth in the nonfarm sector of the economy, both rural and urban, benefiting a wide range of rural and urban poor people. Also, greater food production led to lower food prices for all types of poor people.

A technician teaches farmers about pest-management techniques

Environmental Challenges

Cereal yields have continued to rise on average across Asia since the Green Revolution era, but annual growth rates are slowing. There are several possible reasons for this slowdown: displacement of cereals from better farmlands by more profitable crops like groundnuts; diminishing returns to modern varieties when irrigation and fertilizer use are already at high levels; and the fact that cereal prices have until recently been low relative to input costs, making additional intensification less profitable. But there are concerns that the slowdown also reflects a deteriorating crop-growing environment, and this is supported by growing evidence on the degradation of soils and build up of toxins in intensive paddy systems.

Broader worries have also arisen about the environmental sustainability of the Green Revolution. These wider issues include excessive and inappropriate use of fertilizers and pesticides that pollute waterways and kill beneficial insects and other wildlife; irrigation practices that lead to salt buildup and eventual abandonment of some of the best farming lands; increasing water scarcities in major river basins; and retreating groundwater levels in areas where more water is being pumped for irrigation than can be replenished by the rains.

Environmental concerns have led to new research and a wider array of more sustainable technologies and farming practices. A number of approaches are now being tried to make intensive Green Revolution farming sustainable. More careful and efficient management of soil nutrients, including new ways of applying fertilizer, can increase the efficiency of fertilizer use, thereby reducing production costs and environmental problems. Low- or zero-tillage farming can save labor, fertilizer, and energy, minimize planting delays between crops, conserve soil, reduce irrigation water needs, increase tolerance to drought, and reduce greenhouse gas emissions. Researchers have shown the potential for raising yields in irrigated farming while saving substantially on water use. Integrated pest management combines pest-resistant crop varieties, natural pest control mechanisms, and the judicious use of some pesticides to give farmers significant cost savings on pesticides and improve farmers' health. Still, far too few farmers use these more sustainable technologies and farming practices. Reasons include the high levels of knowledge required for their practice; problematic incentives caused by input subsidies; labor constraints and insecure property rights; difficulties of organizing collective action; and preverse incentives that arise when most of the environmental damage occurs off-site. These constraints require more calibrated policy responses, and developing these remains a major challenge for the future management of Green Revolution areas.

Lessons of the Asian Green Revolution

The Green Revolution was a continuing process of change rather than a single event, and even today scientists and farmers are constantly making improvements to cereal varieties and management practices to help support and advance high levels of productivity. Several important lessons can be drawn from this dramatic period of history.

First, technological barriers to expanded food production among small and large farmers in developing countries can be alleviated. Second, green revolutions do not just happen, but require considerable and sustained nurturing by the state. Third, green revolutions are not necessarily pro poor or environmentally benign, and achieving favorable outcomes requires appropriate supporting government policies.

Overcoming technological barriers to food production

Asia was able to break out of its food production constraint by bringing the force of the 20th-century scientific revolution in agriculture to its farmers. Governments and their international partners invested heavily in agricultural research and development, irrigation, and fertilizer supplies, and farmers made major changes to their traditional and well-honed farming systems. The switch from low-input/low-output farming to high-input/high-output farming was not without its critics, but it sufficed to provide the needed productivity breakthroughs that had otherwise failed to materialize. The initial Green Revolution technology package worked best for wheat and rice in the best-irrigated areas, but within 10 to 15 years the technologies had evolved to accommodate the challenges of many poorer regions growing a wider range of food crops under less-assured irrigation conditions.

Making green revolutions happen

Market forces alone are insufficient for launching green revolutions. Asia's Green Revolution was not a single intervention or a silver bullet, but a set of initiatives and preconditions that came together to ensure that farms of all sizes could participate in a fully functional market chain. These lessons can usefully be divided into a number of preconditions that existed (or were established) and a series of interventions that were implemented to create an enabling and sustained economic environment.

First, if farmers are to adopt Green Revolution technologies, they need access to a holistic package of affordable inputs (fertilizer, improved seed, pesticides, and irrigation water), seasonal credit to buy them each season, and assured access to markets at stable prices. A green revolution takes off only if all these things come together in an integrated way. Achieving these preconditions requires critical accumulated levels of investment in agricultural research and development, extension, roads, irrigation, power, and other infrastructure, as well as effective public and private institutions that serve agriculture. In Asia, these things were built up over several decades in an integrated way—guided by national agricultural development plans—and were already advanced before the Green Revolution.

Second, an enabling economic environment is needed. Although Asian countries discriminated against agriculture in their macroeconomic, tax, and industrial sector policies, they offset many of these biases by subsidizing inputs and adopting price support policies for farmers. The net result was that farmers found it profitable to adopt Green Revolution technologies. Moreover, although the Asian Green Revolution was initiated and driven by governments, the private sector was given an important role, and this helped reduce marketing inefficiencies and corruption.

Third, Asian countries not only invested heavily to launch the Green Revolution, but continued to invest in agriculture to sustain the gains that were achieved.

Making green revolutions pro poor

Green revolutions need to be led by small farmers to be pro poor, but this does not automatically happen without supportive government policies. In Asia, the conditions under which the Green Revolution proved pro poor included (1) a technology package that could be profitably adopted on farms of all sizes; (2) an equitable distribution of land with secure property rights; (3) modern input and credit systems that served small farms at

31

Former UN Secretary General U Thant (center) examines new rice strains

prices they could afford; and (4) product markets and price support policies that ensured small farms received stable and fair prices. Meeting these requirements typically required proactive efforts by governments in the form of land reforms, small farm development programs, and input and credit subsidies.

Making green revolutions environmentally sustainable

Too often, green revolutions have led to environmental problems that impose high off-site costs and undermine the long-term sustainability of the farming system. Deficient management of modern inputs is the primary cause—a problem exacerbated by inadequate extension and training, ineffective regulation of water quality, and input pricing and subsidy policies that made modern inputs too cheap and encouraged excessive use.

More intensive agriculture is not necessarily inconsistent with good management of the environment—technologies like precision farming, integrated pest management, and improved water management practices can increase yields even while reducing water and chemical use. Reforming policies and institutions so they give farmers incentives to manage inputs sustainably rather than unsustainably remains an unfinished agenda.

Conclusion

In spite of the limitations and criticisms of the Green Revolution, its success in heading off famine in Asia and ensuring the region's long-term food security is undeniable. The increases in food production pulled the region back from the edge of famine. Over the course of 25 years, the region went from suffering food deficits that threatened the lives of millions to producing more food than it could consume. The Asian Green Revolution lifted many people out of poverty, jump-started economic growth, and saved large areas of forest, wetlands, and other fragile lands from conversion to cropland. In short, the investments and policies that underpinned the Green Revolution were highly successful in achieving the objectives of the time. They are a testament to the vision and determination of the many farmers, scientists, and policymakers worldwide who made this "revolution" a reality. ■

NOTES

1. The Green Revolution also stimulated gains in agricultural productivity and production in Latin America, but this chapter focuses on its success in Asia.

2. Evenson, R. E., C. E. Pray, and M. W. Rosegrant. 1999. *Agricultural research and productivity growth in India.* IFPRI Research Report 109. Washington, D.C.: International Food Policy Research Institute.

3. World Bank. 2007. *World development report 2008: Agriculture for development*. Washington, D.C.

4. Rosegrant, M. W., and P. B. R. Hazell. 2000. *Transforming the rural Asian economy: The unfinished revolution.* Hong Kong: Oxford University Press.

5. Rosegrant and Hazell 2000; Asian Development Bank. 2000. *Rural Asia: Beyond the Green Revolution.* Manila, Philippines: Asian Development Bank.

6. Pinstrup-Andersen, P., and M. Jaramillo. 1986. The impact of technological change on rice production, food consumption, and nutrition in North Arcot, India. Paper presented at the International Food Policy Research Institute/Tamil Nadu Agricultural University "Growth Linkages" workshop, February 14–16, Ootacamund, India.

7. Pinstrup-Andersen, P., and M. Jaramillo. 1991. The impact of technological change in rice production on food consumption and nutrition. In *The Green Revolution reconsidered: The impact of the high yielding rice varieties in South India,* ed. P. B. R. Hazell and C. Ramasamy. India: Johns Hopkins University Press and Oxford University Press.

8. Bouis, H. 2000. Improving human nutrition through agriculture: The role of international agricultural research. *Food and Nutrition Bulletin* 21 (4): 550–66.

9. Rosegrant and Hazell 2000.

10. Asian Development Bank 2000.

Chapter 4

© CIMMYT

Breeding an "Amaizing" Crop

Improved maize in Kenya, Malawi, Zambia, and Zimbabwe

Melinda Smale and T. S. Jayne

Maize is the world's most widely grown cereal, cultivated in the tropics and in temperate zones, at high and low altitudes, in dry climates and wet ones, on slopes and fields, and in a range of soil types. Large-scale commercial farmers grow it using equipment worth hundreds of thousands of dollars, while poor farmers with small plots, such as those in East and Southern Africa, grow it using little more than a hoe. Given maize's enormous versatility and popularity, when scientists in East and Southern Africa were able to develop more productive maize seeds through innovative breeding programs, their success translated into better livelihoods for millions of farm households.

This story begins on the eve of independence for Kenya, and several decades before the independence of Zimbabwe, with colonial maize-breeding programs geared primarily to the needs of European settler-farmers. In Kenya, the products of these early scientific efforts were as promising as the hybrids that swept across midwestern farmlands in the United States beginning in the 1930s. They served as the basis for generations of new maize hybrids and other improved varieties that spread rapidly among smallholders in newly formed African states from 1965 to 1990. With the spread of modern maize, farmers' yields multiplied several-fold and contributed significantly to improving food production and food security in the region. The experiences of four countries in the region—Kenya, Malawi, Zambia, and Zimbabwe—demonstrate just how influential improved maize and maize breeding were during this period in history.

A New World Import

Maize arrived in Africa relatively recently. During the 1500s, traders introduced maize and cassava—New World crops—into Africa, where they supplemented indigenous staples like sorghum, millet, and yams. Initially, most African farmers adopted maize as a niche crop tucked in their already complex farming systems. But because maize was so well suited to growing conditions in the region, by the end of the 19th century it had become widely cultivated as a secondary food crop.

Between 1900 and 1965, maize pushed aside other crops to become the dominant food crop in Kenya, Malawi, Zambia, and Zimbabwe. Between 2000 and 2005, maize covered more than three-quarters of the land under cereal cultivation in the four countries, and most of the maize being grown consisted of modern (improved) varieties (see Table 4.1).

The initial spread of maize during the colonial era is attributed to several factors. First, it could be grown by newly arrived European settlers—who were novices at farming in the tropics—because it required less capital and technical skill than cotton and tobacco. Second, it could yield higher returns than indigenous cereals and was both easier to process and more marketable, particularly as an export to the British starch market. Third, maize became a form of in-kind wage payment for African workers who left their farms to work on settler-owned farms, mines, and industrial plants, particularly in Zambia, Kenya, and Zimbabwe.

As a result of this close link between maize, European settlers, and colonial governments

This chapter is based on Smale, M., and T. S. Jayne. Forthcoming. Maize in eastern and southern Africa: "Seeds" of success in retrospect. In *Successes in African Agriculture: Lessons for the future*, ed. S. Haggblade and P. B. R. Hazell. Washington, D.C.: International Food Policy Research Institute.

Table 4.1—Maize in East and Southern Africa, 2000–05

Country	Total average annual production (thousand tons)	Maize area as a % of total cereal area	Average per capita consumption of maize as food (kg/year)	Average % of maize used in human consumption
Kenya	2,597	79	86	96
Malawi	1,770	95	121	79
Zambia	868	82	86	94
Zimbabwe	1,076	80	89	72

Note: Consumption data refer to 1997–99. All other data are averages for the period 2000–05.

Source: Aquino, P., F. Carrion, R. Calvo, and D. Flores. 2001. Selected maize statistics: Part 4. In *Meeting world maize needs: Technological opportunities and priorities for the public sector*, ed. P. L. Pingali. Mexico City: International Maize and Wheat Improvement Center; FAO (Food and Agriculture Organization of the United Nations). 2009. FAOSTAT statistical database. Rome.

in the region, state-directed marketing systems emerged that tied grain marketing to the delivery of seeds, fertilizer, and credit on beneficial terms for settler farmers. Yet in spite of this system, which favored settlers over indigenous farmers, maize cultivation still managed to spread rapidly among smallholders. Following independence, as newly independent governments tried to support smallholder farmers, maize was elevated to the center of the "social contract" between these new states and their citizens. Maize thus became the cornerstone of the modern states of Kenya, Malawi, Zambia, and Zimbabwe.[1]

Years of independence
Kenya: 1963
Malawi: 1964
Zambia: 1964
Zimbabwe: 1980

Scientific Achievements in Maize Improvement

The investments in maize research made by colonial governments and settlers, and eventually by independent governments, radically transformed maize production in the region from the 1930s through about 1990. A major element of this success story was the introduction of maize hybrids in East and Southern Africa. Maize hybridization, first demonstrated by scientists in the United States in 1918, is a process in which inbred parent lines of maize are crossed to create seeds with greater yield potential than either parent, an outcome known as "hybrid vigor" (see box next page).[2] The downside is that this vigor tends to decline with each successive

generation of seed saved and replanted by farmers. To realize the full gains conferred by hybridization, farmers need to purchase new seed each season.

Zimbabwe's maize breeders were the first outside the United States to produce double-cross hybrids for commercial use (see box), releasing a hybrid called Southern Rhodesia-1 (SR-1) in 1949. In 1960, the maize-breeding program released the first commercially grown single-cross hybrid in the world, SR-52, which boasted a greater yield advantage and greater uniformity despite seeds that were more costly to produce. SR-52 spread rapidly and widely among commercial farmers, becoming one of the most popular hybrids in the region and a parent of many others. Farmers who grew SR-52 seed using fertilizer and improved agronomic practices increased their yields by 46 percent more than yields from the most common improved local variety.[3]

Following independence in 1980, Zimbabwe's maize breeders continued to chalk up successes. Independence saw the rapid adoption of R200, R201, and R215—fast-growing maize hybrids that were originally bred for European settlers seeking to diversify from tobacco exports; they also provided smallholders with maize seed suitable for cultivation in sandy soils in low-rainfall areas. Although these hybrids were all three-way crosses, which are generally intended for the annual seed purchase and high levels of management typically associated with large-scale commercial farmers, they still performed well for smallholders who could only afford relatively low levels of management.

The Techniques and Technologies of Breeding Better Maize

Maize is predominantly a cross- or open-pollinating crop rather than a self-pollinating crop like rice. In cross pollination, genetic material is exchanged as pollen flows among neighboring plants. Unless cross-pollination is carefully controlled, the progeny resulting from it in a given field will differ from the preceding generation—and from each other—in terms of yield, size, shape, and other characteristics.

When maize *does* self-pollinate, its progeny often have undesirable traits. This is called inbreeding, and after successive generations, it leads to weakened plants called inbred lines. These inbred lines produce small plants, have small cobs, and result in lower yields.

By interbreeding or crossing different varieties of maize, breeders can create "modern" maize that overcomes some of the disadvantages of unimproved and inbred varieties. When two inbred lines are crossed, for example, the progeny's yield can be significantly greater than their parents' yield. This "hybrid vigor" results from the interaction between the sets of genes in the two different inbred lines. The effect of some of the harmful genes expressed in one of the inbred lines is masked by more beneficial ones found in the other parent plant. Maize breeders exploit this process, called heterosis, to develop hybrid cultivars that are now widely grown by farmers.

Breeders produce several main types of maize hybrids:

- Single-cross hybrids—hybrids that result from the cross pollination of unrelated inbred parent lines.
- Double-cross hybrids—hybrids that result from the cross pollination of parent lines that are both single-cross hybrids.
- Three-way hybrids—hybrids that result from crossing three parent lines, where the female parent is a single-cross hybrid and the male is an inbred line.
- Top-cross hybrids—hybrids that result from cross pollinating a single-cross hybrid or an inbred line with an open-pollinated variety.
- Varietal hybrids—hybrids that result from crossing two open-pollinated varieties.

Growing hybrid maize offers some real advantages:

- Hybrids generally produce higher yields than open-pollinated varieties, if grown under suitable conditions.
- Hybrids are uniform in color, maturity, and other plant characteristics, enabling farmers to carry out certain operations, such as harvesting, at the same time.
- The uniformity of the grain harvested from hybrids can have marketing advantages when sold to buyers with strict quality standards.

Hybrid maize also presents some disadvantages:

- To maintain the greatest yield advantage, farmers should buy fresh hybrid seed every planting season.
- Hybrid seed is more expensive than open-pollinated maize seed.
- A farmer needs to produce more than 2 tons of maize per hectare to justify the cost of the seed. Farmers situated in areas with poor growing conditions who cannot afford extra inputs such as fertilizer will not recover the cost of the hybrid seed.
- The grain from a crop grown with hybrid seed should not be used for seed. Farmers cannot replant grain as seed without yield reductions of 30 percent or more.
- Farmers might not always be able to obtain new seed in time for the planting season.

Source: Authors; Morris, M. L. 1998. Maize in the developing world: Waiting for a Green Revolution. In *Maize seed industries in developing countries*, ed. M. L. Morris. Boulder: Lynne Rienner.

Farmer handling maize

These breeding successes in Zimbabwe spread rapidly to neighboring Zambia, where studies suggest that they doubled commercial farmers' yields from 1.3 metric tons per hectare between 1949 and 1953 to 2.7 tons per hectare between 1959 and 1963.[4] Following independence in 1964, Zambia's maize breeders introduced an impressive array of both hybrids and improved open-pollinated varieties. Farmers found that these hybrids out-yielded most other available varieties, even without fertilizer, in all but the most difficult growing environments. They also had other advantages: unlike the single cross SR-52, these double- and three-way crosses lost little yield advantage when farmers saved and replanted seeds from one season to the next. Meanwhile, the improved open-pollinated varieties offered their own distinct advantages to smallholders—ears of these early-maturing, drought-tolerant varieties could be consumed green as a source of food during the hungry period preceding harvest.

Kenya's maize breeders were also successful in breeding improved maize that eventually spread to its large smallholder population. Kenya's program began in 1955 in Kitale, the center of maize pro-duction in the highlands, which were then heavily populated by European settlers. In 1961, the program released an improved, open-pollinated maize variety called Kitale Synthetic II.

After crossing Kitale Synthetic II with dozens of germplasm samples collected from Latin America, Kenya's maize scientists released their first varietal hybrid—Hybrid 611, made from Kitale Synthetic II and Ecuador 573. This hybrid became the basis of all subsequent hybrids developed by the national breeding program.[5] The yield advantage of Hybrid 611 over Kitale Synthetic II was 40 percent, with the added advantage of having lower seed costs than conventional hybrids and less loss of yield advantages when replanted in successive seasons, Hybrid 611 diffused among large- and small-scale farmers in the high-potential areas of western Kenya at rates comparable to those in the U.S. Corn Belt during the 1930s and 1940s.[6]

Malawian smallholders waited much longer for suitable hybrids, for two main reasons. First, Malawi, unlike Zimbabwe or Kenya, did not have a large settler population with an interest in high-yielding maize or the political clout to establish a research system. Unlike Zambia, Malawi had

Table 4.2—Maize performance in Kenya, Zimbabwe, Zambia, and Malawi

Country/episode of success	Annual yield growth (%)	Annual production growth (%)
Kenya, 1965–80	1.44	3.30
Malawi, 1983–93	1.18	3.10
Zambia, 1970–89	4.92	1.85
Zimbabwe, 1980–89	2.21	1.77

Source: FAO (Food and Agriculture Organization of the United Nations). 2009. FAOSTAT statistical database. Rome.

no rich mineral deposits with dense urban populations to feed. Malawi's real maize research clients have always been smallholder farmers, the majority of whom lacked the formal organization and supporting institutions to articulate their needs. These farmers preferred *flint* maize types that processed and stored well on their farms. Second, regional breeding efforts were too focused on *dent* maize types, and flint breeding materials from outside Malawi were not easy to identify. This supply problem was compounded by staffing and funding discontinuities in the national maize breeding programs, and shifting emphasis between efforts to breed hybrids as compared to improved, open-pollinated varieties.

Malawi's first semi-flint hybrids were released in 1990—top-crosses of Malawian lines derived from SR52 and a flint population from the International Maize and Wheat Improvement Center. They had several features small farmers were looking for.[7] Most important was that they satisfied smallholder demand for the flint maize types that processed and stored well on farms.[8] Also important, given the high cost of fertilizer, was the fact that the hybrids grown without fertilizer still yielded more than local maize grown without it, even during the severe droughts that occurred in Malawi during the early-1990s. In particular, MH18 was an early-maturing variety that was more likely to "escape" drought. As top-cross hybrids, they were more likely to retain some of their yield advantage when seed was saved for a season.

The Rapid Spread of Improved Maize

The episodes of success in maize production in the four countries overlapped somewhat, but they varied because of the different conditions and policies within each country. These growth episodes were from 1965 to 1980 in Kenya, 1970 to 1989 in Zambia, 1980 to 1989 in Zimbabwe, and 1983 to 1993 in Malawi.

During these episodes, yields began a steady advance, and overall maize production surged in the four countries at rates that compare respectably with yield and production growth rates in countries such as the United States (see Table 4.2). The share of smallholder farmers growing hybrid maize rose to 43 percent in Malawi, 65 percent in Zambia, and 87 percent in Kenya. It jumped from 40 percent in 1979 to 98 percent in 1985 in

Harvesting maize

Zimbabwe, while total smallholder maize production tripled between 1980 and 1988.

In each country, the growth in maize yields and production was accompanied by the expansion of state marketing infrastructure to smallholder areas, making it easier for government agencies to distribute credit and subsidized inputs like seed and fertilizer, purchase smallholder maize surpluses, and collect loan repayments. Parastatal marketing boards would supply farmers with maize seed and fertilizer on credit then buy the resulting maize harvest from farmers at a fixed, nationwide price, subtracting the cost of any loans. Malawi's Agricultural Development and Marketing Corporation, for example, assumed total responsibility for delivering inputs like seeds and fertilizer to farmers, marketing maize output, maintaining storage facilities, stabilizing maize prices, and transporting maize into food-deficit areas during the hungry season.

In addition, farmers could obtain credit and inputs for growing maize at reduced rates, thanks to government subsidies. For example, Zambian fertilizer subsidies in 1982 averaged 60 percent of the cost of the fertilizer itself, cutting the cost to farmers by more than half.[9]

These state interventions generally benefited smallholders during this 25-year period. On the production side, even when the full costs of seed and fertilizer were taken into account, small farmers growing maize hybrids could earn returns on their land and labor that were nearly twice as much as what they could earn for the local seed varieties cultivated without fertilizer. On the marketing side, smallholders in even the remotest areas profited from policies that set a single purchase price for maize across the entire country.

Yet the effectiveness of the marketing and input credit policies in promoting maize production growth contained the seeds of their own demise. Treasury costs ballooned as small farmers produced more maize than the country could consume and massive stocks accumulated in state warehouses or were exported at a loss. In some cases these costs accounted for 15 percent or more of total government spending and contributed to macroeconomic instability; hence, the maize support prices offered by the marketing boards could not be sustained. As support prices were reduced or withdrawn in many areas farmers opted to sell their grain in illegal parallel markets. The rise of parallel markets also enabled farmers

Maize crop: (left) hybrid and (right) nonhybrid

to avoid repaying the loans they had taken out to buy inputs. These policies eventually led to fiscal crisis and, in some cases, hyperinflation. The maize-breeding programs literally helped to feed millions while also providing a source of income for many smallholder farmers in the region, but the package of policies that accompanied them could not be sustained in the long term.[10]

Ingredients for Success

The main ingredient in each country's episode of success was an innovative breeding program that produced high-quality materials needed to provide smallholders with modern maize. In Kenya, success was partly attributable to the continuity of the breeding program's staff and leadership, and to the fact that the program actually consisted of four separate research stations—one for each of the nation's agroclimatic zones—that released a succession of improved maize varieties suited to each zone. Moreover, the program was backed by consistent and constructive support from aid donors: during these initial years, the Rockefeller Foundation and the United States Agency for International Development (USAID) facilitated the exchange of germplasm between continents as well as the sharing of new research on hybrid genetics. Similarly, Zimbabwe's program succeeded because of its dedicated (and well-paid) scientists who devoted their entire careers to maize research, with the added advantage of being backed by the revenues earned and contributed by commercial farmers.

But good breeding programs are just some of the factors that contributed to the growth and spread of modern maize in Kenya, Malawi, Zambia, and Zimbabwe. All four countries also made complementary investments in agronomic research, extension, seed distribution systems, and rural infrastructure, and all four countries also operated institutions to coordinate grain marketing with seed, fertilizer, and credit delivery. In short, these four countries recognized that smallholder agriculture was an integrated system and, accordingly, they invested heavily in many different ways to promote modern maize as a means of boosting maize yields and production.

The Kenya Maize Research Program, for example, was backed by a larger national maize program that included a dense transport network, marketing boards, preferential pricing policies

Farmer holds a handful of maize, Malawi

for farmers, extension services, and a national seed company. Modern maize spread throughout Kenya as a result of thousands of farming demonstrations carried out by extension agents, seed sales and credit disbursements managed by rural seed stockists, and a supportive policy regime (see Chapter 14).

In Zimbabwe, the government also supported smallholder maize cultivation through input delivery, credit, and marketing programs that had previously served only large-scale European settlers. One of the hallmarks of Zimbabwe's success story was the Seed Maize Cooperative—known in the colonial era as the Seed Maize Association of Southern Rhodesia—that was designed as an autonomous body to transfer monitoring and inspection costs from the government to its maize-producing members, arrange tax breaks, secure exclusive commercial rights over the sale of some seed types, and provide access to subsidized credit. As a result of these interventions, credit allocated to smallholders between 1979 and 1986 rose eightfold, stimulating fertilizer use, increasing maize yields, and encouraging the growth of private investment in input supply. As mentioned above, however, the model could not be financially sustained. By the late-1980s, the government had dramatically scaled back credit disbursement and marketing board collection points, reduced the real prices offered by the marketing board, and faced pressure to legalize parallel private markets.

In Malawi, several factors other than modern maize contributed to small farmers' rapid adoption of maize from the mid-1980s until 1993. During the late-1980s farmers could get hybrid seed and fertilizer at favorable prices. At the same time, improvements were being made in the marketing and distribution of high-quality commercial seed.[11] These improvements began in 1978 when the National Seed Company of Malawi (NSCM) took responsibility from Malawi's Agricultural Development and Marketing Corporation for producing, procuring, and marketing improved maize seed. In 1988 Cargill, a multinational company, acquired most of the NSCM's equity and began aggressively producing, procuring, and marketing seeds in Malawi.

Lessons from East and Southern Africa's Maize Programs

Despite the spread of modern maize among smallholders in East and Southern Africa immediately following independence, the growth in maize yields and production has slowed since about 1990. Unstable weather in the 1990s is much to blame, but the withdrawal of state subsidies and market support in all four countries has also shifted cultivated area from maize to other crops, with unclear effects on total agricultural growth. Ultimately, the fiscal burden associated with state-led marketing and credit policies rendered these systems unsustainable. Subsequent efforts to liberalize the maize sector and maize seed industry in the region have been uneven, erratic, and often ensnared by populist political pressures, leaving national seed research systems chronically underfunded and creating uncertainties that discourage investment throughout the maize production chain.

Conclusion

In spite of the shortcomings and occasional criticisms that accompanied the growth and spread of maize in East and Southern Africa, there is little doubt that the period from 1965 to 1990 represents a success story in agricultural development. A combination of factors—primarily the sustained investment in research and development, dedicated scientists, and supportive public policies—all contributed to maize-driven improvements in rural livelihoods and national food security in the region. ■

NOTES

1. Jayne, T. S. and S. Jones. 1997. Food marketing and pricing policy in eastern and southern Africa: A survey. *World Development* 25 (9): 1505–1527.

2. Morris, M. L. 1998. Maize in the developing world: Waiting for a Green Revolution. In *Maize seed industries in developing countries*, ed. M. L. Morris. Boulder: Lynne Rienner.

3. Rohrbach, D. D. 1988. The growth of smallholder maize production in Zimbabwe: Causes and implications for food security. PhD dissertation, Michigan State University, East Lansing; Eicher, C. 1995. Zimbabwe's maize-based Green Revolution: Preconditions for replication. *World Development* 23 (5): 805–18.

4. Howard, J. A. 1994. The economic impact of improved maize varieties in Zambia. PhD dissertation, Michigan State University, East Lansing.

5. Hassan, R. M., K. Njoroge, M. Njore, R. Otsyula, and A. Laboso. 1998. Adoption patterns and performance of improved maize in Kenya. In *Maize technology development and transfer. A GIS application for research planning in Kenya*. ed. R. M. Hassan. Oxon, U.K.: CAB International.

6. Gerhart, J. 1975. The diffusion of hybrid maize in western Kenya. PhD dissertation, Princeton University, Princeton.

7. Smale, M. and P. W. Heisey. 1994. Maize research in Malawi revisited: An emerging success story? *Journal of International Development* 6 (6): 689–706.

8. Smale, M. 1995. "Maize is life": Malawi's delayed green revolution. *World Development* 23 (5): 819–831.

9. Howard 1994.

10. Jayne and Jones 1997.

11. Smale and Heisey 1994.

Resisting Viruses and Bugs
Cassava in Sub-Saharan Africa

Felix Nweke

Cassava has long played an important role in ensuring food security, particularly among the poor. In Sub-Saharan Africa, where food security is a concern for many, about 95 percent of the cassava produced is used for human consumption. It was initially adopted by farmers as a famine reserve crop because it provided a reliable source of food during drought, locust attack, and during the "hungry season," the period before seasonal food crops are ready for harvest.[1] Cassava appeals to millions of rural and urban households because it is a cheap source of calories. More generally, cassava is also appealing because it is useful as a livestock feed and industrial starch.

Cassava is largely taken for granted today, yet in the 1960s and 1970s it was under severe threat from the twin occurrences of the mosaic virus disease and the mealybug pest. The International Institute of Tropical Agriculture (IITA) in Nigeria led a global research effort to combat these two problems. The two interventions resulting from this research were resoundingly successful and have revitalized cassava production, which has nearly tripled from 33 million tons per year in the early-1960s to 90 million tons per year in the early-2000s.[2] Those additional 1.4 million tons per year are enough to feed 29 million people.[3]

While the food benefits alone are noteworthy, these interventions have had an additional unanticipated impact: they have contributed to overcoming the generations-old perception that cassava is only valuable in Sub-Saharan Africa

as an inexpensive calorie source for the poor and as an emergency crop in case of famine or other food crises. With sharply declining prices that accompanied cassava's production boom, the commensurate uptick in demand for cassava has broadened its appeal as a cash crop, providing an additional source of revenue to producers, especially via sales in urban centers. This dramatic shift in production can be attributed in large part to interventions that controlled the mosaic virus and the mealybug.

A Cassava Primer

Cassava, also commonly known as yucca, manioc, or tapioca, is a perennial shrub from South America that was introduced into West Africa in the 16th century and into East Africa in the 18th century.[4] Cassava is grown principally for its swollen roots though its leaves, which contain a significant amount of protein and other nutrients, are also eaten in some parts of Sub-Saharan Africa. It is currently cultivated in around 40 African countries, covering a wide belt from Madagascar in southeastern Africa to Cape Verde in the northwest.

In Africa, there are four common groups of cassava foods: fresh root, dried root, pasty products, and granulated products. Dried cassava root flour is widely prepared and consumed throughout Africa, especially in rural areas.[5] *Gari*, a common toasted cereal-like cassava food product that is especially popular in Nigeria, is appreciated for its convenience as a ready-to-eat food.

This chapter is based on Nweke, F. 2009. *Controlling cassava mosaic virus and cassava mealybug in Sub-Saharan Africa.* IFPRI Discussion Paper. Washington, D.C.: International Food Policy Research Institute.

© Pietro Cenini/PANOS

Cultivating cassava

Overcoming Mosaic Disease

Transmitted by a white fly and the planting of contaminated cuttings, mosaic disease has been known to reduce cassava yields by an estimated 30 to 40 percent.[6] This disease has been prevalent in East Africa since the 1890s, and efforts to combat it began as early as the 1920s when much of the region was under colonial rule. However, it was not until IITA in Nigeria started breeding specialized cassava in 1971 that serious headway was made. Researchers drew on a rich stock of genetic resources that had been developed during the previous several decades in an effort to combat the disease. In particular, they improved on an already developed but poor performing mosaic-resistant cassava variety by cross-breeding it with genes for high-yielding, good-quality roots and low toxin levels (the latter of which is important because raw cassava can contain toxic levels of cyanide).

By 1977—after just six years of research and development—IITA achieved its goal. The high-yielding, mosaic-resistant cassava varieties that IITA developed are resistant not only to the mosaic disease, but also to other common cassava afflic-

tions including bacterial blight, the mealybug, and the green mite. The mosaic-resistant varieties improved cassava yields by a full 40 percent, from 13.6 to 19 tons per hectare of land.[7] By the turn of the century, Nigeria was producing 32 million tons of cassava per year and became the largest producer worldwide, outpacing Brazil, Indonesia, and the Democratic Republic of Congo.[8]

While the disease-resistant cassava quickly took off in Nigeria, its adoption was slower in neighboring countries mostly due to a lack of political will and perceived need. However, disease-resistant cassava did eventually get picked up in Ghana, sparked by a two-year drought in the early-1980s, and in Uganda upon a major outbreak of a serious form of mosaic disease in 1988. In Uganda, mosaic-resistant cassava increased from 20 percent of the total cassava area under cultivation in 1993 to 80 percent in 1998, and the incidence of the disease declined from more than 90 percent on the local varieties to less than 20 percent on the mosaic-resistant varieties.[9]

A Global Effort Defeats the Mealybug

The mealybug is a pernicious pest that feeds on the cassava plant, injecting a toxin that causes the plant leaf to curl and eventually wither. The cassava mealybug was accidentally introduced in the Congo on infested planting materials brought over from South America in the early-1970s. It soon spread to other African countries and sharply reduced cassava yields. Yield loss in infested plants is extreme, estimated to decimate up to 60 percent of the root and 100 percent of the leaves.[10] Within 10 years of its introduction, the cassava mealybug—especially when coupled with the mosaic virus—threatened to wipe out cassava entirely throughout the continent.[11]

Not only farmers, but also scientists, agricultural policymakers, and political leaders became increasingly alarmed by the scope of losses to cassava wrought by the mealybug. In 1973, an international conference was convened in the Congo to discuss how to manage this problem. Researchers and policymakers reviewed the options and decided that the classical biological control solution—reuniting predators with prey—was the most expedient approach to pursue.

Therefore, researchers returned to the source of the problem for their solution. Because both cassava and the cassava mealybug evolved together in South America, starting in the late-1970s a systematic search for the cassava mealybug and its natural enemies was undertaken in much of Central and South America. Although huge areas were scanned, the mealybug was found only in a very restricted area of South America. Eventually, scientists found a natural enemy, a small parasitic wasp that uses the mealybug as the site for laying its eggs; the mealybug ultimately succumbs to the wasp's developing larvae.

After the wasps were collected and then quarantined in England for a sufficient period of time to ensure that they would not endanger indigenous plants and animals, they were released over a 13-year period (1981 to 1994) in more than 120 locations in 30 African countries. Seven years after the release of the wasp, the mealybug population declined substantially.[12] According to a large-scale survey in Ghana, yield losses due to cassava mealybug were reduced by 2.5 tons per hectare of land.

While simple on paper, the undertaking to control the cassava mealybug in fact required a massive global collaborative effort. At the regional level, based on an agreement among several African countries, the Africa-Wide Biological Control Program was established in 1980, with its headquarters at IITA in Nigeria. IITA, under the auspices of the Africa-Wide Biological Control Program, then organized a network of collaborators in Africa, Europe, and North, Central, and South America to put all the pieces together to tackle the mealybug. This effort included identifying, collecting, rearing, and quarantining the predatory wasp; preparing for its controlled release in Africa; conducting field and laboratory studies; monitoring and conducting studies on impact; and raising awareness about this new solution to the mealybug problem.[13]

Cassava's Production Boom Boosts Food Security and Incomes among the Poor

The control of the cassava mosaic disease and cassava mealybug together resulted in a tremendous increase in production and, subsequently, decreased prices for cassava and products derived from it, such as *gari*. In fact, after accounting for

Preparing cassava, West Africa

Farmer with healthy, disease-resistant cassava plants, western Kenya

inflation, the price of *gari* dropped by a full 40 percent after the mosaic disease and mealybug were brought under control. This dramatic price reduction represents a significant savings for the millions of rural and urban households who consume cassava as their staple food. In terms of fighting hunger, the disease-resistant cassava varieties alone contributed an extra 1.4 million tons of *gari* per year compared with what would have been available from local varieties—enough to feed an extra 29 million people.[14]

Low-income households benefited not only from more affordable cassava products for consumption, but also from increased income from cassava sales. With the production boom that came with the control of mosaic virus and mealybug afflictions, cassava has become a major source of cash income for farm households in many African countries. Studies conducted in the early- to mid-1990s in nearly 300 villages across six African countries revealed that cassava accounted for 25 percent of farm household food crop income, as compared with 15 percent for yam, 14 percent for maize, and 10 percent for rice, with numerous other food crops accounting for the remaining 36 percent.[15]

What Does the Future Hold for Cassava in Africa?

The main question of sustainability that arises with the advent of disease-resistant cassava ironically is borne out of its success. Though increased productivity is yielding a higher gross income, farmers are also facing increasing labor costs because high yields demand a substantial increase in work, especially at the harvesting stage as cassava is an especially heavy and bulky crop. When cassava was produced as a famine reserve crop or as a rural food staple, harvesting could be done piecemeal and as such was not a particularly labor-intensive task. But farmers who produce cassava as a cash crop for urban markets are more compelled to move their product and consequently are straining under the burden of high cassava harvesting labor and refinement costs, which are increasing in direct proportion to yield. Taken together with the declining prices that have come with the production increase, this extra cost may well serve as a disincentive for farmers to sustain production at current levels.

These constraints indeed appear to have dampened production somewhat. From the early-1990s to the early-2000s, after the period of rapid diffusion of disease-resistant varieties in Nigeria, cassava production per capita declined while prices to consumers increased. Progressive farmers who were planting the high-yielding, mosaic-resistant varieties were planting less cassava because of the high labor costs and bottlenecks. However, labor-saving devices such as mechanized methods of cassava-grating for *gari* preparation, are being developed and already spreading throughout Nigeria and Ghana.

The sustainability of the mealybug control effort appears to be more promising. Without question, control of the cassava mealybug using a biological control agent—in this case, its enemy in nature, a particular breed of wasp—is an important scientific success story in African agriculture. The speed of the dispersal of the wasps after their release was high, with wasps observed in a wide area beyond each original release site just two years after their release.[16] There is no reason to expect that wasps will one day disappear from cassava fields unless there are no mealybugs on which their larvae can feed.

Keys to Success

Although these two interventions were quite different in their approach to protecting the cassava crop from near extinction, they share a number of common features. First, their success can be attributed to the collaborative, global approach to problem solving. Cassava is Africa's most significant global commodity. It was brought to Africa some 300 years ago from Latin America and it is rapidly replacing maize as Africa's most important food crop. The research for controlling cassava mosaic disease originated in Tanzania in the 1930s and 1940s under colonial rule. Thirty years later in Nigeria, IITA's research on cassava mosaic virus drew on earlier findings and developed the high-yielding, mosaic-resistant cassava varieties.

The defeat of the mealybug similarly featured a global effort. To tackle the mealybug problem, an Africa-wide biological control center was established at IITA in Nigeria. IITA brought together an international group of scientists and donors who crisscrossed Central and South America and eventually found a parasitic wasp that kills mealybugs in the process of reproduction. Both the cassava mosaic and the mealybug control programs demonstrate the critical role played by global partnerships and cooperation in tackling complex problems that involve multiple players and countries.

Research was another key component of success, not only in the discovery of solutions to the problems plaguing cassava, but also in providing an understanding of the impacts of these solutions. For example, research analysis documents how the rapid adoption of cassava varieties with improved resistance to cassava mosaic disease led to dramatic increases in cassava production in the 1980s and 1990s in Nigeria, Ghana, and Uganda, and how a surge in demand for food products such as *gari* has sparked further expansion of cassava production. That said, more research is needed to further maximize the potential benefits of cassava's booming productivity, for example, in terms of its possible use for industrial purposes and as an export crop.

Both interventions also have benefited from sustained human and financial investments. Strong and committed leadership for more than two decades provided an enabling environment in which hundreds of cassava specialists were successfully trained through graduate degree and other specialized programs. The continuity of scientific leadership is also important in pinpointing and addressing second-generation problems, such as the harvesting labor bottlenecks that arose from planting the high-yielding, mosaic-resistant varieties.

Conclusion

The mosaic and mealybug control programs have been successful and they reinforce each other. The achievements of both control programs in contributing to the high yield of cassava have been sustained for a period of about 25 years. Although these programs appear to have stood the test of time, research efforts on the mosaic and mealybug controls should continue to ensure success in cassava production throughout Sub-Saharan Africa. ■

NOTES

1. Jones, W. O. 1959. *Manioc in Africa*. Stanford: Food Research Institute, Stanford University.

2. FAO (Food and Agriculture Organization of the United Nations). 2009. FAOSTAT statistical database. Rome.

3. CGIAR (Consultative Group on International Agricultural Research). 1996. *Report of the fourth external program and management review of the IITA*. Rome: Food and Agriculture Organization of the United Nations (FAO).

4. Jones 1959.

5. Idowu, I. A. 1998. Private sector participation in agricultural research and technology transfer linkages: Lessons from cassava *gari* processing technology in southern Nigeria. In *Post-harvest technology and commodity marketing*, ed. R. S. B. Ferris. Proceedings of a postharvest conference, November 2–December 1, 1995, in Accra, Ghana. Ibadan, Nigeria: International Institute of Tropical Agriculture.

6. Thresh, J. M., G. W. Otim-Nape, J. P. Legg, and D. Fargette. 1997. African cassava mosaic virus disease: The magnitude of the problem. *African Journal of Root and Tuber Crops* 2 (1 and 2): 13–19.

7. Nweke, F. I., D. S. C. Spencer, and J. K. Lynam. 2002. *The cassava transformation: Africa's best kept secret*. East Lansing: Michigan State University Press.

8. FAO 2009.

9. University of Greenwich. 2000. Uganda: Saving a nation besieged by cassava mosaic disease epidemic. Application nominating the National Agricultural Research Organization (NARO) of Uganda for the King Baudou in International Development Prize, University of Greenwich, Kent, United Kingdom.

10. Herren, H. R. 1981. Biological control of the cassava mealybug. In *Tropical root crops research strategies for the 1980s*, ed. E. R. Terry, K. O. Oduro, and F. Caveness. Proceedings of the first triennial symposium of the International Society for Tropical Root Crops, September 8–12, 1980, in Ibadan, Nigeria. Ottawa: International Development Research Center.

11. Norgaard, R. B. 1988. The biological control of cassava mealybug in Africa. *American Journal of Agricultural Economics* 70 (2): 366–371.

12. Alene, A. D., P. Neuenschwander, V. M. Manyong, O. Coulibaly, and R. Hanna. 2005. *The impact of IITA-led biological control of major pests in Sub-Saharan African agriculture: A synthesis of milestones and empirical results*. Ibadan, Nigeria: International Institute of Tropical Agriculture.

13. Wodageneh, A., and H. R. Herren. 1987. International cooperation: Training and initiation of national biological control programs. *Insect Science and Its Application* 8: 915–918.

14. CGIAR 1996.

15. Nweke, Spencer, and Lynam 2002.

16. Neuenschwander, P., and T. Haug. 1992. New technologies for rearing *Epidinocarsis lopezi* (Hym., Encyrtidae), a biological control agent against the cassava mealybug *Phenacoccus manihoti* (Horn., Pseudococcidae). In *Advances in insect rearing for research and pest management*, ed. T. E. Anderson and N. C. Leppla. Boulder: Westview.

Chapter 6

© RECOFTC

Seeing the Forest Through the Trees
Community forestry in Nepal

Hemant Ojha, Lauren Persha, and Ashwini Chhatre

Forests are critically important in Nepal because more than 70 percent of the country's population derives some part of its livelihood from them. Farmers depend on forests for green fodder to feed their livestock, particularly during the dry season when forests are often the only available source of fodder. They depend on forests for firewood, both as energy for cooking and heating, and as a source of income from sales to others. And they depend on forest products such as wild edibles and medicinal plants for both sustenance and income.

In Nepal, innovative approaches to policymaking, combined with novel methods for organizing community action, have played a critical role in improving and diversifying forest-dependent rural livelihoods during the past three decades. Community forestry programs have been so successful that today, one-third of Nepal's population participates in community forestry, directly managing more than 1 million hectares of natural forest, or one-fourth of Nepal's forest area.

Community forestry, at its most basic level, implies that the state cedes forest land under its control to rural communities. These communities become the primary caretakers and beneficiaries of the natural forests, with the state providing varying degrees of guidance and support through public policies and programs. The key to making these programs work is the active engagement of local communities in the day-to-day and long-term management of forests in a sustainable manner.

While community forestry programs in Nepal have directly contributed to improving rural welfare by increasing household access to both food and income sources, it is the indirect impact of these programs that is the underlying success. Community forestry in Nepal illustrates the vital importance of "getting governance right" or providing the poor with the capacity to own and manage their natural resources. By elevating communities to the role of custodians, managers, and beneficiaries of the country's bountiful forests, and by supporting this effort with a strong legal and regulatory framework and robust civil-society networks, Nepal has strengthened the contribution of communities to both local development efforts and to the country's national development discourse.

The Emergence of Community Forestry in Nepal

For centuries, many rural communities in Nepal have relied on the country's forests for their livelihoods, using the forest's resources in ways that ensured continued availability for future generations. But by the 1970s, things had begun to change. Population growth, along with government mismanagement, was putting new pressures on the forests, and the global environmental movement was drawing attention to the plight of the world's dwindling forests. In Nepal, the forests were in the midst of a double crisis affecting both the sanctity of the Himalayas and the livelihoods of its inhabitants.

This chapter is based on Ojha, H., L. Persha, and A. Chhatre. 2009. *Community forestry in Nepal: A policy innovation for local livelihoods*. IFPRI Discussion Paper. Washington, D.C.: International Food Policy Research Institute.

Community forestry improves access to raw materials, Nepal

In response to this crisis, technical and financial support began to pour in from international agencies to establish forest plantations as a quick fix to the problem of degradation in the Himalayas. But in 1978, the Government of Nepal introduced new regulations that provided local government bodies known as *panchayats* with limited rights to manage designated forest areas. Community forestry programs—initially driven by international agencies, but later taken over by local organizations—began to emerge rapidly in Nepal.

Community forestry gained momentum throughout the 1980s, and in 1993, Nepal introduced the Forestry Act, a radical piece of legislation that allowed forest-dependent communities to directly participate in and take control of forest management at the local level. Nepal's forest-management strategy soon evolved from a traditional protection-oriented, conservation-focused agenda to a much more broad-based strategy for forest use, enterprise development, rural governance, and livelihoods improvement.

At the heart of Nepal's system of community forestry were organizations known as "community forest user groups" (see Table 6.1). These user groups are officially recognized under the 1993 Forestry Act, and provide members with the right not only to use the forest's resources for their own livelihoods, but also the responsibility to manage the use of the forest sustainably. Because they are legal entities, user groups can operate with a high degree of autonomy from arbitrary bureaucratic actions, and they can collaborate with any civil-society or private-sector organization of their choice, rather than relying solely on the government's forest department for services and support.

A user group may include all members of a village, a select subgroup of households, or people from another village or district. The main idea is that the group should be inclusive rather than exclusive of households in the village. In practice, all households of one or more villages become members of a user group, thus representing a range of people with different interests in using the forest's many resources—such as fodder, firewood, wild edibles, spices, medicinal plants, resins, irrigation water, and drinking water.

A user group is led by executive committees that are selected and supervised by annual assemblies of group members. With assistance from forest officials or nongovernmental organizations, user groups develop management plans that outline the goals, activities, and rules governing the use of forest products. Beyond these common structures and procedures, however, user groups have substantial flexibility in defining their own structures and roles. Some operate on the basis of *tole* or hamlet-based decisionmaking, while others are managed by subgroups with their own common interests. Given the diversity of rural Nepal, this flexibility means that each group can tailor itself to local needs, while also nurturing

Table 6.1—Community forestry impacts in Nepal, c. 2008		
Indicator	Number	Share
Community forestry user groups	14,439	
Districts with community forestry operations	75	100 percent
Households engaged in community forestry programs	1.7 million	32 percent of total population
Area (hectares) of forest under management by community forestry user groups	1.2 million	25 percent of total forest area

Source: Nepal Department of Forests. 2009. Community forestry database. Kathmandu, Nepal.

cultures of democratic governance at the local level.

User groups may also raise money from the forests that they manage. Their revenues may come from a variety of sources, including fees collected from members or outsiders in exchange for permission to collect forest products. Under the 1993 Forest Act, while user groups can retain 100 percent of the revenues generated collectively from their forests, they must designate 25 percent of this income for community-development activities. Revenues vary among user groups depending on the size and quality of their forests, and range from US$50 per year in the high hills to $1,200 in the Terai region.[1]

The area of forest managed by any given user group varies substantially, ranging from less than 1 hectare to more than 4,000 hectares, with an average size of 79 hectares.[2] Similarly, the size of each user group can range from less than a dozen to more than 10,000 households, with the average user group having 111 households.[3]

Local Impact, Local Empowerment

Today, though the state retains ownership of forests in Nepal, its role has shifted from policing forest use to assisting community forest groups in the management of their precious natural resources. The handoff of forestry management in 1993 to communities helped rural households expand and diversify their livelihood options.

While poor households had little to gain from using the forests as a source of commercial timber because of the high upfront costs associated with this business, they had much to gain from other uses of the forests. Poor households benefit from the consumption and sale of fodder, firewood, wild edibles, and medicinals, as well as from the income generated through relatively new activities like nursery management, spice cultivation, and resin tapping.[4] Several studies have found that members of user groups in Nepal have gained substantially from forest-based incomes, while other studies have demonstrated that these groups have yet to harness the full revenue potential of their community forests, although more in-depth analysis of these impacts is required.[5] Importantly, forests have also proven to be an important safety net for many of the poorest households, especially those without access to land for agricultural cultivation.

The benefits of community forestry are not limited simply to what individuals and households can consume or sell. Revenues generated by user groups have also been used for community investments. This includes investments in improving irrigation canals, expanding water-distribution systems, supplementing teachers' salaries, providing small loans for community members, and building schools or other public buildings.[6]

There are also several less tangible benefits of community forestry in Nepal. While user groups play an important role in managing forests, they have also been central to promoting social inclusion and grassroots democracy throughout Nepal.[7] These aspects were given a boost in the 1990s with the formation of a network of user groups established to represent local interests at the national level. Known as the Federation of Community Forestry Users (FECOFUN), this nationwide network emerged as a key player in forest-sector policy debates and brought civil-society perspectives into the policymaking process that were previously overlooked and unheard. This effort was no small feat given the prolonged insurgency and political upheavals that have plagued Nepal in recent decades.

Challenges and Remedies

Ensuring that marginalized groups are benefiting equally from community forestry has proven to be a challenge. In some communities, traditionally disadvantaged groups—the poorest households, women and female-headed households, lower caste and *Dalit* (outcast) households, and certain ethnic minorities—have not benefited equally nor enjoyed the same level of participation that would be expected in a community-managed effort. Often, wealthier households and male leadership not only control forest management decisions, but also impede poor households' access to forest products or infringe on the forest areas allocated to them.[8]

Efforts have been made to introduce explicit provisions to protect and support marginalized groups in the community, and to designate forest resources and community revenues to the marginalized. Among women, despite the enduring social norms that discourage women's political participation, greater participation has been observed in recent years, while women-only user groups, though few in number, have been operating successfully. But it is likely that these equality issues, many of which are being articulated on the national policy agenda, will take time to resolve.

A Good Prognosis for Sustainability

Three decades of innovation in community forestry indicate that the intervention is a highly sustainable one. Politically, community forestry is supported by a strong legal and regulatory framework and has won the confidence of many national policymakers, civil-society organizations, and the international development community. The continuing popularity of community forestry can be seen in the increased number of user groups that have formed over time (for example, from 10,969 user groups in 2002 to 14,439 in 2009), the area of forest handed over for community management, and the number of households and families involved.[9] And while support from a variety of stakeholders is needed to sustain community forestry, ultimately its long-term success depends most importantly on the strong interests of local communities in forest governance, their capacity to do the job, and their adoption of a sustainable approach to forest management. So far, communities appear to be up to the task, and user groups have become durable institutions supported by an active and vibrant network of user-group federations, all contributing to the sustainability of community forestry in Nepal.

In economic terms, the prospects are promising, although more needs to be done. Since community forestry began about 30 years ago, the level of donors and government contributions has decreased while the involvement of nongovernmental organizations and user group networks has expanded. User groups currently absorb a little more than 70 percent of their own operating costs (primarily in terms of labor costs and small financial outlays), with donors and the government each contributing the remaining 15 percent.[10]

From an environmental and ecological standpoint, there is strong evidence indicating that community-forestry practices have improved forest conditions. Forest coverage has increased in some areas under community management according to measures drawn from satellite imagery and aerial photography.[11] Forest conditions, as measured by such indicators as sapling densities and diameters, also have improved.[12] To further promote sustainable forestry management, the government and other stakeholders are exploring the possibilities of forest carbon marketing from community forestry.

Keys to Success: An Enabling Political Environment and Strong Civil Society

Three decades of operational innovations, legislative developments, and evolving practice have clearly demonstrated success in terms of enhancing access to forest products, improving livelihoods opportunities for forest-dependent people, and strengthening local organizational capacity. Community forestry appears to have stood the test of time, contributing to the improvement of livelihoods, civic strengthening, and the engagement of Nepal's large rural population. The experience offers several lessons.

- **Learning through experience is the key to success.** Community forestry has evolved into a complex institutional network that requires actors to work collectively in a learning mode. Even when there is an absence of political consensus or a well-defined legal framework, collaborative learning has allowed for continuous improvements in Nepal's model of community forestry.

- **A strong civil-society network is a critical part of community forestry success.** Civil-society networks have played a central role in influencing the development of community forestry, especially in terms of safeguarding community rights and ensuring the autonomy of community action from regressive government actions and intrusive private interests.

- **Diverse practice should be allowed to emerge through flexible regulatory arrangements.** Although conceived as a unified program of community forestry, diverse modalities have emerged in practice. User groups vary from a dozen households to several thousand, and the group structure varies from informal sharing and coordination mechanisms to highly formalized organizations. These are important adaptive responses to the diversity of contexts in Nepal.

Community Forestry: A Global Perspective

During the past decade, more than 22 countries in Africa, Asia, and South America reformed their national forest policies to expand community forestry rights.[a] In fact, by 2008, an estimated 27 percent of the total forested area in developing countries was designated for administration or ownership by communities, and this trend continues to grow.[b]

Most of these policy reforms aim to improve livelihoods for forest-dependent people and achieve more sustainable forest management. They typically provide communities with harvesting rights over forest products, and management responsibilities such as forest monitoring. Governments and communities typically share forest-related revenues based on a predetermined profit-sharing metric.

Nepal stands out as a notable success in being able to move beyond several of the early implementation hurdles that stymie many other countries. For instance, Nepal successfully developed a strong policy and institutional framework, and provided relative autonomy for communities to harvest forest products and undertake a wide range of forest management and enterprise-based activities. Other countries with notable community forestry programs include Cameroon (1.1 million hectares or 5.7 percent of total forest area), Mexico (38.7 million hectares or 59 percent of total forest area), and Tanzania (2.35 million hectares or 6.5 percent of total forest area), where there has also been substantive transfers of forest-resource tenure rights over to communities.[c] India is another country that stands out because of its sheer quantity of forest under collaborative management between communities and government—17 million hectares or 25 percent of the country's forest area.

In spite of its increasing popularity, community forestry has been slow to get off the ground in many other countries. Critiques often focus on a perceived reluctance by governments to cede control to communities, as well as the limited scope for communities to benefit in this system of forestry governance. With continued research on the public policies and grassroots action necessary to make community forestry succeed on a large scale, including research on its impact on a range of indicators at the household and community levels, this intervention is likely to play an increasingly important role throughout the developing world. It may be particularly important in the context of growing global concerns over climate change, where a new emphasis on linking community forestry and carbon markets potentially offers a valuable means of mitigating carbon emissions while generating revenues for poor rural communities.

Prepared by: Lauren Persha, Ashwini Chhatre, and Hemant Ojha

a. Sunderlin, W. D., J. Hatcher, and M. Liddle. 2008. *From exclusion to ownership? Challenges and opportunities in advancing forest tenure reform.* Washington, D.C.: Rights and Resources Initiative; RRI/ITTO (Rights and Resources Initiative/International Tropical Timber Organization). 2009. *Tropical forest tenure assessment: Trends, challenges and opportunities.* Washington, D.C.: Rights and Resources Initiative.

b. RRI/ITTO 2009.

c. White, A., and A. Martin. 2002. *Who owns the world's forests? Forest tenure and public forests in transition.* Washington, D.C.: Forest Trends; Carter, J., and J. Gronow. 2005. *Recent experience in collaborative forest management: A review paper.* CIFOR Occasional Paper 43. Bogor, Indonesia: Center for International Forestry Research.

- **Open and responsive attitudes of government officials are key to a collaborative learning processes.** The development of community forestry was in part triggered by the open and responsive attitude of government officials, and was followed by the gradual development and institutionalization of a multistakeholder process of collaboration. Community forestry is no longer a government program alone or a foreign aid-driven activity, but a complex governance regime for forest-dependent communities. ■

51

NOTES

1. Kanel, K. R., and B. R. Kandel. 2004. Community forestry in Nepal: Achievements and challenges. *Journal of Forest and Livelihood* 4: 55–63.

2. Nepal Department of Forests. 2009. Community forestry database. Kathmandu, Nepal.

3. Kanel and Kandel 2004.

4. Dev, O. P., N. P. Yadav, O. Springate-Baginski, and J. Soussan. 2003. Impacts of community forestry on livelihoods in the middle hills of Nepal. *Journal of Forest and Livelihood* 3: 64–77.

5. Chapagain, B., R. Subedi, and B. Rana. 2009. Beyond elite capture: Community forestry contributes to pro-poor livelihoods in Nepal. Discussion paper. Livelihoods and Forestry Program, Kathmandu, Nepal. Photocopy; Maharjan, M. R., T. R. Dhakal, S. K. Thapa, K. Schreckenberg, and C. Luttrell. 2009. Improving the benefits to the poor from community forestry in the Churia region of Nepal. *International Forestry Review* 11 (2): 254–267.

6. Dev et al. 2003; Adhikari, B., S. DiFalco, and J. C. Lovett. 2004. Household characteristics and forest dependency: Evidence from common property forest management in Nepal. *Ecological Economics* 48: 245–257.

7. Pokharel, B. K., P. Branney, M. Nurse, and Y. B. Malla. 2007. Community forestry: Conserving forests, sustaining livelihoods and strengthening democracy. *Journal of Forest and Livelihood* 6 (2): 8–19.

8. Nightingale, A. J. 2002. Participating or just sitting in? The dynamics of gender and caste in community forestry. Journal of Forest and Livelihood 2: 17–24; Timsina, N. 2002. Empowerment or marginalization: a debate in community forestry in Nepal. *Journal of Forest and Livelihood* 2: 27–33.

9. Acharya, K. P. 2002. Twenty-four years of community forestry in Nepal. *International Forestry Review* 4: 149–156.

10. Pokharel, B. K., P. Branney, M. Nurse, and Y. B. Malla. 2008. Community forestry: Conserving forests, sustaining livelihoods, strengthening democracy. In *Communities, forests, and governance: Policy and institutional innovations from Nepal,* ed. H. Ojha, N. Timsina, C. Kumar, B. Belcher, and M. Banjade. New Delhi: Adroit.

11. Gautam, A. P., E. L. Webb, G. P. Shivakoti, and M. A. Zoebisch. 2003. Land use dynamics and landscape change pattern in a mountain watershed in Nepal. *Agriculture, Ecosystems and Environment* 99 (1-3): 83–96; Nagendra, H. 2007. Drivers of reforestation in human-dominated forests. *Proceedings of the National Academy of Sciences* 104 (39): 15218–15223.

12. Karna, B. K., S. Gyawali, and M. Karmacharya. 2004. Forest condition change: Evidence from five revisited community forests. *Proceedings of the Fourth National Community Forestry Workshop, Department of Forests, Nepal.* Kathmandu, Nepal: Department of Forests.

Chapter 7

Re-Greening the Sahel
Farmer-led innovation in Burkina Faso and Niger

Chris Reij, Gray Tappan, and Melinda Smale

The Sahel—the belt of land that stretches across Africa on the southern edge of the Sahara—has always been a tough place to farm. Rainfall is low and droughts are frequent. The crust of hard soil is, at times, almost impermeable, and harsh winds threaten to sweep away everything in their path. Over the past three decades, however, hundreds of thousands of farmers in Burkina Faso and Niger have transformed large swaths of the region's arid landscape into productive agricultural land, improving food security for about 3 million people. Once-denuded landscapes are now home to abundant trees, crops, and livestock. Although rainfall has improved slightly from the mid-1990s relative to earlier decades, indications are that farmer management is a stronger determinant of land and agroforestry regeneration.

Sahelian farmers achieved their success by ingeniously modifying traditional agroforestry, water, and soil-management practices. To improve water availability and soil fertility in Burkina Faso's Central Plateau, farmers have sown crops in planting pits and built stone contour bunds, which are stones piled up in long narrow rows that follow the contours of the land in order to capture rainwater runoff and soil. These practices have helped rehabilitate between 200,000 and 300,000 hectares of land and produce an additional 80,000 tons of food per year. In southern Niger, farmers have developed innovative ways of regenerating and multiplying valuable trees whose roots already lay underneath their land, thus improving about 5 million hectares of land and producing more than 500,000 additional tons of food per year. While the specific calculations of farm-level benefits are subject to various methodological and data limitations, the order of magnitude of these benefits is high, as evidenced by the wide-scale adoption of the improved practices by large numbers of farmers. Today, the agricultural landscapes of southern Niger have considerably more tree cover than they did 30 years ago. These findings suggest a human and environmental success story at a scale not seen anywhere else in Africa.

The re-greening of the Sahel began when local farmers' practices were rediscovered and enhanced in simple, low-cost ways by innovative farmers and nongovernmental organizations. An evolving coalition of local, national, and international actors then enabled large-scale diffusion and continued use of these improved practices where they benefited farmers.

A History of Drought and Land Degradation

The Sahel, one of the poorest regions in the world, has long been plagued by droughts. The 1968–73 drought caused the deaths of not only many people but also large numbers of animals and trees—a human, economic, and environmental crisis with effects that lasted for years. Groundwater levels plummeted, yields for staple crops—sorghum and millet—declined, and families began leaving the region *en masse*. Most farm households were unable to satisfy half of their annual food needs through their own production nor could they meet the deficit through food purchases.[1]

This chapter is based on Reij, C., G. Tappan, and M. Smale. 2009. *Agroenvironmental transformation in the Sahel: Another kind of "Green Revolution."* IFPRI Discussion Paper. Washington, D.C.: International Food Policy Research Institute.

© Chris Reij

Zai techniques improve soil fertility

During the 1960s and 1970s, foreign aid donors carried out two major projects in Burkina Faso's Yatenga Province—the heart of the country's densely populated Central Plateau—to build earthen bunds designed to reduce soil erosion over thousands of hectares. Conceived without the involvement of local people, however, the projects did not meet farmers' needs. Indeed, farmers failed to maintain the bunds or deliberately destroyed them, and the bunds soon disappeared. Meanwhile, the surface of barren land on the Central Plateau expanded inexorably, and empty, encrusted fields extended across significant parts of the region. Useful tree species were lost, and little natural regeneration occurred. As the landscape was denuded and exposed to severe water erosion, the land and the people became increasingly vulnerable to drought.

The devastating agroenvironmental trends in the Sahel were also weakening the social fabric. Entire families left the region to settle elsewhere, or husbands migrated to coastal countries to earn income, leaving their families behind during increasingly long periods. By 1980, for many farmers, the choice was simple: claim back their land from the encroaching desert or lay down their tools and leave.

Planting Pits and Stone Bunds in Burkina Faso

Around 1980, several farmers close to Ouahigouya, the capital of Yatenga Province, began experimenting with traditional planting pits. To reclaim severely degraded farmland that water could not penetrate, farmers would dig a grid of planting pits (also known as *zaï*) across the rock-hard plots. Their innovation was to increase the depth and diameter of the pits and then add organic matter, such as manure, to the bottom of the basins.

Planting pits improve soil fertility and agricultural production in several ways. They concentrate both nutrients and water precisely where they are needed. Farmers add manure to the pits, which also capture windblown soil, leaves, and litter. Termites are attracted to the organic matter, digging channels that enhance soil architecture as well as water infiltration and retention. By digesting the organic matter, the termites also make nutrients more easily available to the plant roots. The planting pits retain water for long periods of time, allowing crops to survive dry spells. And because farmers can dig the pits during the dry season, they do not have to wait until the rains come to prepare the land for planting. The technique allowed farmers to effectively raise their yields from virtually nothing to 300 to 400 kilograms per hectare in a year of low rainfall, and up to 1,500 kilograms or more per hectare in a good year.[2]

The use of new and improved planting pits spread rapidly, even though the government's agricultural extension service had been crippled by economic reforms and refocused to the country's cotton-growing regions. Several farmer-innovators were central to this process. In 1984, for example, a farmer named Yacouba Sawadogo began organizing semiannual market days to promote planting pits. At the market days, farmers brought a sample of the crop varieties they had cultivated in their *zaï*, deposited seeds with Yacouba, and then later selected the seeds they wanted to plant that season. Initially small, by 2000 Yacouba's market days involved farmers from more than 100 villages. In 1992, a farmer named Ousseni Zoromé began a "*zaï* school," training local farmers on a gravelly site next to the road. When the crop grew, the effort attracted the attention of the minister of agriculture. By 2001, Zoromé's network consisted of more than 20 schools and 1,000 members, with each group charged with rehabilitating its own piece of degraded land. Another farmer, Ali Ouedraogo, trained individual farmers in villages around Gourcy and visited regularly to work with them in their fields and exchange ideas. His students trained other farmers in improved *zaï* techniques and some of the students then experimented with their own techniques.

Over time, and because of these knowledge exchanges, farmers improved and adapted the pits to their own needs. Some farmers used the pits to intensify cereal production, others to produce trees, and others to combine cereal and tree production. Farmers vary the number of pits per hectare and pit dimensions as well as the quantity of organic matter added to the planting pits.

Another innovation based on a traditional farming practice was taking place in this region in the late-1970s and early-1980s. Farmers in Yatenga Province, with support from Oxfam, a nongovernmental organization, began building stone contour bunds to harvest rainwater. For optimum results, the lines of stone had to follow an imaginary line running along land of equal elevation. Around 1980, the development of a simple tool for measuring water levels ensured correct alignment of the contours, something that farmers had been unable to do in the past. The level cost US$6 to make and could be mastered in a day or two by farmers with no reading or writing skills.[3]

The new design allowed runoff to spread evenly through the field and trickle though the small holes in the stones, slowing runoff and causing water to infiltrate the soil. The practice improved the soil by trapping sediments and organic matter within the plots instead of allowing them to wash away with the rain.

These techniques for rehabilitating farmland spread widely among farmers: the total area rehabilitated over the past three decades is estimated to be between 200,000 and 300,000 hectares. The additional food produced on this land helps feed about 500,000 people.[4] A recent study shows that in villages where these soil and water-conservation techniques have long been present, 72 to 94 percent of the cultivated land has been rehabilitated with one or more conservation techniques.[5]

Increasing the Number of On-Farm Trees in Niger

At about the same time, in neighboring Niger, farmers were also putting new twists on old techniques. For centuries, farmers in Sahelian Niger had managed their woodlands to produce continuous harvests of trees. In the 1970s and 1980s, however, they faced significant tree losses from drought and human population pressures. In the early-1980s, they started experimenting with a process known as farmer-managed natural regeneration (FMNR)—a low-cost way of growing and reproducing trees and shrubs that provides useful food, fuel, or fodder.

The original model for FMNR was developed by Tony Rinaudo of Serving in Mission, an international missionary organization. The model grew out of his observation that underneath farmers' cleared fields lay extensive webs of living tree roots and stumps that were continually throwing up new shoots and stems. Here was an invaluable source of new tree stock—a virtual nursery.

Rinaudo and local farmers developed an effective way of regenerating these trees. First, from among the mature root systems in the field, farmers would choose tree stumps based on the usefulness of the species. They would then select the tallest and straightest stems to protect on each stump and remove the rest. Thereafter, they would regularly prune the selected stems to promote their growth and the production of food, fuel, or fodder, while removing new, competing stems as needed. Periodically, they would harvest one of the original stems and choose a newly sprouting stem as a replacement. Farmers could then grow other crops between and around the trees. The techniques were flexible, and farmers adapted them to their own situations and objectives.

Rinaudo, knowing the value of trees to farmers, offered food to farmers during the droughts of 1984 and 1985 in return for protecting on-farm natural regeneration. Many farmers immediately did so, but when food aid stopped, few continued to protect and manage their trees. Those who had cut their trees soon observed the benefits of FMNR, however, and the technique spread.

The trees generated a range of benefits. They reduced wind speed and evaporation. In the 1980s, crops had to be replanted three or four times as they were covered by windblown sand, but today farmers typically plant only once. The trees produce at least a six-month supply of fodder for livestock, and they provide firewood, fruit, and medicinal products that farm households can consume or sell. Moreover, certain tree species, such as the winter thorn acacia (*Faidherbia albida*), enhance fertility by adding nitrogen in the soil.[6]

Many villages now have 10 to 20 times more trees than 20 years ago.[7] In the area where the Serving in Mission project took place, 88 percent of farmers practiced FMNR in their fields, adding an estimated 1.25 million trees each year.[8] Surprisingly, the highest tree densities were found in areas of high rural population density, where one might expect denuded landscapes. Moreover, many of the trees are young and, thus, still increasing in density and cover.

Boosting Crop Production and Improving Food Security

Because these practices were driven primarily by farmer innovation over three decades, involved many dimensions of impact, and included numerous interventions by nongovernmental organizations and donors, assessing their impacts quantitatively is more difficult than would be the case for single, formal agricultural development projects or programs. Nonetheless, on-the-ground studies, supported by aerial photography and satellite imagery, attest to the magnitude of their success.

Researchers examining the impacts of contour stone bunds and *zaï* have found increases in cereal yields, varying from 40 percent to more than 100 percent.[9] One study of 17 sites rehabilitated with stone bunds found that cereal yields averaged almost 800 kilograms per hectare—325 kilograms per hectare higher than the average yield on control plots.[10]

Zaï alone usually have a greater impact on yields than stone bunds alone, but farmers reap the greatest returns from using both together. And farmers who also used at least five tons of manure per hectare achieved even higher yields, harvesting 1,000 to 1,250 kilograms per hectare.[11]

Farmers in the Central Plateau of Burkina Faso have rehabilitated at least 200,000 hectares of land using these techniques. If cereal production increased by an average of 400 kilograms per hectare—a conservative estimate—farmers have increased their annual harvest there by 80,000 tons, or enough to feed about 500,000 people. With these increases, farm households that suffered from food deficits of six months or more during the early-1980s have been able to reduce their deficit periods from six months to two or three months, or to zero in some cases.

Using satellite imagery, researchers at the United States Geological Survey have been able to identify where tree densities and tree cover in Niger have increased over time and where these changes are likely attributable to FMNR. Estimates

Improving soil fertility through rehabilitation of degraded lands

from high-resolution images acquired during 2003 to 2008 peg FMNR at nearly 5 million hectares.

Because of FMNR, farmers in Niger are producing an estimated additional 500,000 tons of cereals a year. This additional production covers the requirements of 2.5 million people out of a total population of about 15 million in 2009. FMNR also has an indirect impact on food security through tree crop products, which farmers can harvest and sell in local markets. Moreover, despite a near-doubling of the population since 1980, Niger has been able to maintain per capita production of millet and sorghum, which make up more than 90 percent of the typical villager's diet. Per capita production remained at approximately 285 kilograms between 1980 and 2006.[12]

A New Agricultural Landscape

The land management techniques adopted by farmers in Burkina Faso and Niger have changed barren agricultural landscapes in those countries into complex agricultural systems with more vegetation and more varied vegetation. In the Central Plateau of Burkina Faso, rehabilitated plots have an average of 126 trees per hectare, compared with 103 trees per hectare on control plots. Moreover, the trees on rehabilitated land are larger and represent a wider range of species.[13] The level of water in wells has improved significantly since land rehabilitation started, and farmers have created small vegetable gardens around several

© Chris Reij

wells, adding to their incomes and improving nutrition. Increased water recharge appears to result from increases in rehabilitated lands and not from increases in rainfall.

Although millet and sorghum remain the dominant crops in Burkina Faso, farmers are also increasingly growing cowpea and sesame. In some villages, they have begun reintroducing small plots of cotton on rehabilitated land. More on-farm trees and more livestock also add to diversity. With their increased supplies of fodder and crop residues, farmers can keep livestock closer to their fields, contributing to more intensive and profitable livestock production. In turn, livestock produce manure that can be used to improve soil fertility. Twenty years ago, most manure was used as a source of domestic energy, but now it is largely returned to the fields. In many places, a market has sprung up for manure, as well as for transporting manure by donkey cart.

These developments have also brought changes in how rural people earn their livelihoods. After the harvest, men once commonly migrated to urban areas for employment, but some indicators suggest that this pattern is changing as more men remain in the villages where they can now earn sufficient incomes from agriculture.

In recent years, the changed landscape has also been critical to managing crises. Between October 2005 and June 2006, when much of Niger was facing a food crisis caused by drought compounded by other factors, including the export of cereals to the urban markets of northern Nigeria, villages that had protected and managed natural regeneration were much less affected by the food shortages than villages that had not.

Sahelian women may have gained the most from the land rehabilitation techniques. The innovations have greatly improved the supply of fuelwood over the past 20 to 30 years, allowing women to reallocate the time once spent on collecting fuelwood to other activities, including producing and preparing food and caring for children. Women in the Zinder Region who own baobab trees also earned substantial annual income (up to $210) from the sale of tree leaves used to make sauce for the daily porridge.[14] Farmers report that women involved in FMNR have a stronger economic position and better capacity to feed their families a nutritious, diverse diet.

Lessons for Policy and Practice

These stories are among the first examples of the success of poor farmers in enhancing food security while adapting to climate change. Therefore, they carry important lessons about effective partnerships for agricultural development.

First, innovation by local people ("barefoot science") is as important as cutting-edge research. The most successful innovations are often simple, low-cost improvements on practices that are already locally available and known to farmers.

Second, a single technique or practice alone is generally not enough to achieve meaningful environmental and economic impacts but can act as a trigger for other innovations. Where farmers undertook multiple innovations simultaneously, they accomplished more rapid environmental improvements because soil, water, and vegetative regeneration proved to be mutually reinforcing.

Third, a single menu of technical options can be adopted on a large scale, but to achieve this, the menu must be flexible, adaptable, and testable by farmers under their own social, economic, and environmental conditions. Farmers can then choose the practices that best meet their needs.

Fourth, in resource conservation, individual farmers adopting innovations on single fields or farms can achieve impacts, but when communities work together collectively, they will produce more sustainable benefits.

Fifth, farmers are more likely to adopt resource conservation innovations if at least one innovation or component provides significant benefits in the first or second year.

Finally, spreading technical innovations requires coordinated, flexible configurations of actors. In Burkina Faso and Niger, the widespread dissemination of innovations resulted from long-term collaboration between individual farmers, farmer groups, local and international nongovernmental organizations, bilateral and multilateral donors, and national governments. In the Sahel, the projects that became successes tended to start fairly small in scale and to closely involve local farmers in designing technical solutions. Charismatic leaders, both local and from outside the community, stimulated change through their own choices and actions and provided personal role models for others. In a number of the stories recounted, leaders were willing to take socially risky actions that diverged from customary behavior. These types of strong local leaders will need to play a large role in tackling tough conservation problems.

Conclusion

In 1980, no one would have predicted the extent of re-greening in the Sahel today. Farmers in Burkina Faso and Niger have found low-cost ways of intensifying agriculture that allow production to grow along with population. Studies of these projects refute the popular perception that because dryland environments are difficult and market infrastructure is often lacking, investing in them does not pay. Moreover, the longevity of these innovations—two to three decades—attests to their social and political sustainability.

These techniques alone will not solve all problems. Some of the techniques require a great deal of labor, and in the case of stone bunds, funding from outside the community is often required to purchase the necessary quantity of stones and cover the high costs of transporting them. They are most effective under specific environmental conditions. *Zaï*, for example, function best in areas with rainfall between 300 and 800 millimeters.[15] Yet these innovations are important tools to help crop production in the Sahel address the needs of a burgeoning population. And the process by which these innovations emerged— through experimentation, exploration, and exchanges by and among farmers themselves—is possibly the most vital lesson learned from the Sahel.[16] ■

NOTES

1. Broekhuyse, J. T. 1983. *Transformatie van Mossi land.* Amsterdam, The Netherlands: Koninklijk Instituut voor de Tropen.

2. Kaboré, P. D., and C. Reij. 2004. *The emergence and spreading of an improved traditional soil and water conservation practice in Burkina Faso.* Environment and Production Technology Division Discussion Paper No. 114. Washington, DC: International Food Policy Research Institute.

3. Wright, P. 1985. Water and soil conservation by farmers. In *Appropriate technologies for farmers in semi-arid Africa,* ed. H. W. Ohm and J. G. Nagy. Purdue, Ind.: Purdue University, Office of International Programs in Agriculture.

4. Botoni, E., and C. Reij. 2009. *La transformation silencieuse de l'environnement et des systèmes de production au Sahel: Impacts des investissements publics et privés dans la gestion des ressources naturelles.* Ouagadougou, Burkina Faso and Amsterdam, The Netherlands: Comité Permanent Inter-Etats pour la Lutte contre la Sécheresse au Sahel and Vrije Universiteit Amsterdam.

5. Belemviré, A., A. Maïga, H. Sawadogo, M. Savadogo, and S. Ouedraogo. 2008. *Evaluation des impacts biophysiques et socio-économiques des investissements dans les actions de gestion des ressources naturelles au Nord du Plateau Central du Burkina Faso. Rapport de synthèse Etude sahel Burkina Faso.* Ouagadougou, Burkina Faso: Comité Permanent Inter-Etats pour la Lutte contre la Sécheresse au Sahel.

6. Larwanou, M., M. Abdoulaye, and C. Reij. 2006. *Etude de la régénération naturelle assistée dans la région de Zinder (Niger): Une première exploration d'un phénomène spectaculaire.* Washington, D.C.: International Resources Group for the United States Agency for International Development.

7. WRI (World Resources Institute). 2008. Turning back the desert: How farmers have transformed Niger's landscapes and livelihoods. In *World resources 2008: Roots of resilience: Growing the wealth of the poor.* Washington, D.C.: WRI.

8. Larwanou, Abdoulaye, and Reij 2006.

9. Reij, C., G. Tappan, and M. Smale. 2009. *Agroenvironmental transformation in the Sahel: Another kind of "Green Revolution."* IFPRI Discussion Paper. Washington, D.C.: International Food Policy Research Institute.

10. Matlon, P. J. 1985. *Annual report of ICRISAT/Burkina Economics Program.* Ouagadougou, Burkina Faso: ICRISAT (International Crops Research Institute for the Semi-arid Tropics).

11. Sawadogo, H. 2008. *Impact des aménagements de conservation des eaux et des sols sur les systèmes de production, les rendements et la fertilité au Nord du Plateau central du Burkina Faso.* Ouagadougou, Burkina Faso: Comité Permanent Inter-Etats pour la Lutte contre la Sécheresse au Sahel.

12. WRI 2008; Wentling, M. 2008. *Niger: Annual food security report and future prospects.* Niamey, Niger: United States Agency for International Development.

13. Belemviré, A. 2003. *Impact de la conservation de l'eau et des sols sur la régénération naturelle assistée. Développement Rural et Environnement au Burkina Faso: La réhabilitation de la capacité des terroirs sur la partie Nord du Plateau central entre 1980 et 2000.* Rapport de travail no. 1. Ouagadougou, Burkina Faso: Conseil National pour la Gestion de l'Environnement.

14. Sawadogo, H., F. Hien, A. Sohoro, and F. Kambou. 2001. Pits for trees: How farmers in semi-arid Burkina Faso increase and diversify plant biomass. In *Farmer innovation in Africa: A source of inspiration for agricultural development,* ed. C. Reij and A. Waters-Bayer. London: Earthscan.

15. Roose, E., V. Kaboré, and C. Guenat. 1993. Le zaï: Fonctionnement, limites et amélioration d'une pratique traditionnelle de réhabilitation de la végétation et de la productivité des terres dégradées en région soudano-sahélienne (Burkina Faso). *Cahiers ORSTOM, Série Pédologie* 28 (2): 159–173.

16. Haggblade, S., and P. B. R. Hazell, ed. Forthcoming. *Successes in African agriculture: Lessons for the future.* Baltimore: John Hopkins University Press.

Chapter 8

© Theodor Friedrich/FAO

Innovating in the Pampas
Zero-tillage soybean cultivation in Argentina

Eduardo Trigo, Eugenio Cap, Valeria Malach, and Federico Villarreal

The United States, Canada, the former Soviet Union, and many other countries have learned valuable lessons about the dire consequences of overexploiting land for intensive crop production. The emergence of dust bowls in the United States in the 1930s and in the Kazakhstan plains of the Soviet Union in the 1960s illustrated how unsustainable farming practices can cause long-lasting ecological and agricultural damages and losses.

Argentina faced similar risks as it began to intensify the cultivation of soybean in the 1970s in the Pampas region, an expansive area of fertile land stretching from the Andes Mountains in the east to the Atlantic Ocean in the west, an area more commonly associated with cattle ranching and the gauchos, Argentina's cowboys.

While soybean is a commercially lucrative crop, its cultivation negatively impacts soil fertility, particularly when farmed intensively following the cultivation of other crops such as wheat and maize. However, what could have been a disaster instead became an unmitigated success. The widespread adoption of zero-tillage cultivation practices, improved soybean varieties, and other technologies together enhanced yields, boosted production, and conserved soil fertility. Today, Argentina is a global leader in soybean production and exports, providing the international market with supplies of both food and feed that have helped keep global prices low.

The Essentials of Zero Tillage

Although soybean was introduced in Argentina in the early decades of the 20th century, commercial cultivation began in earnest in the 1950s. Protein-rich soybean is commonly used in livestock feed, and as global demand for livestock products—both dairy and meat—increased as incomes grew during the latter half of the 20th century in many countries, some Argentine farmers saw the financial benefits of shifting to soybean cultivation. The land area under soybean production in Argentina expanded rapidly during the 1970s, contributing significantly to an increase in Argentina's agricultural output.

But while this new crop meant higher economic benefits—derived from new demand and the possibility of growing two crops, soybean and wheat, instead of one—it required a much tighter and more careful management schedule resulting from, among other factors, increased climatic risks, higher demands for weed-control strategies, the need for more efficient use of machinery, and the need for greater technical assistance.[1] The fact that soybean was a new, relatively unknown crop, plus the greater complexity of the cropping system, required expert knowledge on how to bring all the pieces together in an effective way. Access to new and reliable information became a key issue for the success of soybean cultivation in Argentina.

Moreover, this new crop had a considerable impact on the land. On many farms where soybean cultivation followed wheat or maize farming, the conventional practice was to burn the remains of the crop cultivated in the period preceding soybean to minimize the time that the land was left uncultivated, thus extending the period available to till, seed, and grow the soybean.

This chapter is based on E. Trigo, E. Cap, V. Malach, and F. Villarreal. 2009. *The case of zero-tillage technology in Argentina*. IFPRI Discussion Paper. Washington D.C.: International Food Policy Research Institute.

But this practice created problems such as soil erosion, water runoff, and loss of organic matter. The practice was so environmentally damaging that it actually started to undermine productivity, even in the best-endowed areas. By the early-1990s, soil degradation was estimated to have reached levels as high as 47 percent in the Arrecifes River basin and 60 percent in the farmland of the Carcaraña River basin, two of the most important areas in Argentina's Pampas region.[2]

As a result of these problems, both scientists and farmers were interested in exploring cultivation practices that were less aggressive with regard to the preparation of the soil, less conducive to soil erosion, and less detrimental to productivity. Their exploration was accompanied by debates about appropriate technologies, farm shows to demonstrate alternative cultivation practices, and foreign study tours to learn about practices in other countries. It was in this context that the development of zero-tillage cultivation practices began in Argentina.

Zero tillage (also called no-tillage farming) is a resource-conserving cultivation practice that depletes organic matter from the soil at a lower rate than conventional tilling and improves the soil's capacity to retain moisture. Under zero-tillage cultivation, crops are planted in untilled soil by making a narrow hole or trench of sufficient width and depth to cover seeds and apply fertilizer. The opening is typically prepared by a tractor-drawn driller, although in some countries such as India, draught animals are used instead of a tractor (see Chapter 9). The soil remains covered by plants from previous crops, and herbicides are used to break these plants down and return their nutrients to the soil. The seeds that emerge from the undisturbed soil draw on the nutrients from these plant residues for their growth.

The method was first popularized in the 1950s and 1960s in industrialized countries with the introduction of commercial herbicides. Farmers in the United States began experimenting with zero tillage in the 1970s, and scientists at the U.S. Department of Agriculture, the University of Illinois, and the University of Kentucky contributed greatly to the technology's further development. By the end of the decade, the pipeline of zero-tillage technology—cultivation techniques, drillers, herbicides, and so on—was substantial, with promising applications not only in the United States, but also in Canada, the United Kingdom, and Germany, among other countries. In Latin America, zero tillage was introduced by the Instituto de Pesquisas Agropecuarias Meridional (IPEAME) in Londrina, in the state of Paraná, Brazil, in cooperation with the German Agency for Technical Cooperation (GTZ).[3]

Zero tillage (and reduced tillage, which involves a minimal amount of tilling and land

Soybean production, Argentina

preparation) has several advantages. It can improve water retention, reduce soil erosion, lower the chances of drought-related crop failures, and lessen the need for labor that would be otherwise required for soil preparation and weeding. These advantages together help reduce or even neutralize decades-long erosion processes, improve soil fertility, maintain or increase crop yields, and lower production costs.

The Emergence of Zero Tillage in Argentina

The successful introduction of zero-tillage cultivation practices in Argentina—not only for soybean, but also for wheat, maize, sunflower, and sorghum, although on a much smaller scale—is a unique story in many ways. Zero-tillage cultivation was advanced by the emergence of a farmer-driven network that brought together researchers, extension agents, private input suppliers, agricultural machinery producers, and others to adapt zero-tillage techniques and equipment to the needs of farmers in the Argentine Pampas.[4]

The story begins as early as 1968, when the National Institute of Agricultural Technology (INTA), Argentina's largest agricultural research institution, started to notice the soil erosion problems that affected crop yields and output. This issue led to the establishment of a soil conservation program at INTA (later known as INTA's Conservationist Agriculture Project), which played a significant role in developing both scientific capacity to address soil-fertility issues, and specialized machinery needed to practice zero-tillage cultivation.

But INTA was not the only one to notice the effects of inadequate soil-management practices. In fact, zero tillage was being explored by a number of individuals representing various interests—farmers, technical-assistance providers, agricultural-input companies, and researchers—as early as 1975. Through informal exchanges of information and experience, the idea that zero-tillage cultivation could be adapted to the needs of Argentine farmers gained substantial footing.

In working together to identify problems, try alternatives, and share information, these informal exchanges between and among private and public actors laid the groundwork for a formal network that spearheaded the widespread promotion and use of zero-tillage cultivation practices. A shared perception of the nature of the problem and a convergence of interests among these various actors was the initial glue that led to the creation of the Argentine Association of No-Till Farmers, known by its Spanish acronym, AAPRESID.

AAPRESID was formed in 1989 as a nongovernmental organization composed of farmers with an interest in conservation. Its main goal was to bring together researchers, extension agents, and private input-supply companies to get zero tillage off the ground, but it also acted as a lobbying group to help its members acquire necessary farm equipment, and to secure loans and tax exemptions for farmers adopting zero-tillage practices on their farms.

AAPRESID's 20 or so founding members were mainly medium-and small-scale farmers and technical-assistance providers, all of whom were already involved in the movement to promote zero-tillage agriculture in Argentina. AAPRESID grew rapidly in tandem with the speedy increase in the adoption of zero-tillage farming throughout the country. Soon, the majority of key players in the agribusiness sector became members, and by 1996, AAPRESID was firmly established as the main force driving the development and expansion of zero-tillage cultivation.

Accelerating the Cultivation of Soybean

Three events contributed to a boost in zero-tillage cultivation of soybean and other crops in Argentina in the 1990s. First, new soybean varieties were introduced in 1996 that were genetically modified to be resistant to the herbicide glyphosate (sold commercially in many countries under the brand name of Roundup Ready®). Glyphosate, commonly used as a weed killer, is particularly useful in zero-tillage cultivation because it breaks down plant residues and returns their nutrients to the soil. Using glyophsate in combination with the herbicide-tolerant soybean meant that farmers could apply the chemical, break down plant residue and weeds, and plant soybean quickly. This technique was aided by the use of drillers that seeded rather than plowed the soil in a way that encourages erosion.

Second, there was a significant decline in the global price of glyphosate during roughly the same time. The herbicide's price began falling when its patent, held by Monsanto, a U.S.-based crop science and agricultural inputs company, expired. The patent expiration allowed for new competition and lower prices in the local market for the herbicide.

Third, there was a change in Argentina's economic policy regime with respect to agriculture. The government eliminated agricultural export taxes and reduced import duties on inputs and capital goods during the early-1990s. This change, together with the deregulation of a number of key markets for both agricultural goods and services, created favorable conditions that eventually led to the increase of both grain and oilseed production, the latter of which includes soybean.

As a result of these convergent events, overall grain and oilseed production in Argentina grew from 26 million tons in 1988–89 to more than 67 million tons in 2000–01. Cultivation of grain and oilseed crops using zero tillage expanded from about 300,000 hectares of land in 1990–91 to more than 22 million hectares in 2007–08 (see Figure 8.1).

As of 2007, Argentina's soybean production accounted for more than 20 percent of global production, up from less than 5 percent as late as 1982. Argentina is now the third-largest exporter of soybean, after the United States and Brazil (see Figure 8.2).

Controversy and Opportunity

There is much global debate about the use of chemical herbicides and genetically modified, herbicide-tolerant soybean in Argentina. These two inputs are central to making zero-tillage cultivation possible, and studies show that their environmental impacts are, at worst, no more significant than alternative inputs, and at best, when combined with zero-tillage practices, beneficial for soil fertility.[5]

There is also some debate in Argentina over the influence of zero-tillage soybean cultivation on farming systems beyond the Pampas. Additional research is needed to better understand the potential impacts of a shift in farming systems— from mostly extensive livestock production to relatively intensive agricultural production—in the more marginal areas outside the Pampean region.

Irrespective of these issues, more than 22

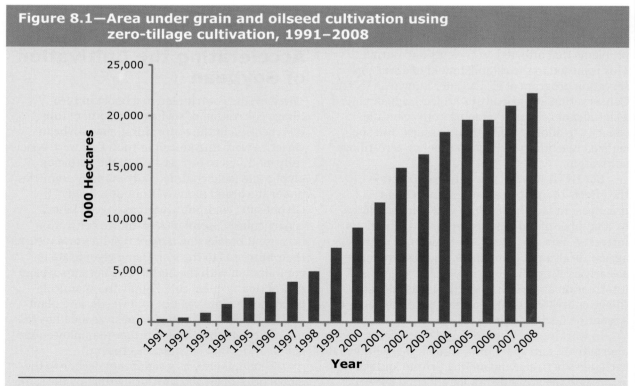

Figure 8.1—Area under grain and oilseed cultivation using zero-tillage cultivation, 1991–2008

Adapted from AAPRESID (Asociación Argentina de Productores en Siembra Directa). 2007. *Base estadística*. www.aapresid.org.ar. Rosario, Argentina; SAGPyA (Secretaría de Agricultura, Ganadería, Pesca y Alimentos). 2009. *Estimaciones agrícolas*. www.sagpya.mecon. gov.ar. Buenos Aires, Argentina.

million hectares of land were brought under zero-tillage cultivation in Argentina between 1991 and 2008, with valuable benefits for soil fertility, farmer incomes, export earnings, and global stocks of both food and feed. The use of zero tillage, along with the introduction of herbicide-resistant soybean varieties and other factors, improved soil fertility by reversing decades of erosion and the long-term threat of unsustainable land exploitation.

In economic terms, about 8.3 percent of the total value of production of soybean and maize in Argentina—around US$12 billion—could be attributed to zero tillage, complementary technological innovations, and economic factors described earlier. For farmers alone, the cumulative savings associated with the use of zero tillage since 1991 comes to about $4.7 billion. Moreover, the industry that emerged from the introduction of zero tillage—farm equipment production, extension services, input supplies, farming, and other related activities—is estimated to have generated some 200,000 new jobs in Argentina's agricultural sector between 1993 and 1999.[6]

Lessons Learned

The success of zero tillage in Argentina can be attributed to a combination of appropriate research and technology and the will to make it work. Beyond the quantitative impacts that have benefited Argentine farmers and global consumers, the social and economic processes that brought about the boom in zero tillage are themselves a success story.

Argentina's switch from conventional planting to zero-till cultivation demonstrates that change is often more than the introduction and adoption of a new technology. Rather, change can involve the entire reorganization of the agricultural sector. The diffusion of zero-tillage cultivation practices in Argentina has had long-lasting effects on the ways in which key economic players—farmers, businesses, and government—interact to improve agricultural production. It has had a durable impact on the structure and composition of Argentina's agricultural sector. And it has had a long-term impact on the soil—on the sustainability of intensive agriculture—in the country.

In particular, this story is anchored by a partnership among very diverse stakeholders—farmers, scientists, extension agents, input suppliers, and farm-equipment producers—who identified a problem and, in the process of sharing information and developing solutions, coalesced around an innovative network that allowed for the tremendous growth in zero-tillage cultivation.

And with the rise of Argentina as a major soybean exporter, this combination of technologies, practices, and ideas has provided the country with valuable export earnings while also supplying the international market with a food and feed crop that has contributed to keeping global food prices low. ∎

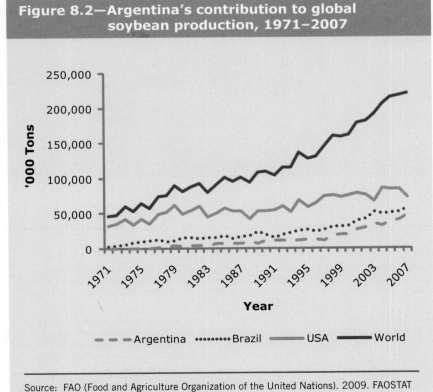

Figure 8.2—Argentina's contribution to global soybean production, 1971–2007

Source: FAO (Food and Agriculture Organization of the United Nations). 2009. FAOSTAT statistical database. Rome.

Cultivating the Cerrado in Brazil

The world's savannahs have long been written off as wastelands due to their highly weathered, acidic, nutrient-poor soils that inhibit agricultural production. The Cerrado region of Brazil—an area covering approximately 204 million hectares of land (or 24 percent of Brazil's entire land area) and representing 15 percent of world's savannah area—was one such region, until the 1970s.[a]

From a scientific perspective, the Cerrado region's potential was unleashed when scientists at the Brazilian Agricultural Research Corporation (Embrapa) formulated a mixture of phosphorus, lime, and other inputs that could dramatically improve soil fertility and thus the agricultural potential of the region. But removing this technical impediment is only part of the story. Complementary investments by the Government of Brazil and hard work by farmers who took a chance by investing their livelihoods in the Cerrado also played key roles in the region's development. For example, a critical contribution came from Embrapa's investments in the development of crop varieties and cultivation practices that were appropriate to the savannah's climate and soil and, therefore, encouraged the expansion of agricultural production in the region. Similarly valuable contributions came from direct government support in the form of road and irrigation development in the region, and indirect support in the form of low-interest loans to purchase fertilizers and machinery and to access veterinary services.

By the late-1970s, large-scale farming and cattle ranching began to expand dramatically in the Cerrado. Today, with an estimated 40 to 50 percent of the Cerrado under productive use, the region accounts for 59 percent of Brazil's coffee production, 55 percent of its beef, 54 percent of its soybean, 28 percent of its maize, and 18 percent of its rice.[b] By bringing the Cerrado into production, Brazil has been transformed into a global powerhouse for food and agriculture, and has been able to contribute to keeping both domestic and global food and feed prices relatively low.

Importantly, the development of the Brazilian Cerrado offers valuable insights for other developing countries aiming to increase food and agricultural production as a means of reducing food insecurity, increasing incomes, and improving livelihoods—particularly in Sub-Saharan Africa, where the largest concentrations of savannah areas still exist.

Prepared by: Levon Yeganiantz and Antonio Flavio Dias Avila

a. Yeganiantz, L., E. Alves, A. Flavio Dias Avila. 2009. *Cerrados development in Brazil: A case study.* Mimeo; World Food Prize. 2006. *2006 international symposium (transcripts).* Des Moines: The World Food Prize Foundation.

b. Spehar, C. R. 2008. Grain, fiber and fruit production in the Cerrado development. In *Savanas: Desafios e Estratégias para o Equilíbrio entre Sociedade, Agronegócio e Recursos Saturais*, ed. F. G. Faleiro and A. L. Farias Neto. Planaltina, Brazil: Embrapa Cerrados. World Food Prize 2006.

NOTES

1. Senigagliesi, C., and S. Massoni. 2002. Transferencia de tecnología en Siembra Directa: Un análisis de lo realizado en el INTA. In *Siembra Directa II.* Buenos Aires, Argentina Ediciones INTA.

2. Secretaria de Agricultura, Ganadería y Pesca (SAGyP). 1995. *El deterioro de las tierras en la República Argentina: Alerta Amarillo.* Buenos Aires, Argentina.

3. Derpsch, R. 1999. *Expansión mundial de la siembra directa y avances tecnológicos.* Proceedings of the VII Congreso Nacional de Siembra Directa de AAPRESID, August 18–20, Mar del Plata, Argentina. Rosario, Argentina: Asociación Argentina de Productores en Siembra Directa.

4. Ekboir, J., ed. 2002. *CIMMYT 2000-2001 world wheat overview and outlook: Developing no-till packages for small-scale farmers.* Mexico City: International Maize and Wheat Improvement Center.

5. Casas, R. 2003. El aumento de la materia orgánica en suelos argentinos: El aporte de la siembre directa. Proceedings of the XI Congreso Nacional de AAPRESID. Rosario, Argentina: Asociación Argentina de Productores en Siembra Directa.

6. Trigo, E. J., D. Chudnovsky, E. J. Cap, and A. López. 2002. *Los transgénicos en la Agricultura Argentina: Una historia con final abierto.* Buenos Aires, Argentina: Libros del Zorzal.

Chapter 9

©IRRI

Leaving the Plow Behind

Zero-tillage rice-wheat cultivation in the Indo-Gangetic Plains

Olaf Erenstein

The Indo-Gangetic Plains—named for the Indus and Ganges Rivers—is the breadbasket of the Indian subcontinent. This large swath of land, running from Pakistan across northern India and southern Nepal and into Bangladesh, is South Asia's center of wheat and rice production. Since the mid-1990s, hundreds of thousands of farmers, nudged by stagnating crop yields, have adopted a new way of farming known as zero tillage.

Zero tillage (see Chapter 8) is a cultivation practice that not only helps preserve soil fertility and conserves scarce water, but also boosts yields and increases farmers' profits by reducing their production costs. Instead of plowing their fields and then planting seeds, farmers who use zero tillage deposit seeds into holes drilled into the unplowed fields. An estimated 620,000 wheat farmers in northern India have adopted various forms of zero tillage on an estimated 1.76 million hectares of land under rice and wheat cultivation, with average income gains amounting to US$180–340 per household per year.

"Drilling" for Crops

The Green Revolution (see Chapter 3) transformed the Indo-Gangetic Plains. The technological package of improved wheat and rice seed, chemical fertilizer, and irrigation, accompanied by supportive policies, led to rapid productivity growth and the advent of rice–wheat systems. In rice–wheat systems, farmers cultivate two crops a year. During the cool, dry winter they grow wheat—the traditional mainstay of food security in the northwest Indo-Gangetic Plains—and during the warm monsoon season, they switch to growing rice. This pattern of cultivation now covers an estimated 14 million hectares of land in the region.[1]

Since the 1990s, however, productivity growth in rice–wheat systems has stagnated for both crops.[2] The main culprits appear to be land degradation—or, the decline in soil quality associated with inappropriate soil and water management—and the tendency for farmers to plant wheat too late to achieve the highest possible yields. By the time farmers have finished harvesting their rice, they are often hard-pressed to prepare their fields and plant wheat in a timely fashion. Rising productivity in rice and wheat has long been the linchpin of food security and rural economic growth in the region, so the slowdown in productivity growth generated serious concern.

A promising option to help address this problem has arisen in the form of zero-tillage cultivation. What if farmers do not have to plow their fields before planting wheat? Eliminating this step not only saves precious time, but also avoids disturbing the soil in ways that contribute to soil degradation and the growth of weeds. By sowing seeds in unplowed fields in small slots or trenches that are carved out by tractor-drawn seed drills, farmers can also avoid drying out the soil and, thus, can use water more sparingly.

The success of zero-tillage cultivation in Argentina, Brazil, Canada, and the United States provided the initial impetus for zero tillage in the

This chapter is based on Erenstein, O. 2009. *Zero tillage in the rice-wheat systems of the Indo-Gangetic Plains: A review of impacts and sustainability implications.* IFPRI Discussion Paper. Washington, D.C.: International Food Policy Research Institute.

Indo-Gangetic Plains. But the zero-tillage practices used on large mechanized farms in the aforementioned countries did not immediately translate into viable practices for small-scale, resource-poor farmers in South Asia.

At first, the specialized agricultural machinery required to plant seeds in a zero-tillage system was not available in the region. In the mid-1980s, though, the International Maize and Wheat Improvement Centre (CIMMYT) introduced a prototype drill in Pakistan. Using this prototype, scientists from Pakistan's National Agricultural Research Centre developed zero-tillage methods suitable for local conditions. In India, CIMMYT introduced a prototype in 1989, and, in 1991, the first prototype of an Indian zero-tillage seed drill was developed at the G. B. Pant University of Agriculture and Technology in Pantnagar.

The goal, however, was to develop a model that local manufacturers could produce and sell at an affordable price. Working with CIMMYT and the Rice-Wheat Consortium for the Indo-Gangetic Plains (a consortium of national and international agricultural research institutions and other partners), both countries undertook programs to

further develop and commercialize zero-tillage drills. Private sector companies improved and adapted the prototype drills, based on feedback from farmers. Most farmers using zero-tillage technology in the region now rely on locally manufactured zero-till seed drills, drawn by tractors, with 6 to 11 tines that sow wheat directly into unplowed fields with a single pass of the tractor.

India in particular was highly successful at developing local manufacturing capacity to adapt and produce zero-tillage drills at a competitive cost. In 2003, the average price of a zero-till drill was $325 in India, compared with $559 in Pakistan.[3] Close links between scientists and farmers in India also helped. Private manufacturers placed machines in villages, where farmers could try them out, allowing for rapid feedback and the refinement of implements. State and local government officials helped disseminate the new technology and even subsidized the equipment to lower its cost to farmers. The Rice-Wheat Consortium helped build the public–private partnership, nurtured it through its formative stages, and facilitated technology transfers from international and national sources.

© IRRI

Rice-wheat inter-cropping

Falling Costs, Rising Incomes

The spread of zero-tillage technology began in the late-1990s and accelerated in the early-2000s, particularly in the northwest Indo-Gangetic Plains of India, where zero- or reduced-tillage wheat accounts for between one-fifth and one-fourth of the wheat area.[4] Surveys of farm households from 2003–04 found that 34.5 percent of sampled farmers in India's Haryana and 19 percent in Pakistan's Punjab used zero tillage (although many of them did not use zero tillage on their entire wheat crop).[5] The spread of zero tillage has been slower in Pakistan than in India, hampered by, among other things, bureaucratic struggles within the national system about whether or not zero tillage was viable as well as a smaller presence of the Rice-Wheat Consortium. In the Indo-Gangetic Plains of India, about 620,000 farmers use zero- and reduced-tillage wheat, which is now estimated to cover 1.76 million hectares of land. Studies show that the payoffs to the investments in the research and development of zero- and reduced-tillage techniques by the Rice-Wheat Consortium of the Indo-Gangetic Plains and CIMMYT were substantial, aided by accelerating farmers' adoption of these practices by at least five years.[6]

In India, a review of zero-tillage wheat studies showed that adopting farmers could increase their incomes by about $97 per hectare of land, for two reasons—zero tillage raised their wheat yields and reduced their production costs.[7] Adopter farm households could increase their annual overall incomes by $180 to $340. Large-scale farm surveys confirmed both a significant yield effect and cost-saving effect in Haryana (see Figure 9.1). But similar farm surveys in Punjab in Pakistan found zero tillage to be primarily a cost-saving technology for wheat cultivation, with no significant yield effect.

The biggest contributor to farmers' increased income is the cost-saving effect. Using zero tillage, farmers spend much less time and fuel using tractors to prepare the land and plant wheat. The tractor-drawn zero-tillage drills allow farmers to make just one pass through their fields rather than the eight passes typically needed during traditional cultivation. As a result, farmers achieve an immediate—and recurrent—cost savings amounting to

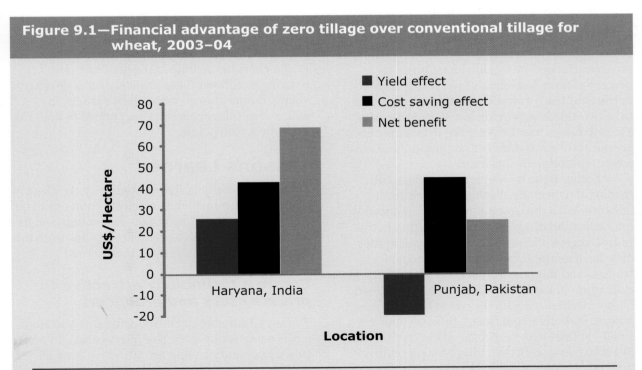

Figure 9.1—Financial advantage of zero tillage over conventional tillage for wheat, 2003–04

Source: Erenstein, O. 2009. Adoption and impact of conservation agriculture–based, resource-conserving technologies in South Asia. In *Proceedings 4th World Congress on Conservation Agriculture, February 4–7, 2009, New Delhi, India*. New Delhi: World Congress on Conservation Agriculture.

about 15 to 16 percent of their operational costs, or about $52 per hectare of land in India.[8]

In addition, zero tillage has been shown to increase wheat yields in India by 5 to 7 percent, further boosting farmers' returns.[9] The rise in yields is closely associated with the timelier planting of wheat. If farmers cannot manage to plant wheat before mid-November, heat stress at the end of the wheat season can reduce their yields by 1 to 1.5 percent a day.[10] By allowing farmers to plant wheat more quickly after the rice harvest, zero tillage can reduce these yield losses.

Zero tillage has reportedly increased families' food consumption in some areas, probably through higher disposable income. And the adoption of zero-tillage cultivation has helped households free up time and money for various other productive, social, and leisure endeavors as well.

Doing More to Reach the Poor

Zero tillage has so far primarily benefited farmers in the northwest Indo-Gangetic Plains of India, who typically operate more intensive and productive rice–wheat systems, have greater institutional support, and suffer from less poverty than do farmers in the eastern Indo-Gangetic Plains. The eastern plains, an area with 500 million people, are characterized by smallholders (70 to 90 percent of farm households farm fewer than 2 hectares of land) and widespread poverty (more than two-thirds survive on less than $2 per day).[11] Yet zero tillage has the potential to generate even greater yield gains and cost savings in these areas, where agriculture is less intensive.

Another issue is whether zero-tillage cultivation practices are displacing agricultural laborers. With the Green Revolution–induced intensification of agricultural production in the Indo-Gangetic Plains, farm labor opportunities have been an important source of income for landless and migrant workers. Yet given that wheat cultivation in the Indo-Gangetic Plains is already highly mechanized with the use of tractors, diesel pumps, and other equipment, this risk appears small—at least with respect to wheat cultivation. But if farmers adopt zero tillage for rice cultivation, laborers could indeed lose their earnings from the labor-intensive process of transplanting rice seedlings into wet fields. It is thus important

to carefully examine the implications of disseminating this technology more widely.

A Step toward Agricultural Sustainability

Zero-tillage cultivation is having positive environmental impacts in the Indo-Gangetic Plains. It saves fossil fuel, reduces greenhouse gas emissions, and cuts water use. Research has shown that farmers can save 36 liters of diesel fuel per hectare of land, an 80 percent savings over conventional wheat tillage.[12] More research is needed to quantify the full range of environmental impacts.

Still, zero tillage should be used as a stepping stone to a broader agricultural concept known as conservation agriculture, which involves minimal disturbance of the soil, retention of residue mulch on the soil surface, and a rational use of crop rotations—an approach increasingly recognized as essential for sustainable agriculture. Zero tillage currently foregoes many of the benefits associated with conservation agriculture because it is applied to only one of the two cropping seasons, without adequate residue management or crop rotation. Reducing the tillage of rice still presents a challenge, particularly in terms of water and weed management and available rice varieties. Researchers in the Indo-Gangetic Plains are working to address these challenges and develop viable "double no-till" rice–wheat systems in which zero-tillage practices are applied to both rice and wheat cultivation.

Lessons Learned

Despite the wealth of information on zero tillage in the Indo-Gangetic Plains, much still remains to be learned about the spread of the technology and its impacts. Nonetheless, several key lessons from the success of zero tillage present themselves.

Create a technology attractive to private users and producers

The key to successfully introducing a new technology is a financially attractive intervention. In many cases, interventions that are attractive from an environmental or social point of view do not get off the ground because of a lack of interest by commercially minded actors—farmers who produce for the market or equipment distributors who sell to farmers. Zero tillage proved attractive from a private viewpoint—for both technology suppliers and technology users—in the Indo-Gangetic Plains.

It is important to show that the technology delivers on its promises in the farmers' villages and fields. Research and development should actively involve farmers through, for instance, participatory projects, farmer-to-farmer exchanges, and traveling seminars. Moving agricultural experts away from the yield paradigm can be a challenge. Producing the same with less can be an attractive proposition to farmers because it enhances their bottom line, but it implies a shift in mindset that has traditionally focused on producing more per unit of area.

Another critical aspect is to link farmers with knowledgeable and accessible technology suppliers, including local manufacturers who can make equipment that will do the job well at a competitive price and adapt and repair it as needed. The successful business model that emerged for zero-tillage drills also benefited from the fact that the zero-tillage drills are applicable across the Indo-Gangetic Plains—a large area with many farmers.

Pay attention to context

Context was imperative in the success of zero tillage in India. The slowdown in productivity growth in rice–wheat systems and concerns about production costs and sustainability opened the door to resource-conserving technologies like zero tillage. Concerned by stagnating productivity, many farmers became interested in prospects

Harvesting wheat with a sickle, India

for improving their bottom line. The increasing problem of herbicide tolerance of the weed Phalaris minor in the Indian state of Haryana also helped break through farmers' reluctance to even try zero-tillage technology. Researchers were interested and excited by the prospects of enabling change in farmers' fields. Policymakers were interested in technological solutions to enhance the sustainability of South Asia's breadbasket while avoiding more demanding institutional changes.

Use institutions and people to promote the technology

The Rice-Wheat Consortium played a pivotal and innovative role as facilitator, information provider, technology clearinghouse, and capacity builder. By providing resources to help get the technology out into farmers' fields and manufacturers' workshops, and by offering a forum in which interested parties could interact, the consortium played a critical role in spreading zero-tillage technology in the Indo-Gangetic Plains. Key champions in the agricultural research and development system also picked up the technology and promoted it despite initial resistance.

Conclusion

Hundreds of thousands of farm households in the Indo-Gangetic Plains have increased their farm income by adopting zero-tillage cultivation, while also generating significant benefits for the environment—reductions in water and fuel use and improvements in soil conservation. Concerted efforts by an array of stakeholders that spanned public and private sectors, national and international research systems, and included several persevering champions provided the institutional support for this technological opportunity to materialize. The success of zero-tillage wheat so far could serve as a stepping stone to conservation agriculture and equitable rural development. And by raising farmers' incomes and preserving the natural resource base on which agriculture depends, zero tillage is laying the groundwork for improved food security in South Asia's Indo-Gangetic Plains in the years to come. ■

NOTES

1. Timsina, J., and D. J. Connor. 2001. Productivity and management of rice-wheat cropping systems: Issues and challenges. *Field Crops Research* 69 (2): 93–132.

2. Ladha, J. K., D. Dawe, H. Pathak, A. T. Padre, R. L. Yadav, B. Singh, Ya. Singh, Y. Singh, P. Singh, A. L. Kundu, R. Sakal, N. Ram, A. P. Regmi, S. K. Gami, A. L. Bhandari, R. Amin, C. R. Yadav, E. M. Bhattarai, S. Das, H. P. Aggarwal, R. K. Gupta, and P. R. Hobbs. 2003. How extensive are yield declines in long-term rice–wheat experiments in Asia? *Field Crops Research* 81: 159–180.

3. Erenstein, O., U. Farooq, R. K. Malik, and M. Sharif. 2007. *Adoption and impacts of zero tillage as a resource-conserving technology in the irrigated plains of South Asia*. Comprehensive Assessment of Water Management in Agriculture Research Report 19. Colombo, Sri Lanka: International Water Management Institute.

4. Several factors make it difficult to reliably measure zero-tillage adoption in the Indo-Gangetic Plains, one of which is the very use and interpretation of the term "zero tillage." Survey respondents may understand this term to mean (1) the use of the zero-till drill (with or without tillage), (2) the practice of not tilling (with or without the zero-tillage drill), or (3) the practice of "reduced tillage"—that is, cultivation using a minimal degree of tilling. See Erenstein, O. 2009. Adoption and impact of conservation agriculture–based, resource-conserving technologies in South Asia. In *Proceedings 4th World Congress on Conservation Agriculture, February 4–7, 2009, New Delhi, India*. New Delhi: World Congress on Conservation Agriculture.

5. Erenstein et al. 2007.

6. Laxmi, V., O. Erenstein, and R. K. Gupta. 2007. *Impact of zero tillage in India's rice–wheat systems*. New Delhi: International Maize and Wheat Improvement Center and Rice-Wheat Consortium; Laxmi, V., O. Erenstein, and R. K. Gupta. 2007. Assessing the impact of NRMR: The case of zero tillage in India's rice-wheat systems. In *International research on natural resource management: Advances in impact assessment*, ed. H. Waibel and D. Zilberman. Wallingford, U.K.: Food and Agriculture Organization of the United Nations and CAB International.

7. Erenstein, O., and V. Laxmi. 2008. Zero tillage impacts in India's rice-wheat systems: A review. *Soil & Tillage Research* 100 (1–2): 1–14.

8. Erenstein et al. 2007; Erenstein and Laxmi 2008.

9. Erenstein and Laxmi 2008.

10. Ortiz-Monasterio, J. I., S. S. Dhillon, and R. A. Fischer. 1994. Date of sowing effects on grain yield and yield components of irrigated spring wheat cultivars and relationships with radiation and temperature in Ludhiana, India. *Field Crops Research* 37 (3): 169–84.

11. Erenstein 2009.

12. Erenstein, O., U. Farooq, R. K. Malik, and M. Sharif. 2008. On-farm impacts of zero-tillage wheat in South Asia's rice-wheat systems. *Field Crops Research* 105 (3): 240–252; Erenstein and Laxmi 2008.

Chapter 10

© IRRI

Pumping up Production
Shallow tubewells and rice in Bangladesh

Mahabub Hossain

As a result of extreme population pressures on declining arable land, Bangladesh has historically struggled with food security. Exacerbating the situation are unpredictable monsoon seasons, flooding, and drought that can cause severe crop damage and yield losses. Despite these endemic challenges, Bangladesh has more than doubled the production of cereal grains since it became an independent nation in 1971.

This surge in productivity can be largely attributed to the proliferation of relatively simple and affordable shallow tubewells along with the development of high-yielding, dry season rice, known locally as *boro* rice. In fact, *boro* rice production has increased from 10 percent of the country's rice total rice production in 1966–67, when the Green Revolution was initiated, to 61 percent in 2008. The additional rice cultivated with the improved *boro* rice variety now feeds nearly 22 million people annually.

In addition to improving food security, *boro* rice has helped stabilize prices of staple food and has been the major factor behind the country's recent downward trend in inflation, as well as in the reduction of poverty by almost 1 percent per year.[1]

Shift in Government Policy Provides the Catalyst for Growth

Modern, small-scale irrigation technologies—devices such as deep tubewells, shallow tubewells, hand tubewells, and low-lift pumps—have played an important role in Bangladesh's agricultural sector since the early-1960s. Their use began in 1962–63 with the supply of low-lift pumps for lifting water from surface sources to adjoining fields. The low-lift pumps spread quickly in the depressed basins of the northeastern and central regions where surface water was easily available in the dry season. By the mid-1970s, nearly 35,000 shallow tubewells were fielded, irrigating nearly 0.57 million hectares of land. By 1982–83, deep tubewells and shallow tubewells together were irrigating 0.61 million hectares of land, 40 percent of the country's total irrigated area.[2]

However, high import duties meant that low-cost pumps and other irrigation equipment from Japan were largely inaccessible for most small-scale farmers. Instead, these farmers were forced to rely on a handful of state-owned companies that controlled the procurement, installation, and distribution and management of irrigation equipment, as well as the distribution of fertilizer and seeds. In spite of substantial government subsidies on equipment and inputs, farmers' total dependence on the government effectively suppressed production capacity as the government struggled to keep up with demand and to efficiently manage the distribution of equipment.

Despite the conventional wisdom of the time warning against privatization, it was clear that Bangladesh's policy of direct involvement in the input market was inefficient and unsustainable.

This chapter is based on Hossain, M. 2009. *The impact of shallow tubewells and boro rice on food security in Bangladesh.* IFPRI Discussion Paper. Washington, D.C.: International Food Policy Research Institute.

Recognizing this reality, in 1979 the government initiated a policy to liberalize modern agricultural inputs, allowing for privatization in the import and marketing of irrigation equipment and chemical fertilizers. The policy reform was completed in 1988–89 with the removal of a ban on the import of small engines, the elimination of import duties, and the withdrawal of restrictions on importing a variety of standard farm equipment. By early 1989, the cost of installing a shallow tubewell to irrigate 4 to 5 hectares of land had fallen to about 60 percent of its subsidized price before privatization.[3]

This policy shift improved farmers' access to minor irrigation equipment and opened the door to the rapid expansion of groundwater irrigation. With the reduction in prices, medium- and small-scale farmers could afford the investment, which they financed mostly with their own savings. The total area of land irrigated increased from 2.06 million hectares in 1988 to 3.56 million hectares in 2001 and 5.05 million hectares in 2008, or an average rate of increase of 150,000 hectares per year. Most of the increase can be attributed to

groundwater exploitation through tubewells, with shallow tubewells accounting for 85 percent of the total increase. Today nearly 70 percent of farm households in Bangladesh use shallow tubewells for irrigation—equivalent to two-thirds of the country's total irrigated area, or some 3.2 million hectares of land.[4]

Boro Rice Leads the Way to Improved Yields and Food Security

About a decade before market liberalization, scientists were working to improve traditional *boro* rice yields. This led to the development of modern varieties of dry-season irrigated *boro* rice, which now are the highest yielding among Bangladesh's three seasonal rice varieties. However, without an irrigation system, *boro* can only be grown in extreme low-lying lands in depressed basins that, given Bangladesh's agroecological conditions, severely limited its production potential. Further, in order to thrive, *boro* rice is relatively dependent

© Chris Stowers/PANOS

Water pump used instead of manual irrigation on rice field

on fertilizer, the supply of which was limited under a government-managed distribution system. *Boro* rice production increased dramatically once these two limitations were vanquished, mostly because privatization led to the spread of minor irrigation equipment and restrictions on fertilizer supply loosened.

With the expansion of shallow tubewells and other irrigation systems, *boro* rice cultivation has gradually spread from the very low-lying lands to higher elevations, replacing the traditional rice varieties known as *aus* (which is drought-tolerant but low-yielding) and deep-water *aman* (a long-duration crop but susceptible to damage by flooding). During 1989–2008, the area of land planted with *aus* and *aman* rice declined by 1.7 million and 0.5 million hectares, respectively, as it was replaced with *boro* rice. In fact, though the total acreage of land under rice cultivation did not change, production has increased from 23 million tons in 1989–90 to 43 million tons in 2007–08, due to the rapid expansion of *boro* rice cultivation. Modern variety *boro* rice is cultivated on nearly all irrigated land in the dry season, and it has accounted for almost the entire increase in Bangladesh's rice production since 1988 (see Figure 10.1).

The increase in rice production after the policy change that eased access to agricultural inputs is estimated at 5.9 million tons per year. The changes that came with the government's liberalization of markets also created 238,000 new full-time jobs.

Increased Production, Decreased Prices

Though *boro* rice is relatively intensive in terms of the amounts of water, fertilizer, and other inputs needed for cultivation, its high yields mean that the costs, when measured against the amount of rice produced, are still lower compared with other varieties. For example, the cost of production per ton of output for *boro* was 22 percent lower than *aus* in 1988 and 17 percent lower in 2007. Reduced production costs for farmers have helped keep rice prices within affordable limits of low-income

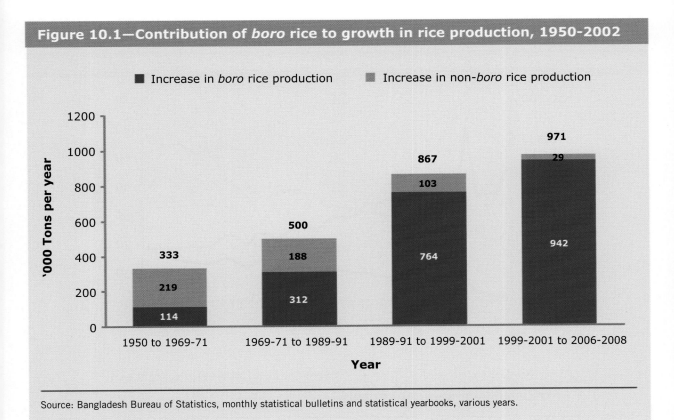

Figure 10.1—Contribution of *boro* rice to growth in rice production, 1950-2002

■ Increase in *boro* rice production ■ Increase in non-*boro* rice production

Source: Bangladesh Bureau of Statistics, monthly statistical bulletins and statistical yearbooks, various years.

rice consumers. The price of rice declined by 0.42 taka per kilogram (kg) (US$6.14 per ton) per year during 1976–88 and a further 0.55 taka per kg ($8.04 per ton) per year from 1988 to 2007 (see Figure 10.2). The cheaper price of rice that followed increased production has been particularly benefi-cial for low-income urban consumers and the rural landless, who spend on average nearly 50 percent of their budget on food (compared with 30 percent for all consumers). In tandem with this outcome, the incidence of poverty declined by 1 percent per year during the 1980s and 1990s. The progress was more rapid at 2 percent per year during 2000–05.[5]

Emergence of a Water Market Benefits Small Farmers

Privatization has led to an increase in the share of farms owning shallow tubewells from just 4.6 percent in 1988 to 22 percent in 2007, and the cost of the tubewells has declined from $670 to $220 during the past two decades. However, ownership is skewed toward larger landholders, with 2007 data showing shallow tubewells in the hands of almost 90 percent of farmers operating farms of more than 2 hectares of land, compared to only 6 percent of farmers operating up to 0.4 hectares. The latter group constitutes 52 percent of farm households in Bangladesh.

But while most marginal farmers do not own shallow tubewells, they have universal access to irrigation through a water market that emerged with the proliferation of the shallow tubewells. Due to the fragmented and scattered nature of landholdings in Bangladesh, land parcels near a tubewell are usually owned by a number of farmers in addition to the tubewell owner. Consequently, the tubewell owner can sell water to operators of adjoining plots to optimize use of the well. This has given rise to active local markets for water transactions, pushed down the costs of water use, provided tubewell owners and users with an incentive to use water wisely and economically, and contributed to widespread adoption of modern rice varieties in the dry season.

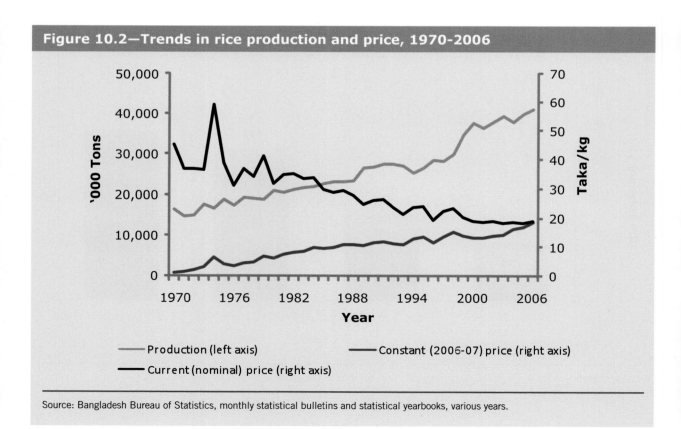

Figure 10.2—Trends in rice production and price, 1970-2006

Production (left axis)   Constant (2006-07) price (right axis)
Current (nominal) price (right axis)

Source: Bangladesh Bureau of Statistics, monthly statistical bulletins and statistical yearbooks, various years.

Environmental Impact

The expansion of *boro* rice cultivation has raised some environmental concerns. One is the prospective decline in soil fertility due to growing more than one crop on the same piece of land, a practice that has increased with the availability of irrigation and the shorter time to maturity of modern rice varieties. However, such double cropping of rice is widely prevalent in medium and high lands only. Also, it is not yet clear whether double cropping and the concomitant yield increases do indeed threaten soil fertility.

Another concern is that *boro* rice is pushing out major noncereal crops such as pulses and oilseeds, important sources of protein and micronutrients for the poor (see Chapter 15). The area of land on which pulses and oilseeds are cultivated indeed has declined over time, though it is unclear whether this is entirely because of the expansion of *boro* rice cultivation.

A third point pertains to the heavy use of pesticides with *boro* rice, which is having an adverse impact on the quality of surface water and the fish habitat. The incidence of pesticide use is very high with *boro* rice compared with other rice varieties. In 2008, more than 80 percent of farmers used pesticides in the cultivation of modern *boro* rice compared with only 9 percent for wheat and about 16 percent for other traditional rice varieties.

Finally, the overexploitation of groundwater resources may be damaging the country's drinking water. Cultivating rice during the dry season is requiring a heavy use of groundwater through shallow tubewells. The National Commission on Agriculture noted that the potential recharge of the aquifer that could be extracted by shallow tubewells had almost been exploited by 1996. Since then, the use of shallow tubewells has expanded, which suggests that the groundwater resources have already been overexploited. To address this problem, other options could be considered, such as harvesting rainwater and a synchronized use of surface water and groundwater for further expansion of *boro* cultivation in Bangladesh.

Another concern related to the country's drinking water is arsenic contamination, which has been shown to be a serious problem in Bangladesh.[6] However, its link with the exploitation of groundwater for *boro* cultivation has yet to be firmly established.

Lessons Learned: The Right Equipment and the Right Policies Plant the Seeds for Improved Food Security

In the 1960s when the long-term irrigation policy and water-resource development plans were formulated, policymakers and civil society generally agreed that private investment-based minor irrigation was inappropriate for Bangladesh because they feared that small farmers and share tenants would be marginalized by such a system. When the privatization of the input market began to take hold in Bangladesh in the early-1980s, this sentiment remained largely unchanged, with concerns that privatization would create inequity in access to irrigation water and promote further inequality in the distribution of agricultural income.[7]

Yet the experience shows a different outcome. The relaxation on import duties on minor irrigation equipment and the encouragement of private trade in the input market did not stand in the way of progress. Farmers' increased access to small-scale irrigation equipment such as shallow tubewells has allowed for high-yielding *boro* rice in Bangladesh to be cultivated on low-lying lands as well as on medium-low and medium-high elevations.

With the Bangladesh government's decision to deregulate input markets, particularly for minor irrigation equipment, the area of land under *boro* rice cultivation expanded tremendously. The gross effect of market liberalization for minor irrigation equipment is an additional 5.9 million metric tons of rice production per year, enough to feed an additional 22 million people. ■

NOTES

1. Ravallion, M. and B. Sen. 1996. When method matters: monitoring poverty in Bangladesh. *Economic Development and Cultural Change* 44 (4): 761–792; Narayan, A. and Z. Hassan. 2009. *Breaking down poverty in Bangladesh*. Dhaka, Bangladesh: University Press Ltd.

2. Ahmed, R. 1995. Liberalization of agricultural input markets in Bangladesh: Process, impact and lessons. *Agricultural Economics* 12: 115–128; Ahmed, R., S. Haggblade, and T. E. Chowdhury. 2000. *Out of the shadow of famine: Evolving food market and food policy in Bangladesh*. Baltimore and London: Johns Hopkins University Press; Mandal, M. A. S. 1987. Imperfect institutional innovation for irrigation management in Bangladesh. *Irrigation and Drainage Systems* 3: 239–258.

3. Gisselquist, D. 1992. Empowering farmers in Bangladesh: Trade reforms open doors to new technology. Paper presented to the Annual Conference of the Association for Economic Development Studies in Bangladesh. Washington D.C.: World Bank.

4. Bangladesh Ministry of Agriculture. 2008. *Minor irrigation survey report 2007-08*. Dhaka, Bangladesh: Ministry of Agriculture.

5. Ravallion and Sen 1996; Narayan and Hassan 2009.

6. Kinniburg, D. G. and P. L. Smedley, eds. 2001. *Arsenic contamination of groundwater in Bangladesh. Phase 1*. Final technical report of the British Geological Survey and Department of Public Health Engineering WC/00/19. www.bgs.ac.uk/arsenic/bphase1/b_intro.htm. Harvey, C. F., C. H. Swartz, A. B. Badruzzaman, N. Keon-Blute, W. Yu, M. A. Ali, J. Jay, R. Beckie, V. Niedan, D. Brabander, P. M. Oates, K. N. Ashfaque, S. Islam, H. F. Hemond, and M. F. Ahmed. 2002. Arsenic mobility and groundwater extraction in Bangladesh. *Science* 298: 1602–1606; Brammer, H. 2009. Mitigation of arsenic contamination in irrigated paddy soils in South and Southeast Asia. *Environment International* 35: 856–863.

7. Osmani, S. R. and M. A. Quasem. 1990. *Research monograph 11: Pricing and subsidy policies for Bangladesh agriculture*. Dhaka, Bangladesh: Bangladesh Institute of Development Studies; Quasem, M. A. 1985. Impact of the new system of the distribution of irrigation machines in Bangladesh. *The Bangladesh Development Studies* 13 (3): 127–140; Howes, M. 1985. *Whose water? An investigation of the consequences of alternative approaches to small scale irrigation in Bangladesh*. Dhaka, Bangladesh: Bangladesh Institute of Development Studies.

Chapter 11

Pushing the Yield Frontier

Hybrid rice in China

Jiming Li, Yeyun Xin, and Longping Yuan

In the second half of the 20th century, a race was underway in China between a blistering rate of population growth and vigorous efforts to feed an expanding populace by increasing rice production. Efforts in the 1960s to boost rice production gained ground with the introduction of semidwarf rice varieties that increased yields from 2 to 3.5 tons per hectare by 1975. These gains were respectable, but not sufficient. So Chinese scientists started developing even higher-yielding rice.

In 1976, Chinese scientists had made a crucial breakthrough, successfully commercializing what is known as three line hybrid rice, raising yields to more than 5 tons per hectare by 1983. As the technology advanced, nationwide rice yields averaged more than 6 tons per hectare by 1995. And by 2004, yields of super hybrid rice cultivated in selected regions had achieved yields of more than 10 tons per hectare.[1]

By pushing rice yields steadily and dramatically upward, the development of hybrid rice has allowed China to feed an additional 60 million people a year while reducing the land allocated to rice production by 14 percent since 1978. Hybrid rice now accounts for 63 percent of all land under rice cultivation in China, helping to make it the world's largest rice-consuming country that also is self-sufficient in rice production.[2]

Breakthroughs in Rice Breeding

Historically, food security has been one of China's greatest challenges. Since 1950, China's arable land has been halved from 0.18 to 0.10 hectare per person, while its population has more than doubled from about 560 million to 1.3 billion.[3] Rice imports could not meet China's burgeoning demand—only a small share of global rice production reaches world trading systems. Agricultural production has thus become one of China's top priorities.

China began its effort to develop hybrid rice in 1964 (see box next page). In hybrids, the offspring plants of two genetically distinct parents offer higher yields or other positive traits superior to those of their parent plants (see Chapter 4). But scientists faced special challenges in developing hybrid rice because rice, unlike maize, is a self-pollinating crop, with small florets that contain both male and female organs. To overcome this

Inspecting a hybrid rice strain

This chapter is based on Li, J., Y. Xin, and L. Yuan. 2009. *Hybrid rice technology development: Ensuring China's food security.* IFPRI Discussion Paper. Washington D.C.: International Food Policy Research Institute.

Scientist examines new hybrid rice seed varieties

difficulty, China's rice breeders developed a system that combined three lines, or types, of rice rather than just two. First, a male sterile plant (called the A line) is bred, or crossed, with a genetically identical plant that is not sterile (called the maintainer line, or B line). The resulting plant is another male sterile plant that can then be crossbred with a genetically distinct plant (called the restorer line, or R line). The offspring is then a plant with fertile hybrid seeds.

Scientists spent years searching for and developing A, B, and R lines that could produce rice plants with strong hybrid vigor. China's Ministry of Science and Technology and Ministry of Agriculture put their weight behind this effort, naming the three-line hybrid rice technology one of 22 key research projects in 1971. From 1972 to 1975, scientists tested thousands of hybrids, comparing them with yields from other rice varieties commonly cultivated by farmers. The hybrids beat the yield results of these other varieties by 20 to 30 percent, signaling that hybrids had the potential to generate a significant jump in the country's rice yields.[4]

Still, the early hybrids faced a number of challenges: they were all based on a narrow genetic base, they were susceptible to disease, they produced only one late crop a year, and they produced relatively few grains when cultivated for seed production. As a consequence, farmer adoption of hybrids stagnated. It was not until the late-1970s and early-1980s that scientists introduced more A lines to diversify the genetic base of hybrid rice and develop hybrids with different crop maturity dates and lower vulnerability to diseases and pests. By planting hybrids that were best suited for the agroecological conditions of their land and

History of Hybrid Rice Technology Development in China

1964	China begins research on three-line hybrid rice breeding
1974	Scientists develop first sets of three lines (A, B, and R lines) for a three-line system of breeding hybrid rice
1976	China starts hybrid rice commercialization
1977	Scientists develop systematic techniques for hybrid rice seed production
1987	Hybrid rice acreage surpasses 10 million hectares; China establishes a national two-line system hybrid rice program
1990	Hybrid rice acreage exceeds 15 million hectares
1995	Scientists develop two-line system of breeding hybrid rice
1996	China launches national program to breed super hybrid rice
2000	China achieves super hybrid rice Phase I objectives (10.5 tons per hectare)
2004	China achieves super hybrid rice Phase II objectives (12.0 tons per hectare)
2006	China starts work on super hybrid rice Phase III objectives (13.5 tons per hectare)

by adopting appropriate cultivation practices, Chinese farmers were rapidly able to reap the yield benefits of this new development in rice.

Hybrid rice cultivation also received a boost from concurrent policy reforms that occurred in China during the 1980s—primarily the transition from the collective production system before 1979 to the household responsibility system after 1981 (see Chapter 19), and the liberalization of the rice retail market in 1993. These policy shifts gave rice farmers more freedom to decide what types of rice to cultivate and encouraged hybrid rice breeders to develop hybrids designed to meet consumer preferences rather than strictly meeting production quotas.

Winnowing of harvested hybrid rice

Ramping Up Seed Production

Still, producing enough good-quality, affordable seed to meet the farmers' growing demand for hybrid rice remained a challenge. Without sufficient quantities of seed for farmers, the gains generated through years of research would be lost. Scientists devoted themselves to studying genetics, environmental conditions, and water and fertilizer management in hybrid seed produc-

tion, and by 1975, they had developed a systematic package of techniques for producing hybrid rice seed. An army of about 30,000 people from rice-growing provinces, including farmers, researchers and technicians, converged on Hainan Island in 1975 to produce hybrid seeds. They succeeded in producing enough seeds to provide the raw material needed to launch large-scale commercial seed production in 1976, which was followed by large-scale hybrid rice cultivation in both southern and northern rice-growing regions (Figure 11.1).

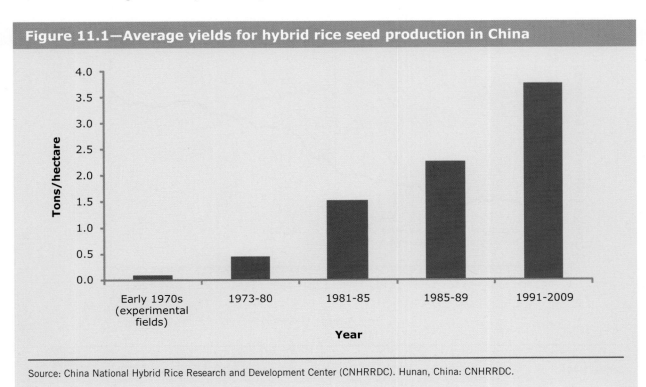

Figure 11.1—Average yields for hybrid rice seed production in China

Y-axis: Tons/hectare (0.0 to 4.0)

X-axis (Year): Early 1970s (experimental fields), 1973-80, 1981-85, 1985-89, 1991-2009

Source: China National Hybrid Rice Research and Development Center (CNHRRDC). Hunan, China: CNHRRDC.

This seed production effort had not only helped to ensure that plenty of high-quality seeds would be available for commercial hybrid rice production, but it also lowered costs for seed businesses and farmers, promoting the fast and steady expansion of hybrid rice production throughout China. Many large hybrid rice seed businesses emerged in the late-1970s with the encouragement and support of the state.

Pushing the Yield Boundaries

In the early-1970s a Chinese scientist discovered a male sterile rice plant whose sterility could be controlled by length of daylight or temperature. In 1987, scientists proposed a way of using this material (called environment-conditioned genic male sterility, or EGMS) to develop hybrids using just two lines. By controlling the male sterility or fertility on the same plant under different environmental conditions, scientists could eliminate a step in the hybrid development process. Besides simplifying the process of developing a hybrid, the new two-line system was more effective in terms of both seed production and commercial rice production. In trials in southern China between 1998 and 2003, a number of two-line hybrids showed remarkable yield increases over the three-line hybrids.[5] Dozens of two-line hybrids were released into commercial production, and by 2008, two-line hybrids occupied 3.3 million hectares of land under rice cultivation, about 11 percent of total rice acreage and 22 percent of total hybrid rice acreage.[6]

But China has worked to push the yield boundaries still further. Encouraged by efforts in Japan and at the International Rice Research Institute to develop super-high-yielding rice, China proposed a super hybrid rice program in 1996. The program set ambitious yield targets: it aimed to achieve 10.5 tons per hectare between 1996 and 2000 (Phase I), 12 tons per hectare between 2001 and 2005 (Phase II), and 13.5 tons per hectare between 2006 and 2015 (Phase III). Indeed, the program achieved its phase-one target in 2000 and its phase-two target in 2004. By 2006, the Ministry of Agriculture had certified 34 rice hybrids as "super rice."[7] Chinese rice breeders are now working on phase three.

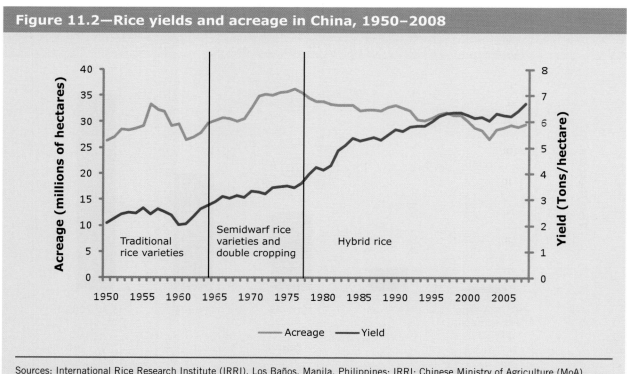

Figure 11.2—Rice yields and acreage in China, 1950–2008

Acreage (millions of hectares)

Yield (Tons/hectare)

Traditional rice varieties

Semidwarf rice varieties and double cropping

Hybrid rice

—— Acreage —— Yield

Sources: International Rice Research Institute (IRRI). Los Baños, Manila, Philippines: IRRI; Chinese Ministry of Agriculture (MoA). Beijing: MoA.

More Food, Jobs, and Land

Hybrid rice technology has been essential to China's self-sufficiency in rice production. China's total rice production increased from 136.7 million tons in 1978 to 197 million tons in 2008—a 44.1 percent jump—as the hybrid rice program raised the national average yield from 3.4 tons per hectare to 6.7 tons per hectare (a 67.5 percent increase in yield) (Figure 11.2). This growth in production has allowed China to feed an additional 60 million people per year. The concurrent reforms in China's land tenure system also played an important role in promoting hybrid rice cultivation and improving production incentives for farmers.

The fact that hybrid rice's yield advantage has enabled China to cultivate it using less land is also clearly important. China reduced its total rice-growing acreage from about 34.4 million hectares in 1978 to 29.4 million hectares in 2008, a 14.5 percent decrease. Farmers could thus diversify into production of other crops, including high-value crops such as fruits and vegetables, on land not used for rice farming.[8] China's commercialized rice hybrids also have adapted better than conventional inbred rice to a whole range of climatic and geographic conditions, including high-stress environments. Their vigorous root system, strong stem, thick leaves, and high photosynthesis efficiency give them a significant yield advantage in rice-growing regions where environmental stresses are more acute.

Hybrid rice technology has had an impact on China's labor market as well. Hybrid rice research, extension, seed production, and allied industries employ tens of thousands of people, while the hybrid rice cultivation itself has helped to release rural labor into other off-farm areas of employment, such as rural industries.

Keys to Success

One of the most important elements in the successful development and dissemination of hybrid rice was the full support and commitment of the Chinese government. From the research programs of the mid-1960s to today, the government has provided generous funding, conducive policies, and information campaigns that promoted the research, development, and deployment of hybrid rice.

Coordination and collaboration were also critical for developing the new rice technologies. Commercializing both the three-line and two-line

Consuming rice, China

hybrid rice varieties took years of cooperative research by hundreds of rice scientists from research institutes and universities. A sophisticated three-tier seed system and four-level research extension network also were key contributors to the success. The three-tier seed system included provincial seed companies to purify parental lines, prefectural seed companies to multiply A lines, and county-level seed companies to produce hybrid seeds. This system ensured a high quantity and quality of the hybrid rice seed for commercial production. The four-level extension network consisted of county, commune, brigade, and production teams to evaluate, select, and promote hybrid rice and appropriate cultivation practices.

Finally, hybrid rice would not have been successful in China without the emergence of a hybrid rice seed industry. Cultivation of hybrid rice increased from 140,000 hectares in 1976 to 18.6 million hectares in 2008, with a commensurate increase in demand for hybrid seed.[9] With a combination of policy support and financial subsidies from the state in the initial phases, the seed industry has gone from a small venture in seed production to a vibrant business sector that now manages large and competitive production and distribution systems.

Lessons from China's Experiences

China's experiences offer a number of lessons. From an institutional and policy standpoint, full government support and commitment were imperative. Government policies and standards made hybrid rice attractive, profitable, and sustainable, and government support was important—especially in the early stages—for research; seed production; and farmers' purchases of hybrid seed, pesticides, and fertilizers.

Furthermore, a national, high-ranking scientist coordinated and oversaw the progress of technology development. Adequate human resources—from full-time researchers all the way to extension workers devoted to publicizing the technology—ensured helpful participation from multiple disciplines related to the technology.

In addition, an effective seed production infrastructure was essential, along with minimum seed quality standards and long-term maintenance of genetic purity of parental lines and hybrid seeds. Given that different ecological rice-growing regions or markets need unique hybrids, it was critical that research and extension infrastructures were regional.

Lastly, comprehensive training programs, which included plot demonstrations, technology workshops, technical briefings, frontline demon-strations, field tours, and mass media campaigns, helped popularize the remarkable yield improvement of hybrid rice.

Conclusion

Even in the wake of the successes of the past several decades, hybrid rice in China faces a number of challenges. Rice farming, which contributes to soil erosion and salinization, has caused considerable environmental stresses. Existing hybrid rice varieties have gradually lost resistance to disease and insects. To maintain and increase yields, Chinese hybrid rice breeders must continually develop new hybrids with multiple resistances to diseases and insects. Yet with a majority of educated young and middle-aged workers moving to metropolitan areas, producing and promoting hybrid rice will become more difficult. Continued investment in agricultural research and continuous innovation in developing, promoting, and sharing new technologies are essential in sustaining the gains achieved by hybrid rice technologies developed in China. ∎

NOTES

1. Yuan, L. P. 2007. Proposal of implementing the "planting-three-produce four" high-yielding project on super hybrid rice. *Hybrid Rice* 22 (4): 1.

2. Chinese Ministry of Agriculture. Beijing: Ministry of Agriculture.

3. Riley, N. 2004. China's population: New trends and challenges. *Population Bulletin* 59 (2): 1–36.

4. Lin, S. C. and L. P. Yuan. 1980. Hybrid rice breeding in China. In *Innovative approaches to rice breeding.* Selected papers presented at the International Rice Research Conference, 1979, in Los Baños, Philippines. Manila, Philippines: International Rice Research Institute.

5. Yang, S. H., B. Y. Cheng, and W. F. Shen. 2004. Progress of hybrid rice breeding in Southern China. *Hybrid Rice* 19 (5): 1–5.

6. Lu, X. G., S. S. Virmani, and R. C. Yang. 1998. Advances in two-line hybrid rice breeding. In *Advances in hybrid rice technology,* ed. S. S. Virmani, E. A. Siddiq, and K. Muralidharan. Proceedings of the 3rd International Symposium on Hybrid Rice, November 14–16, 1996. Hyderabad, India, and Manila, Philippines: International Rice Research Institute.

7. Qi, Y. L., S. S. Shi, X. C. Yu, G. W. Sheng, and J. D. Hu. 2007. China's super hybrid rice breeding research progress and strategy. *Chinese Agricultural Science Bulletin* 23 (9): 263–68.

8. Virmani, S. S. Progress and issues in development and use of hybrid rice in the tropics. 2002. In *Sustainable rice production for food security: Proceedings of the 20th session of the International Rice Commission, Bangkok, Thailand, 23–26 July 2002,* ed. D. V. Tran and R. Duffy. Rome: Food and Agriculture Organization of the United Nations.

9. Chinese Ministry of Agriculture. Beijing: Ministry of Agriculture.

Chapter 12

© Douglas Smith

Improving Crops for Arid Lands
Pearl millet and sorghum in India

Carl E. Pray and Latha Nagarajan

Millions of small-scale farmers in India live in harsh environments where rainfall is limited and irrigation and fertilizer are unavailable. India's arid and semiarid lands constitute more than 50 percent of the country's geographic area and are home to 60 percent of the rural population. Farmers in states such as Andhra Pradesh, Gujarat, Karnataka, and Rajasthan have long grown sorghum and pearl millet—hardy crops that can thrive in almost any soil and survive under relatively tough conditions. Production from these crops was low, however, and so were returns to farmers, until improved, higher-producing varieties were developed and distributed starting in the 1970s. Since then, a succession of more productive and disease-resistant varieties has raised farmers' yields and improved the livelihoods of about 6 million millet-growing households and 3 million sorghum-growing households.

The success and sustainability of these improved varieties resulted from three inter-ventions by the Indian government and the international community: increased investments in crop improvements during the 1970s, the devel-opment of efficient seed systems with a gradual inclusion of the private sector in the 1980s, and the liberalization of the Indian seed industry in the late-1990s. Thanks to these interventions, improved varieties have delivered benefits to some of the poorest people and areas in India.

An evolving partnership between public research and private industry has played a central role in getting these improved varieties out to millions of poor and small-scale farmers in India's arid and semiarid lands. By allowing farmers to grow the same amount of millet or sorghum using half as much land, these improved varieties have made it possible for farmers to shift farmland to valuable cash crops—that is, crops they can sell in the market—and thereby raise their incomes.

Dryland Farming in India

Millions of Indian farmers must eke out a living by cultivating crops in areas where rainfall is low and unreliable. Among the crops suited to these harsh conditions are millet and sorghum, which belong to a group of annual grasses that produce small grain seeds and are often cultivated as cereals. Millet comes in many varieties, including pearl millet, finger millet, little millet, and foxtail millet, but here "millet" refers to pearl millet only. Millet and sorghum are widely grown in Africa, Asia, and Russia and can be used as grain or forage. They are resistant to drought, grow quickly (the period from planting to harvest is typically three to four months), and can be cultivated in a wide range of soil types.

In India, sorghum is predominantly grown in arid and semiarid regions, particularly in the states of Andhra Pradesh, Karnataka, Maharashtra, and Tamil Nadu. Farmers can grow it with as little as 400–500 millimeters of rain a year. If rainfall is slightly higher—500–600 millimeters a year— farmers tend to prefer pearl millet over sorghum and grow it extensively in the dry western and northern regions of the country, specifically in the states of Gujarat, Haryana, and Rajasthan.

This chapter is based on Pray, C. E., and L. Nagarajan. 2009. *Pearl millet and sorghum improvement in India.* IFPRI Discussion Paper. Washington D.C.: International Food Policy Research Institute.

Sorghum and millet are the principal sources of energy, protein, vitamins, and minerals for millions of the poorest people in harsh and unfavorable agricultural environments. These crops currently constitute an estimated 11.4 percent of the global cereal area harvested and 4.1 percent of the total output of world cereals.[1]

The Indian Government Invests in Millet and Sorghum Research

The first advances in millet and sorghum research in India resulted from the efforts of a range of government institutions. In the early 1960s, the Indian Council of Agricultural Research (ICAR),

with assistance from the Rockefeller Foundation, initiated research on hybrid sorghum and pearl millet. Success came relatively quickly. The first sorghum hybrid (CSH-1), bred in India, was officially released for commercial cultivation in 1964, followed by the first pearl millet hybrid (HB 1) in 1965.

In 1967, to help organize and focus research on these two crops, ICAR initiated the All India Coordinated Millet Improvement Project, and two years later, the All India Coordinated Sorghum Improvement Project. These programs organized government research and in many locations tested for improved characteristics of hybrids and varieties—through state agricultural universities, research institutes, and experiment stations.

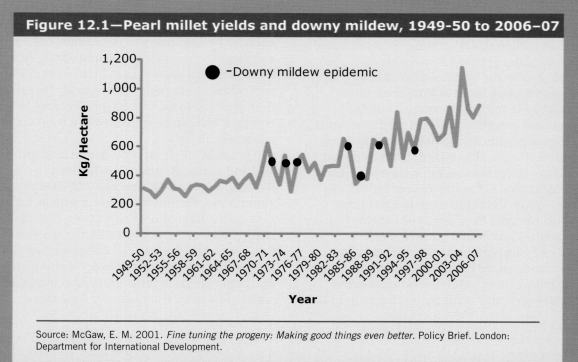

Pearl Millet and Downy Mildew

Plant researchers must continually issue new varieties of pearl millet to stay ahead of the threat of downy mildew. During the past few decades, a boom-and-bust pattern has developed: an improved variety of pearl millet is released to the public, generating hefty gains in productivity; a few years later, the variety becomes susceptible to downy mildew, yields fall, and the cycle begins again (see Figure 12.1).

So far, the only solution appears to be constant research to improve pearl millet's resistance to the disease. In recent years, both public and private entities have released pearl millet varieties that are resistant to downy mildew and have achieved widespread adoption, but it may only be a matter of time before these varieties, like the ones released before them, become vulnerable to the fungus and must be replaced.

Figure 12.1—Pearl millet yields and downy mildew, 1949-50 to 2006–07

Source: McGaw, E. M. 2001. *Fine tuning the progeny: Making good things even better*. Policy Brief. London: Department for International Development.

The creation of the International Crops Research Institute for the Semi-Arid Tropics (ICRISAT) in 1972 further stimulated research on sorghum and pearl millet and contributed substantially to the research effort on these crops.

Joint efforts by these institutions resulted in the release of a succession of pearl millet hybrids offering yield advantages. Since the mid-1960s, average grain yields have nearly doubled, even though much of the production of millet has shifted to more marginal production environments. Production of pearl millet in India currently stands at 9 million tons and hybrids cover more than half of the total national pearl millet area of 10 million hectares.[2] Researchers face a constant challenge from downy mildew, however—a fungus that can cause crop losses of up to nearly 100 percent (see box previous page).[3]

Similarly, tremendous advances in sorghum improvement resulted from decades of a partnership between ICRISAT and the Indian national agricultural research system. Although the first set of sorghum hybrids was released in the mid-1960s, many other popular hybrids have followed, augmenting the spread of sorghum hybrids and pushing up productivity, especially for *kharif* sorghum, or rainy season sorghum. The hybrids reflect impressive advances in diversifying parental lines and incorporating resistance to major pests and diseases.

Cultivating a Seed Industry

At the beginning of the Green Revolution, it became clear to the Indian government and to key state governments that state extension services and emerging private seed companies could not distribute enough seed to allow for the large-scale adoption of new varieties. The government decided to create state seed corporations, the first of which evolved out of the G. B. Pant University of Agriculture and Technology in Pantnagar. This corporation then became a model for the National Seed Corporation and other state seed corporations. The Indian government, with the financial support of the World Bank and technical assistance from the Rockefeller Foundation, financed the development of state seed corporations in most major Indian states in the 1960s. Gradually these state seed corporations replaced state departments of seed production and formed the nascent foundations of a formal seed industry.

Often, formal seed industries are taken for granted, especially in industrial countries, where agriculture is extremely productive. But in India, as in many other countries, seed industries are still emerging. The problem stems from the limited profitability of seeds. When farmers are able to plant and save seeds from one season to the next without losing much in terms of yield and output, there is little need for them to purchase new seeds—and little opportunity for seed producers to sell new seeds.

It is only when commercial seeds offer clear advantages in terms of quality and performance that farmers become more willing to purchase them. When improvements are bred into a crop, for example, farmers must buy or otherwise gain access to the improved seed to realize the benefits of breeding. Farmers must also buy seeds for hybrids, the yields of which tend to drop when grain from harvests is saved and planted in the next season (see Chapter 4).

But seed industries do not emerge simply by themselves. The right rules and regulations must be in place to encourage private investment in the industry and to limit the role of the public sector where it is a less-efficient purveyor of seed to farmers. In India, this institutional framework for the development of a seed industry emerged with the Indian Seed Act in 1966. The nascent Indian seed industry was heavily regulated under the act, however, with limited entry and formation of large firms—domestic or foreign. Private seed imports for both commercial and research purposes were restricted or banned, ostensibly to protect smallholders from predatory corporate practices.

A Private Seed Industry Emerges

Since the 1970s, the private sector has played an ever-increasing role in developing improved varieties of millet and sorghum and distributing them to farmers, through innovative partnerships with public-sector agencies. In 1971, India began deregulating the seed sector, relaxing restrictions on seed imports and private firms' entry into the seed market. This change, combined with a new seed policy in 1988, spurred enormous growth in private-sector seed supplies in India. Currently, the Indian market for agricultural seed is one of the biggest in the world.

Millet and sorghum sold at market, India

Sorghum and pearl millet breeding by private companies began around 1970, when four companies had their own sorghum and pearl millet breeding programs. By 1985 this number had grown to 10 companies. In 1981, a private company developed and released the first hybrid pearl millet.

One major reason for the spurt in private-sector growth was the strong public-sector research on sorghum and millet. International agricultural research centers such as ICRISAT exchanged breeding material with public and private research institutions. National agricultural research centers such as ICAR and agricultural universities provided breeder seed not only to the national and state seed corporations, but also to private seed companies to be multiplied and distributed through their company outlets, farmer cooperatives, and private dealers. For private firms, public institutions like ICRISAT, ICAR, and state universities provided invaluable genetic materials free of charge.

Today, more than 60 private seed companies supply improved pearl millet to small-scale farmers and account for 82 percent of the total seed supply, while more than 40 companies supply improved sorghum, accounting for 75 percent of supply. Many of these companies benefit not only from the availability of public research on improved pearl millet and sorghum, but also from innovative partnerships that specifically aim to disseminate new materials to the private sector. The most recognized of these partnerships is ICRISAT's hybrid consortia, developed in 2000–01. Private companies pay a membership fee to ICRISAT to receive nonexclusive access to hybrid parent lines that can then be used for the development and marketing of their own seed products. Although no single company has a monopoly over an individual line—all companies can use them for their own purposes as they choose—the market is currently large enough to allow all companies to compete for the smallholders' business.

The ultimate beneficiaries of this public–private system are the millions of small-scale farmers who grow sorghum and millet. Public research agencies contribute genetic materials and scientific expertise to improve crop varieties when the incentives for private-sector involvement are limited. Then, private companies take on the final development of new varieties and seed distribution—tasks to which they are often better suited than are public agencies. In this way, the benefits of crop improvements are delivered directly to farmers, who find them worthwhile enough to support financially.

Impacts of Improved Millet and Sorghum

During the past four decades, farmers have benefited from rising millet and sorghum yields (see Figure 12.2). Although yields of pearl millet stagnated for a time, perhaps owing to frequent outbreaks of downy mildew, they rebounded again in the mid-1980s, when ICRISAT released varieties with greater resistance to the fungus.

Farmers have readily adopted the improved varieties of sorghum and millet. By 1992–94, about 55 percent of the hectares of land under sorghum and pearl millet cultivation in India were planted with improved varieties, nearly doubling the productivity of both crops compared with the unimproved varieties. The area under cultivation with improved varieties continues to rise and so does productivity. In addition, as the number of varieties to choose from increases, farmers seek out more appropriate varieties for their growing conditions and consequently tend to experience more stable yields. Six million hectares of land under pearl millet cultivation (more than 60 percent of the total pearl millet area) in India are now planted with more than 70 hybrids, of which at least 80 percent are from the private sector, many based on genetic materials from ICRISAT.[4]

Because sorghum and millet are central to poor people's diets in arid and semiarid regions of India, when yields rise, the benefits to those people are direct and immediate. In rural areas of the state of Maharashtra, sorghum accounts for 48 percent of total per capita cereal consumption, and in rural Rajasthan and dry areas of Gujarat, pearl millet accounts for more than 50 percent of cereal consumption, contributing to about 20–40 percent of people's total energy and protein intake.[5]

Besides providing more pearl millet and sorghum to consume, the improved varieties also offer significant economic returns to farmers. It has been conservatively estimated that the annual returns to India's farmers from pearl millet varieties developed by ICRISAT total US$50 million—more than 12 times the cost of its investment in pearl millet research.[6]

Sustainability of the Interventions

Sorghum and pearl millet policies and the programs that support them appear to be sustainable for several reasons. Farmers' demand for a range of millet crops and millet varieties in the arid and semiarid regions of India (including the states of Karnataka, Andhra Pradesh, Rajasthan, and Gujarat) is unlikely to diminish in the near future because currently few substitute crops for these harsh growing environments exist. Moreover, new sources of demand are emerging for sorghum, such as for biofuels and animal and poultry feeds.

Moreover, the public and private seed industry continues to receive valuable genetic materials from the public-sector research system and thus finds the development of new pearl millet and sorghum products profitable. Although 80–90 percent of the benefits from the adoption of sorghum and millet hybrids went to farmers, the spread of privately released hybrids shows that private firms are also benefiting enough to induce them to invest in the research and development of cultivars for small farmers in unirrigated regions.[7]

It is noteworthy that the amount of land cultivated with sorghum and millet has steadily declined. Still, overall production of pearl millet is increasing, primarily because of higher yields. These higher and more stable yields for pearl millet have enabled farmers to plant millet on a smaller area of land and to use a larger area for other crops, particularly cash crops. Sorghum yields have risen more slowly than those for millet, and thus overall sorghum production has declined along with the area under cultivation. During the rainy season, the area of land under sorghum cultivation in particular has declined considerably, owing to competition from other high-value crops such as maize, cotton, and soybean.

In India's more-favored growing environments, where farmers have access to irrigation and rising incomes are changing food-consumption patterns, the area sown to sorghum and other millet crops is gradually giving way to rice, wheat, maize, and other specialty crops. This trend is in part due to government pricing and promotion policies that favor wheat, rice, and

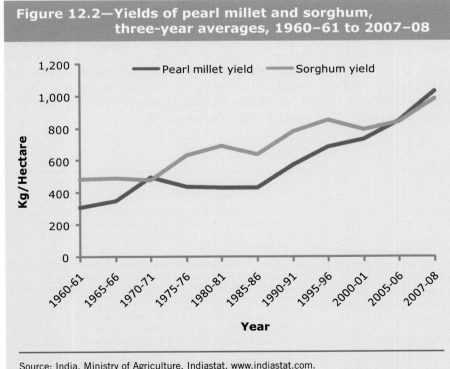

Figure 12.2—Yields of pearl millet and sorghum, three-year averages, 1960–61 to 2007–08

Source: India, Ministry of Agriculture. Indiastat. www.indiastat.com.
Note: For 2007–08, actual data, rather than three-year averages, were used to denote the current trend.

maize. If at some point the government decides that it cannot afford to continue subsidizing wheat, rice, and maize production, demand for sorghum and pearl millet is likely to increase.

Learning from India's Experience

All three elements of the Indian interventions to improve sorghum and pearl millet hybrids were important. First, the investments in public-sector plant-breeding and crop-management research were made by the national government, state governments, and international agricultural research centers. When hybrids of sorghum and millet were first being developed, all three of these groups contributed genetic material that benefited farmers directly and provided the basis for private researchers to develop new varieties.

Second, the government invested in seed production in public and private institutions. The Indian government and state governments, with the help of donors, made major investments in government seed corporations that multiplied the seeds of not only wheat, rice, and maize, but also pearl millet and sorghum. Seed laws were written and enforced to allow small private-sector seed companies to enter into the seed business and make profits. The government also provided training for people involved in the seed industry in both public and private institutions.

Third, India liberalized the seed sector starting in the mid-1980s. Instead of allowing state seed corporations to become regional monopolies,

the government opened the doors to investment by large Indian firms and allowed foreign direct investment in the sector. This change, coupled with continuing investments in public plant breeding and public–private partnerships, has continued to provide private firms with a steady stream of genetic materials for developing proprietary hybrids. India also benefits from a seed law that allows companies to sell truthfully labeled seed without having to go through costly and time-consuming certification and registration processes for new hybrids and varieties. The result is a vibrant and sustainable supply of seed of new cultivars that are drought-tolerant and resistant to many pests and diseases.

Conclusion

Since the mid-1960s, yields of pearl millet and sorghum in India have doubled. In contrast to the major Green Revolution crops, very few yield increases of millet and sorghum is attributable to irrigation, given that 90 percent or more of these crops is grown in unirrigated, rainfed conditions. This doubling of yields has allowed farmers to grow the same amount of food using half as much land, further allowing them in many cases to shift land to valuable cash crops and increase their incomes. In addition, millet and sorghum contributed to food security because they are considerably more resistant to drought, pests, and diseases than other major food grains. Furthermore, because the wealthy tend to eat rice and wheat, the benefits of these new technologies have gone primarily to poor Indian consumers. ■

NOTES

1. FAO (Food and Agriculture Organization of the United Nations). 2009. FAOSTAT statistical database. Rome.

2. Thakur, R. P., V. P. Rao, K. N. Amruthesh, H. S. Shetty, and V. V. Datar. 2003. Field surveys of pearl millet downy mildew: Effects of hybrids, fungicide, and cropping sequence. *Journal of Mycology and Plant Pathology* 33: 387–94.

3. Breese, W. A., C. T. Hash, A. Sharma, and J. R. Witcombe. 2002. *Improving pearl millet, the staple cereal crop of some of the world's poorest people, whilst keeping one step ahead of downy mildew.* Poster presented at the Plant Pathology and Global Food Security Presidential Meeting at Imperial College, London, July 8–10.

4. Dar, W. D., B. V. S. Reddy, C. L. L. Gowda, and S. Ramesh. 2006. Genetic resources enhancement of ICRISAT mandate crops. *Current Science* 91 (7): 880–84.

5. Parthasarathy R. P., P. S. Birthal, B. V. S. Reddy, K. N. Rai. and S. Ramesh. 2006. Diagnostics of sorghum and pearl millet grain-based nutrition. *International Sorghum and Pearl Millet Newsletter* 47: 93-96.

6. CGIAR (Consultative Group on International Agricultural Research).1996. A new generation of pearl millet on the horizon. *CGIAR News* 3 (3). www.worldbank.org/html/cgiar/newsletter/Oct96/6millet.html.

8. Pray, C. E., S. Ribeiro, R. A. E. Mueller, and P. P. Rao. 1991. Private research and public benefit: The private seed industry for sorghum and pearl millet in India. *Research Policy* 20 (4): 315–24.

Chapter 13

© Arne Hoel/World Bank

Navigating Through Reforms

Cotton reforms in Burkina Faso

Jonathan Kaminski, Derek Headey, and Tanguy Bernard

Historically, cotton has been a key cash crop in many West African countries. It is not typically viewed as a food security crop because cotton fiber (or lint), its primary commodity, is not consumable. But if cotton cultivation can contribute to increasing household incomes, and if such changes in incomes can translate into increases in the quality and quantity of food consumed in the household, then cotton is an important crop to many small farmers. This is the case in Burkina Faso, where cotton has played an important role in both the economy and culture for many generations.

Dating back to the French colonial rule and continuing through independence in 1960, Burkina Faso's cotton expansion strategy has involved substantial government intervention, a feature also common in many countries in the region. This system revolved around "contract farming" arrangements by which a state-controlled cotton company provided inputs (such as research on cotton improvement, farmer education services, fertilizers, loans, and marketing services) in exchange for the farmers' output through exclusive purchase rights. This arrangement, where the state protects farmers from free-market perils including large-scale market fluctuations and difficulties in accessing credit, seemingly would contribute to positive outcomes, such as the faster adoption of modern inputs, high repayment rates, and production growth.

But despite growth in the cotton industry in the 1960s and 1970s, this state-led strategy had become widely criticized by the late-1980s. The state cotton company had exorbitant operating costs, which reduced farmers' earnings, and was accused of corruption, while inefficiencies in the structure of farmers' groups meant that farmer repayment rates to the state ran only at around 40 percent. By the early-1990s, the entire Burkinabè cotton sector was in serious financial jeopardy.

Although these types of problems were evident in nearly all of Africa's cotton-producing countries, governments across the continent responded quite differently and with mixed success: some governments, such as Mali's, resisted reform and others, such as Benin's, embraced wholesale liberalization. Being quite systematic in its approach, Burkina Faso pursued a third path, careful to introduce reforms gradually and to learn lessons from its neighbors.[1]

This more nuanced reform approach has been the driving factor behind Burkina Faso's threefold increase in cotton production since the early-1990s, which led the country to become Africa's leading cotton producer in 2006 and its leading exporter in 2007. By comparison, production stagnated in both Mali and Benin, where it had been much higher in the past. Since Burkina Faso's reforms began, the number of households cultivating cotton has nearly doubled to more than 175,000 from 1996 to 2006, and cotton-related work has generated an estimated 235,000 new jobs that have directly and indirectly benefited around 1.8 million people. Despite recent financial problems and falling cotton prices, the Burkinabè model represents a remarkable success.

This chapter is based on Kaminski, J., D. Headey, and T. Bernard. 2009. *Institutional reform in the Burkinabè cotton sector and its impacts on incomes and food security: 1996-2006.* IFPRI Discussion Paper. Washington, D.C.: International Food Policy Research Institute.

Burkina Faso's Cotton Story

Cotton has long been an integral part of the Burkinabè economy. After relatively slow growth under the French colonial administration in the 1920s, cotton production expanded and continued to increase rapidly in 1960 after the transition from French rule. An important continuous presence throughout the West African cotton sector was the French Company for the Development of Textile Fibers (CFDT), which continued to provide new seed varieties, extension services, and other inputs and marketing services after independence and even after Burkina Faso established a state-controlled cotton company, SOFITEX, in 1979. In partnership with CFDT, SOFITEX continued to operate the state-led system in which farmers, organized in cooperatives known as Village Groups, were provided with improved seeds, extension services, fertilizers, pesticides, and marketing services in exchange for the exclusive marketing of their cotton crops.

But while the state-led CFDT cooperation system introduced new production techniques and high-yielding crop varieties, which resulted in a twofold increase in crop yields during the 1980s, the state's heavy hand led to some significant drawbacks. Poor financial management, corruption, and rampant overspending throughout the system, combined with falling cotton prices in international markets during the late-1980s, signaled that the system was not working well. Corruption also became widespread among Village Group leaders and SOFITEX officials, weakening the credibility of the state-led system. As a result of these shortcomings, the prices paid to farmers declined from 1988 to 1992, Village Groups accumulated large debts, and production started to collapse in the early-1990s. At this stage, the need to reform the sector was urgent, and both donors and the Burkinabè government recognized that the cotton sector was too important to ignore.

Despite broad agreement that the sector was in trouble, the major players within it—including the World Bank and the French international aid agency, Agence Française de Développement—did not immediately agree on the best reform path. On one side, the World Bank emphasized the inefficiency in the state's management of the sector, leading to weak returns to farmers. On the other side, the Agence Française de Développement , the CFDT, and some officials in the Burkinabè govern-

ment believed that disorganized farmers would be at a disadvantage upon losing protection and support from the state in the face of full-scale liberalization. Hence, the reform path that emerged was both a political compromise and an effort toward maintaining the best elements of the state-led model while removing or minimizing the worst.

Cotton Sector Reforms

The first stage of Burkina Faso's reform process focused on strengthening local institutions and building capacity in preparation for eventual market liberalization. One of the first priorities was to build and strengthen farmers' organizations. This specific reform targeted one of the most immediate problems—the low repayment rates by farmers' groups for state-provided credits—but it was also aimed at increasing farmers' participation in the cotton sector. The problem with the existing Village Groups was that they required cotton farmers to be pooled together with other farmers. This meant that the other farmers got a free ride off the relatively profitable cotton sector, which discouraged cotton production and reduced repayment rates. So to improve cotton farmers' social capital and production incentives, the government introduced legislation to allow cotton farmers to form and manage their own voluntary membership groups (Groupement de Producteurs de Coton, or Cotton Producer Groups) in 1996. As a result, group repayment rates increased from 50 to 60 percent before the reforms to more than 90 percent afterward.[2] Moreover, thousands of farmers joined cotton groups, and the Cotton Producer Groups arguably facilitated the rapid expansion of cotton farming in the country. In this phase, local capacity was further strengthened with the formation of a cotton union in the late-1990s; by 1999, the government had allocated 30 percent of its SOFITEX shares to the union.

Another reform looked to maintaining the benefits of contract farming—such as potentially higher repayment rates and higher input use—while inducing greater efficiency through private-sector participation. The government took a number of steps to begin the process of liberalizing cotton markets, starting with allowing the private sector to provide functions for which the state had no comparative advantage (for instance, in areas such as input provision, transport services, and cotton refinement, but not research and develop-

Gathering harvested cotton

ment).[3] Further liberalization in 2004 provided two private companies with exclusive purchase rights in "concession areas" of the country's cotton-producing areas, along with a monopoly on contract farming arrangements with the Cotton Producer Groups.

By 2006, the government had significantly reduced its role in the cotton sector, having delegated most responsibilities to the new cotton union and the Cotton Producer Groups. In addition, it had established an interprofessional association to promote cooperation among important stakeholders, including cotton farmers, bank representatives, government officials, research institutes, and other private stakeholders. This association became an important institution for resolving conflicts and promoting the development of the sector, particularly at a time of decline in cotton prices since the early-2000s.

Impacts on Production and Exports

In terms of production, the numbers reflect a dramatic increase after the reform. Cotton production (both seed and lint) increased from 150,500 tons in 1995 to 690,000 tons in 2007, which translated into an increase in US$165 million in cotton export earnings.[4] Before the reforms, cotton production accounted for just 3.3 percent of national agricultural production in terms of value; by 2006, it had reached more than 8 percent.[5] Further, the number of cotton-producing households nearly doubled, from around 95,000 in 1996 to more than 175,000 in 2006.[6] This growth pattern was largely driven by the intervention, since the reformulation of the farmers' groups successfully improved incentives for cotton production and improved relationships between farmers' groups and cotton firms.

The indirect contributions of cotton sector growth to GDP growth are also significant, especially in terms of foreign exchange earnings. Cotton exports before the reforms represented less than 30 percent of Burkina Faso's annual export earnings, but reached as high as 70 percent during the reform period and are now regularly around 50 percent of export earnings.

An indirect indicator of the success of the reforms is that Burkina Faso has overtaken Mali and Egypt to become the current African leader in cotton production as of 2006 and lint-cotton

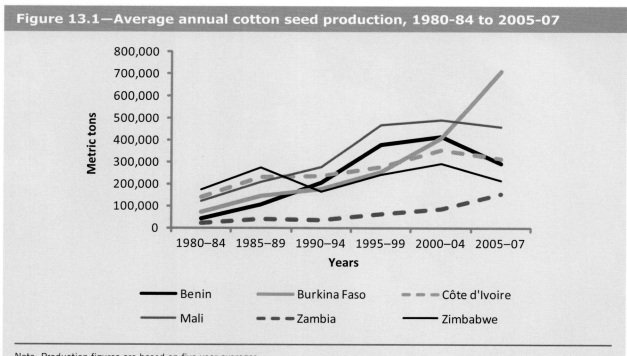

Figure 13.1—Average annual cotton seed production, 1980-84 to 2005-07

Metric tons (y-axis): 0 to 800,000

Years (x-axis): 1980–84, 1985–89, 1990–94, 1995–99, 2000–04, 2005–07

Legend: Benin, Burkina Faso, Côte d'Ivoire, Mali, Zambia, Zimbabwe

Note: Production figures are based on five-year averages.

Source: FAO (Food and Agriculture Organization of the United Nations). 2009. FAOSTAT statistical database. Rome.

exports as of 2007, based on a threefold increase in production since the early-1990s. In 2007, Burkina Faso's cotton production exceeded Mali's by 66 percent, which is especially noteworthy considering that Mali had significantly outpaced Burkina Faso on this front for the previous two decades (see Figure 13.1).

Contributions to Employment and Rural Welfare

Cotton sector reforms in Burkina Faso have resulted not only in extensive growth in production but also in a corresponding increase in employment opportunities and rural welfare, benefitting an estimated 1.8 million people. In terms of job creation, the share of cotton farmers has almost doubled between 1994 and 2003, reflecting an increase in agricultural employment from 11.3 percent to 19.9 percent during this same period. This amounts to an estimated 235,000 new jobs for farmers in the sector, some of whom were land croppers or migrants returning to Burkina Faso from war-torn Côte d'Ivoire after 2001. The cotton reforms eased the absorption of this new labor force in allowing migrants to quickly access inputs and form their own farmers' groups.[7]

But new employment opportunities were not the only impact of the reforms. Cotton production affects food security through its impact on farm income, which households can spend on food purchases and on food production. Household incomes rose sharply among cotton farmers during 1995 to 2003, with estimates varying from 19 percent to 43 percent. Poverty rates among cotton farmers also fell sharply from 62 to 47 percent between 1994 and 2003, although it should be noted that poverty rates among the rest of the population also fell during this period.[8]

In terms of food production, the relationship with cotton is complicated because while food crops can compete with cotton for land, cotton farmers also grow food as part of an intercropping strategy. So, somewhat counterintuitively, food production actually increased in cotton-producing areas during the reform period: as farmers grew more cotton, they also produced more food by intercropping.[9] In 1996, around 40 to 45 percent of people involved in cotton cultivation reported that they were food secure; as of 2006, this figure had increased to 70 percent.

However, there is no evidence that rates of malnutrition have declined for the broader population, suggesting that the cotton success story has principally influenced food consumption only among cotton-producing households. This situation exists probably because, unlike food production, cotton growth does not alleviate poverty by lowering the economywide price of food, which is one of the most direct determinants of poverty reduction. For this reason, expanded cotton production should not be viewed as the primary means of solving the country's broader malnutrition problems.

Are Burkina Faso's Cotton-Sector Reforms Sustainable?

The success of Burkina Faso's reform approach hinges, to a large extent, on government policies as well as on the ability of the Cotton Producer Groups and the cotton union to manage the responsibilities that the government transferred to them. Though difficult to predict because the reforms and their impacts are still ongoing, the constraints that the Cotton Producer Groups continue to face—particularly a lack of resources as well as hints of corruption in the cotton union—suggest that further reforms will likely be needed to ensure a continuous and smooth transfer of power from the state.

Perhaps most disconcerting is the recent financial difficulty that the sector has faced, which is largely linked to cotton pricing. Because international cotton prices are volatile, governments have long tried to smooth out part of the international price volatility at the farm level to reduce farmers' risk and income variation. However, the dangers are twofold: prices can be smoothed to the point where they are out of synch with real world price movements, and stabilization funds can be easily mismanaged and abused. Though Burkina Faso did try to move to a pricing formula that was more closely aligned with international prices, the formula was poorly implemented and the cotton stabilization fund was mismanaged. While in this sense the Burkinabè government's cotton reforms were unsuccessful, government officials do at least appear to be addressing the problem by outsourcing the management of the stabilization fund to the West African Development Bank. Meanwhile, the government intervened again to recapitalize cotton firms as a means of shoring up the sector before new private investors come on board. This effort shows that although decision-making under the new institutional structures in the sector has not been error-free, problems have been addressed relatively quickly and in an appropriately consultative manner. Indeed, the closer collaboration among SOFITEX, the farmers' union, and the private sector that has evolved may well be one of the most significant outcomes of the entire reform process.

The environmental sustainability of cotton production is also critical, especially in a region known for degraded soils and thought to be highly vulnerable to climate change. One concern is

that increased cotton production has gone hand in hand with a requisite increase in land use, including marginal lands that may have more fragile soils. For cotton production, it is critical to improve and maintain soil fertility by applying appropriate amounts of both chemical and organic fertilizers. Currently, however, there are concerns that farmers are not applying the recommended levels of either type of fertilizer. As such, some new initiatives have been established to improve soil management, including pilot organic farming projects and extension programs to help farmers obtain environmentally friendly inputs, such as organic fertilizer.

New Solutions to Old Problems: Bt Cotton in China and India

In 1996, a new chapter for global cotton production began with the commercial introduction of genetically engineered (GE) cotton. Despite pests being a major economic constraint to cotton production, conventional breeding had proven to be unsuccessful in developing insect-resistant cotton varieties. It was only through the use of GE technology that it was possible to develop varieties resistant to insects. The first generation of such varieties are known as Bt cotton and contain a gene introduced from the soil bacterium *Bacillus thuringiensis* (Bt) that produces a toxin lethal to specific types of bollworms.

Bt cotton spread rapidly from the United States to Australia, Mexico, Argentina, China, and South Africa (all of which commercialized Bt cotton in the mid- to late-1990s) as well as to India, Colombia, Egypt, Brazil, and, most recently, Burkina Faso.[a] Studies show that over the years Bt cotton has benefitted farmers overall, although there is great variability in study findings on Bt cotton by location, year, and assessment method used.[b] This is particularly true in China and India, where Bt cotton is viewed as a boon for many small-scale, resource-poor farmers—or, those farmers whose cotton land holdings average just 2.0 hectares in India and fewer than 0.75 hectares in China.[c] Documented gains have come mainly from the reduction of pesticide use and increased yields, which together have contributed to improvements in farm incomes.

In China, Bt cotton was developed both independently by the Chinese Academy of Agricultural Sciences (CAAS) and in a partnership between CAAS and Monsanto, a global crop-science company. Once Bt cotton was commercialized in 1997, it spread rapidly throughout most of China's cotton-growing provinces. As of 2008, Bt cotton accounted for more than 70 percent of all cotton cultivation area in China, or about 3.8 million hectares, and was being cultivated by an estimated 7 million smallholders. Annual farm surveys from the main cotton production districts in China document the use of less pesticide for Bt cotton varieties (in comparison to non-Bt varieties), ranging from approximately 85 percent less pesticide use in 1999 to 46 percent in 2006. Less pesticide use has translated not only into lower costs of production, but also into fewer reported cases of insecticide poisoning.[d] The reduction in pest damage resulting from the cultivation of Bt cotton has increased productivity, with reported yield increases of around 6 percent, with significant variability in both directions.[e]

In India, Bt cotton was initially developed through a joint venture between Mahyco, an Indian seed company, and Monsanto, and commercialized in 2002 (although farmers were cultivating unapproved Bt cotton illegally prior to this time). As of 2008, Bt cotton was cultivated on more than 80 percent (approximately 7.6 million hectares) of India's cotton area by an estimated 5 million smallholders. On average, farmers cultivating Bt cotton reduced pesticide use 42 percent, secured yield increases of 30 percent, and increased their cotton profit by 47 percent,

The Burkinabè Cotton Reforms: Keys to Success

Burkina Faso's gradual approach to cotton-sector reforms differed from that of several other cotton-producing African countries, some of which stuck to the troubled status quo while others embarked on overly hasty liberalization paths. The problem with the latter approach is that it introduces a real risk of market failures that could result in more harm than good. On the other hand, keeping the pre-reforms status quo was clearly untenable.

Burkina Faso's success is grounded in a number of factors. For both political reasons and a genuine desire to preserve the better elements of the state-led model, Burkina Faso adopted a cautious and pragmatic approach to reform. This approach has facilitated institution building—such as the farmers' groups and the cotton union—and allowed policymakers to observe and improve upon the outcomes of the reforms. For example, while reforming farmers' groups improved incentives for farmers to work cooperatively and increase production, the success of this effort also provided a strong case for strengthening key institutions as part of the liberalization process. Also, creating the cotton farmers' union served political ends and also helped farmers become greater participants in decision-making. In addition, the partial privatization of the cotton sector was

although the variability is as significant as it is in China.[f] Nevertheless, Bt cotton has contributed significantly to increases in both cotton area under cultivation and total cotton production in India, moving the country from the third largest importer in 2002–03 to the second largest exporter (after the United States) in 2007–08.[g]

Despite these gains, controversy continues to surround Bt cotton. Concerns include: the high variability in performance of Bt cotton under different agroclimatic conditions and pest pressures; the differences in farmers practices and the lack of information in the hands of farmers; the cost of the technology; the challenges for small farmers who must navigate through markets in which large companies own the Bt traits and supply costly seeds; and the risk to develop resistance to the Bt toxin and overwhelm the gains afforded by the technology. But based on the evidence thus far, Bt cotton seems to be providing new opportunities for small farmers to increase cotton yields and output, with the potential to increase both incomes and food security.

Prepared by: Patricia Zambrano and David J. Spielman

a. James, C. 2008. *Global status of commercialized biotech/GM crops: 2008*. ISAAA Brief 39. Ithaca: International Service for the Acquisition of Agri-biotech Applications.

b. Smale, M., P. Zambrano, G. Gruère, J. Falck-Zepeda, I. Matuschke, D. Horna, L. Nagarajan, I. Yerramareddy, and H. Jones. 2009. *Measuring the economic impacts of transgenic crops in developing agriculture during the first decade: Approaches, findings, and future directions*. Food Policy Review 10. Washington, D.C.: International Food Policy Research Institute.

c. James 2008; Huang, J., H. Chen, J. Mi, R. Hu, and E. Osir. 2009. Farmers' seed and pest control management for Bt cotton in China. In *Biotechnology and agricultural development: Transgenic cotton, rural institutions and resource-poor farmers*, ed. R. Tripp. London: Routledge.

d. Huang et al. 2009.

e. Smale, M., A. Niane, and P. Zambrano. Forthcoming. Une revue des méthodes appliquées dans l'evaluation de l'impact economique des plantes transgéniques sur les producteurs dans l'agriculture non-Industrialisée: La première décennie. *Economie Rurale*.

f. Smale, Niane, and Zambrano 2009.

g. Sadashivappa, P., and M. Qaim. 2009. Effects of Bt cotton in India during the first five years of adoption. Paper presented at the International Association of Agricultural Economists' 2009 Conference, August 16–22, Beijing; Gruère, G. P., P. Mehta-Bhatt, and D. Sengupta. 2008. *Bt cotton and farmer suicides in India: Reviewing the evidence*. IFPRI Discussion Paper 808. Washington, D.C.: International Food Policy Research Institute; James 2008.

driven by pragmatism rather than ideology; some elements of state involvement had always worked well, so it made sense to preserve those elements while allowing the private sector to operate where it had a greater advantage. Moreover, the granting of private sector regional monopolies partly acted as an experiment through which policymakers could gauge the potential of this sector.

The broader principles that underlie this success story then are those that relate to the process of reform rather than the specific details—especially Burkina Faso's pragmatic approach of introducing reforms gradually, sequencing and prioritizing them. Given the very similar institutional and agroecological conditions of neighboring cotton-producing countries, particularly Mali, it is possible that the more specific policy initiatives of the Burkinabè cotton reforms could potentially be applied to these countries as well. ■

NOTES

1. Tschirley, D., C. Poulton, and P. Labaste. 2009. *Organization and performance of cotton sectors in Africa: Learning from reform experience.* Washington, D.C.: World Bank; Bourdet, Y. 2004. A tale of three countries—structure, reform and performance of the cotton sector in Mali, Burkina Faso, and Benin. Country Economic Report 2004: 2. Stockholm, Sweden: Swedish International Development Cooperative Agency.

2. Bernard, T., M-H. Collion, A. de Janvry, P. Rondot, and E. Sadoulet. 2008. Do village organizations make a difference in African rural development? A study for Senegal and Burkina Faso. *World Development* 36 (11): 2188–2204; Kaminski, J. 2006. *Retrospective survey on ten years of changes in the cotton sector of Burkina Faso: Interviews of stakeholders, field survey of representative producers and GPCs, and price information on local markets.* Toulouse, France: Toulouse School of Economics.

3. Research and development is still carried out by public research centers, but under a public–private partnership with cotton firms, other research centers in France, and the state.

4. FAO (Food and Agriculture Organization of the United Nations). 2009. FAOSTAT statistical database. Rome.

5. FAO 2009.

6. Kaminski 2006.

7. Kaminski 2006.

8. Grimm, M., and I. Gunther. 2004. A country case study on Burkina Faso. Research paper for the Operationalising Pro-Poor Growth Project, a joint initiative of the Agence Française de Développement, German Federal Ministry for Economic Cooperation, German Agency for Technical Cooperation, KfW Development Bank, U.K. Department for International Development, and the World Bank. University of Gottingen, Gottingen, Germany.

9. DGPSA (Direction Générale des Produits de Santé et des Aliments). 2008. *Permanent agricultural survey, 1994–2004.* Ouagadougou, Burkina Faso: Ministry of Agriculture.

Unlocking the Market
Fertilizer and maize in Kenya

Joshua Ariga and T. S. Jayne

From the early-1990s to 2007, maize farming and marketing in Kenya underwent a major transformation. The government reduced its role in markets for fertilizer and maize while also dedicating significant resources to constructing roads, building other types of rural infrastructure, developing improved maize varieties, and promoting improved agronomic practices. These moves, along with other favorable changes in the wider economy, set off a chain of positive events—major private investment in fertilizer and maize marketing, more fertilizer consumption, higher maize yields, and lower maize prices—that have improved the welfare of both maize farmers and maize consumers in Kenya.

Overall, the government's reforms worked together to make it easier for farmers to get access to and afford fertilizer for their crops, and for some of these farmers to sell surplus maize above household requirements. Although government action catalyzed the changes, actions by farmers and private fertilizer importers and dealers went a long way to make this possible. Small farmers have increased their use of fertilizer per cultivated hectare of maize by 33 percent in the past 10 years, contributing to higher maize yields, increased farm incomes, and improved national food security.

Still, this success story is a fragile one. Widespread post-election violence in 2008, drought, unstable world markets in 2008 and 2009, and policy changes have threatened the positive developments in Kenya's maize and fertilizer sectors as well as the country's overall agricultural outlook. Continued success will depend on the return to greater political stability, renewed clarity and transparency regarding the operations of the state in input markets, and sustained public investments in support of market development and the welfare of small farmers.

Facing the Food Price Dilemma

In the early-1990s in Kenya, policymakers were struggling with the problem posed by the classic food price dilemma: how can a country keep food prices at tolerable levels for consumers while at the same time giving farmers adequate incentives to feed the nation and raise farm incomes? For many years, the solution pursued by Kenyan policymakers was to strike a balance between these two competing objectives by controlling the prices of maize and maize meal. The state-run National Cereals and Produce Board (NCPB) generally bought maize from farmers at higher-than-market prices and sold maize to industrial maize millers at below-market prices.

The government was also heavily involved in the fertilizer market. It assigned the Kenya Farmers Association the task of importing fertilizer, over half of which was financed by foreign aid donors by the late-1980s. It designated a state-run corporation, the Kenya National Trading Corporation, to distribute fertilizer donated by foreign governments. Import quotas kept fertilizer imports from rising too high. The Kenyan government also set the price of fertilizer to make it affordable for small-scale and poor farmers.

This chapter is based on Ariga, J., and T. S. Jayne. 2009. *Private sector responses to public investments and policy reforms: The case of fertilizer and maize market development in Kenya.* IFPRI Discussion Paper. Washington, D.C.: International Food Policy Research Institute.

Farmer applies fertilizer to maize, Kenya

By the early-1990s, it was becoming clear that Kenya's system of state-controlled maize and fertilizer markets was unsustainable. Because the NCPB had to cover the gap between the prices at which it bought and sold maize, it incurred massive deficits during the 1980s. At the same time, the state system of buying and selling maize was becoming increasingly inefficient and corrupt, driving sellers and buyers to illegal markets outside of the state's control. Fertilizer dealers found it unprofitable to supply fertilizer to remote areas at the prices set by the government. Designed to improve farmers' access to fertilizer, the controlled fertilizer pricing structure thus had the opposite effect in distant and hard-to-reach areas of Kenya. At the same time, a tide of worldwide support for market liberalization was rising, based on the belief that greater reliance on markets would encourage competition and lower marketing costs to the benefit of both farmers and consumers.

Reforming Markets for Fertilizer and Maize

In the early-1990s, the Kenyan government launched a series of reforms designed to spur agricultural productivity by encouraging private investment in fertilizer distribution. It removed fertilizer import restrictions, allowed private actors to participate in importing, trading, and distributing fertilizer, eliminated controls on access to foreign exchange, and removed customs duties and taxes imposed on fertilizer imports. By 1996, donor-financed imports had dwindled to 5 percent of total consumption, and small-scale farmers relied exclusively on the private sector and cooperatives for fertilizer.

Reforms, however, went even further. In late 1993, under pressure from international lenders, the government eliminated controls on the movement and price of maize and eliminated subsidies on maize sold to registered millers. By 1995, private traders were officially allowed to transport maize across districts. Starting in 1995/96, and under pressure from external donors, the government dramatically reduced NCPB's operating budget. By the early-2000s, less than 4 percent of small farm households sold maize directly to the NCPB.[1]

Currently, most of the maize purchased by the NCPB comes from large-scale farmers in the maize-surplus parts of the country. Although the NCPB's purchases now account for less than one-third of the maize sold by all Kenyan farmers, its operations still significantly affect market prices. NCPB purchase and sale operations tend to raise market prices, particularly during good harvest years, and therefore protect against downward price risk.

Although the liberalization process, especially in its early years, was marked by unpredictability, vacillation, and perceptions that state resources were being channeled to particular firms, it generated a dramatic response from the private sector and was largely satisfactory to small farmers.

Easing the Way for Fertilizer Use

The reforms to maize and fertilizer markets, coupled with the freeing of the foreign exchange regime in 1992, created a new policy environment in Kenya. Private firms surged into fertilizer importing, wholesaling, distribution, and retailing. By 1996, Kenya had 12 major importers, 500 wholesalers, and roughly 5,000 retailers distributing fertilizer in the country.[2] The number of retailers was estimated to rise to between 7,000 and 8,000 by 2000.[3] Some of the largest importers were cooperatives and estate firms supplying their members, most of whom were small-scale farmers participating in contract-farming arrangements for tea, coffee, and sugarcane.

Thanks to the increase in the number of fertilizer retailers, the average distance small farmers had to travel to get to the nearest fertilizer retailer fell from 8.1 to 3.4 kilometers between 1997 and 2007. Over the same period, the average distance they had to travel to get to the nearest hybrid maize seed stockist declined from 5.6 to 3.4 kilometers. The rise in the number of rural fertilizer and hybrid seed retailers, as well as accelerated public investment in road infrastructure since 2003, expanded small farmers' access to fertilizer, reduced their transaction costs, and helped raise the demand for modern inputs and the productivity of smallholder maize production.

A key factor in increasing fertilizer use has been cost and price. The cost added on to the price of fertilizer between offloading at Mombasa port and delivery to the farm has decreased substantially since the liberalization of fertilizer marketing, with much of the cost savings passed on to the farmer through lower retail prices.

Another important factor in keeping fertilizer prices low is increased competition among local importers and wholesalers. Competition has led importers and wholesalers to exploit cheaper ways of transporting fertilizer and use cheaper international sources of credit while also pursuing more efficient business practices by merging local firms with more established international fertilizer firms. If inflation is taken into account, fertilizer prices in Kenya are currently about equal to what they were in the mid-1990s even though world fertilizer prices are substantially higher than they were in the mid-1990s.

With increased availability and competitive prices, many more farmers are using fertilizer. The proportion of small-scale farmers using fertilizer on maize during the main growing season rose from 56 percent in 1996 to 70 percent in 2007, although these rates vary considerably throughout the country. The highest proportion of smallholders using fertilizer occurs in the

highlands of central and western Kenya, where more than 80 percent of all maize-growing smallholders apply fertilizer on maize. Fertilizer application rates rose from 84 kilograms per hectare of land in 1997 to 111 kilograms per hectare in 2007, a 34 percent increase. Overall, total national fertilizer use doubled between the mid-1990s and late-2000s (see Figure 14.1).

Maize Yields Rise and Prices Fall

Between 1997 and 2007, maize yields increased by roughly 18 percent. This yield improvement is not reflected in official government maize production statistics, which do not take into account the increasingly large number of farmers who are growing maize on the same fields as other crops, or the shift over time in the proportion of maize area grown in relatively semi-arid regions. This shift was facilitated by the release of improved maize

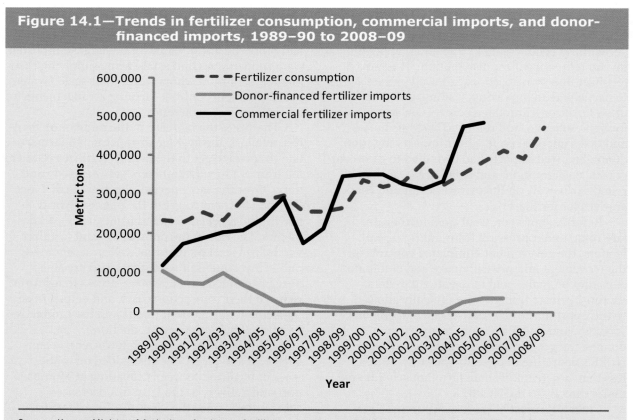

Figure 14.1—Trends in fertilizer consumption, commercial imports, and donor-financed imports, 1989–90 to 2008–09

Source: Kenyan Ministry of Agriculture for data on fertilizer consumption and donor-financed imports; author interviews with fertilizer importers for fertilizer import data.

cultivars well suited to mid- and low-altitude areas of the country.

Maize farmers have also found it easier to sell their increased production of maize. More private maize assemblers—that is, traders who buy directly from farmers and assemble maize for bulk distribution—are now spread across rural areas where maize surpluses are expected. More than 90 percent of Kenya's maize sales are now made to private traders, who are more accessible than they were in the past. In the lowlands of Eastern Province, for example, the average distance between farm and private buyer declined from 6.55 to 1.62 kilometers between 1997 and 2007, and in the high-potential areas of western Kenya this distance declined from 1.80 to 0.40 kilometers. This improved penetration of maize assemblers in rural areas has likely reduced farmers' costs and resulted in tangible benefits.

Since the mid-1990s, maize meal, a staple in Kenyan diets, has become more affordable. The average daily wage for an urban Kenyan consumer employed in the formal sector bought three times more staple foods in 2006/07 than it did in 1995/96. Although the recent food price crisis partially reversed this trend, the quantities of staple foods affordable per daily wage in urban Kenya during the 2008/09 marketing season were still roughly double their levels of the mid-1990s. And in rural Kenya, because of the removal of bans on the movement of maize between districts, grain is now easier and cheaper to purchase in drier lowlands and marginal zones where food deficits are more common. Many farmers in these marginal areas are net consumers, who must buy food because they do not produce enough for their own subsistence.

More Improvements Are Possible

The case of fertilizer and maize markets in Kenya shows how public policy changes and investments can be a catalyst for greatly expanded private markets for agricultural inputs like fertilizer and outputs like maize. Nonetheless, Kenya could improve the well-being of small farmers and consumers even more by pursuing a number of other reforms, which can serve as useful lessons

Preparing maize for consumption, Kenya

for other countries as well.

First, well-managed and efficient transport and storage arrangements can further reduce the cost of distributing grain and fertilizers. At Kenya's port of Mombasa, the offloading of commodities from ships is frequently delayed, and the regional railway system is deteriorating. The limited transport capacity requires fertilizer importers to rent storage facilities near the port, thereby raising costs. Improving Kenya's railway system, in particular, could greatly reduce the cost of fertilizer to farmers in the upland production region.

Second, the government should reduce the cost and complexity of port operations. In Kenya, port fees, levies, and other charges should be rationalized and aggregated. In addition, documentation procedures need to be reduced, and some services should be provided electronically.

Third, fertilizer packages should be tailored to local demand from small farmers, who require and are able to purchase only small packets. In addition, fertilizer quality control needs to be more actively enforced.

Fourth, fertilizer use could be made more profitable for farmers if it were combined with training on cultivation practices, soil fertility, water management, and efficient use of fertilizer and improved seed technologies that are responsive to fertilizers.

Fifth, by offering farmers credit, inputs, and know-how, farmer organizations can provide an important resource to help small farmers make use of higher levels of inputs like fertilizer and achieve better production and marketing practices.

Conclusion

When Kenya liberalized markets for fertilizer and maize and invested in various types of
public goods to support small-scale agriculture,
thousands of private actors plunged into these
markets, encouraging both an impressive rise in
fertilizer use and significantly increased maize
yields on the plots of small farmers. A recent
nationwide survey revealed farmers' satisfaction
with the reformed maize markets: more than 65
percent of farmers reported that they prefer the
current liberalized maize marketing system over
the previous state-controlled system.[4]

In 2008, however, the positive developments
in Kenya's maize and fertilizer markets were
threatened by civil disruption, drought, and the
unprecedented surge in world fertilizer prices.
Early-2008 witnessed the destruction of physical
infrastructure in western Kenya (such as grain
storage facilities) and the closing of many fertilizer
supply stores. Moreover, the incentives to use fertilizer in Kenya have been adversely affected both
by drought and by world events, as the price of fertilizer in relation to that of maize in Kenya reached
its highest level in at least 18 years. Sustaining
the success of the past two decades will require
a return to political stability, a commitment to a
clearly defined and relatively limited state role in
fertilizer markets, and continued public investments in market development and the welfare of
small farmers. ■

NOTES

1. Tegemeo Institute/Egerton University. Various years.
    Household surveys. Nairobi.

2, Allgood, J. H., and J. Kilungo. 1996. *An appraisal of the
    fertilizer market in Kenya and recommendations for
    improving fertilizer use practices by smallholder farmers:
    A field report.* Muscle Shoals: International Fertilizer
    Development Center.

3. International Fertilizer Development Center. 2001. An
    assessment of fertilizer prices in Kenya and Uganda: Domestic
    prices vis-à-vis international market prices. Muscle Shoals.

4. Tegemeo Institute/Egerton University. Various years.

Counting on Beans
Mungbean improvement in Asia

Subramanyam Shanmugasundaram, J. D. H. Keatinge, and Jacqueline d'Arros Hughes

Beginning in the 1960s, agricultural scientists, policymakers, and farmers undertook a huge effort to increase the production of staple grains, especially in Asia, in what was described as the Green Revolution (see Chapter 3). This heavy focus on cereal production boosted food production and incomes for millions of rural people—but it also pushed a number of other crops to the sidelines. For example, legumes—including soybean, chickpea, and mungbean—had long been important in Asian diets, but in the 1960s yields of these crops were either stagnant or declining.

In the early-1970s, scientists at AVRDC – The World Vegetable Center decided that the potential benefits of mungbean were too important to ignore. They recognized mungbean's potential to supply nutrients and protein to Asia's hungry, offer farmers a new income-generating opportunity, improve soil fertility, and diversify crop rotation practices—if only mungbean could be fit into the cropping practices of Asian farmers.

In response to this challenge, AVRDC launched a research program aimed at increasing both the yields and output of the crop by breeding improved varieties. By working with national research partners in 27 Asian countries to adapt these varieties to local conditions, the program has succeeded in releasing 112 improved mungbean varieties to an estimated 1.5 million farmers. Farmer adoption rates have been substantial, and the release and dissemination of improved varieties have contributed to a 35 percent increase in mungbean production in Asia with consequent benefits to farmers' well-being.[1]

Mungbean: Part of a Balanced Diet

Mungbean, along with chickpea and pigeon pea, is a major legume crop that supplements the largely cereal-based diets of the poor in Asia. When consumed together, cereals and legumes (also known as pulses) contribute significantly to a healthy and balanced diet. Cereals are deficient in the amino acid lysine, which legumes can provide; legumes are low in sulfur-rich amino acids, which cereals can provide. High in protein and easy to digest, mungbean consumed in combination with cereals can thus significantly increase the quality of protein in a meal.

Mungbean is also valuable because, like other legumes, it converts nitrogen from the air into helpful compounds that contribute to plant growth and soil fertility. This process, known as nitrogen fixation, is mediated by naturally occurring bacteria that live on small nodules on the mungbean's roots. The bacteria produce nitrogen compounds that help the plant to grow and, when the plant dies and decomposes, increase the fertility of surrounding soil.

The importance of legumes was emphasized by AVRDC when it was established in Taiwan in 1971. The Center's aim was to enhance the diets, cropping systems, and incomes of poor farmers in Asia through the production and consump-

This chapter is based on Shanmugasundaram, S., J. D. H. Keatinge, and J. d'Arros Hughes. 2009. *The mungbean transformation: Diversifying crops, defeating malnutrition.* IFPRI Discussion Paper. Washington, D.C.: International Food Policy Research Institute.

© AVRDC-The World Vegetable Center

Mungbean cultivation, Asia

tion of vegetables. To do so, the Center selected two legumes for crop improvement—soybean and mungbean.

When AVRDC began its research on mungbean, Asian farmers were growing traditional varieties that posed several vexing problems. They took a long time to harvest—90 to 110 days to reach maturity—and thus could not be easily rotated in-between cereal crops.[2] They also tended not to mature in the field all at once, meaning that farmers had to spend long hours harvesting the crop multiple times, while their pods (the casings in which the beans grow) tended to shatter easily, resulting in significant crop losses. In addition, mungbean crops were susceptible to insects and diseases, especially the mungbean yellow mosaic virus. And though these varieties required a great deal of labor, they produced only about 400 kilograms of small seeds per hectare of land.

After some discussion, plant scientists agreed on the goals of their mungbean improvement program. The ideal mungbean, they decided, would, among other things:

- carry all of its pods on the top of the plant for easy harvesting;
- have a stable potential yield of more than 2 tons per hectare;
- mature quickly, in about 60 to 75 days;
- mature at a uniform rate so that farmers could complete the harvest in one go;
- have larger seeds than traditional varieties; and
- be resistant to pests and diseases like

Cercospora leaf spot, powdery mildew, mungbean yellow mosaic virus, bean fly, pod borer, and bruchid weevil.[3]

Having agreed on a blueprint, AVRDC recognized that the development of this ideal mungbean required a strong relationship with national agricultural research organizations in countries where improved mungbean could be cultivated. To this end, AVRDC established the South Asia Vegetable Research Network (SAVERNET) in partnership with its key collaborators—scientists at national agricultural research organizations in Bangladesh, Bhutan, China, India, Myanmar, Nepal, Pakistan, Sri Lanka, and Thailand.

Under SAVERNET, AVRDC scientists and scientists in participating countries screened and exchanged germplasm (that is, genetic materials) to identify desirable traits with which to develop improved mungbean lines. Working closely with farmers, they evaluated the performance of promising varieties under different agroecological conditions in different countries and during different seasons. Results were consolidated and shared among the network members. Over time and with technical support from AVRDC, the national partners in each country gradually assumed greater responsibility over their national mungbean improvement programs.

Research breakthroughs, however, were not immediate in all countries. Although mungbean research showed spectacular success in Southeast Asia and China, the main region in need of improved varieties was South Asia, where the mungbean yellow mosaic virus severely con-strained the crop's production. In 1992, AVRDC established an informal network with scientists in Pakistan to collaborate on finding a solution. Shuttle breeding—that is, growing two crops a year by sending germplasm back and forth between AVRDC in Taiwan and the Nuclear Institute for Agriculture and Biology in Pakistan—enabled scientists to develop improved mungbean yellow mosaic virus–resistant varieties for South Asia. In 1997, the South Asian members of SAVERNET organized a mungbean subnetwork to disseminate these virus-resistant varieties. Within four years and with crucial support from the United Kingdom Department for International Development (DFID), scientists managed to release these improved, virus-resistant varieties, which yield at least 2 tons per hectare and mature in 55 to 65 days, throughout the region—in Bhutan, Bangladesh, India, Nepal, Pakistan, and Sri Lanka.

Farmers did not immediately take to the improved mungbean varieties in all countries; they had to be convinced. AVRDC's national partners in different countries demonstrated the value of improved mungbean by conducting demonstrations in farmers' fields, organizing field days (events for sharing agricultural information), promoting adoption through model farmers, and encouraging both public and private seed companies to multiply and distribute improved mungbean seed so that farmers could replicate these demonstrations.

Ultimately, these efforts succeeded. Between 1997 and 2002, mungbean cultivation in South Asia took off, and by 2005, improved mungbean was being cultivated on 1.5 million hectares of land.

Beyond AVRDC and its partners, much of the credit for this success goes to the farmers who were active in the research and development of improved mungbean. They were instrumental not only in evaluating the improved varieties under farm conditions, but also in producing seed that could be shared with other farmers. For example, under a Seed Village Program launched in India's Punjab state in 2003, a total of 270 farmers, each planting mungbean on just 0.4 hectares of land, succeeded in producing about 2,700 tons of high-quality seed that was distributed to other farmers in the next season.

Impacts of the Mungbean Transformation

Mungbean has been transformed from a marginal to a relatively important crop and, in the process, has contributed to improving rural household income, expanding employment opportunities, diversifying diets, increasing nutritional security, and enhancing soil fertility in Asia.

Since the 1980s, improved mungbean has led farmers to plant the crop on more and more land (Figure 15.1). Today, improved mungbean

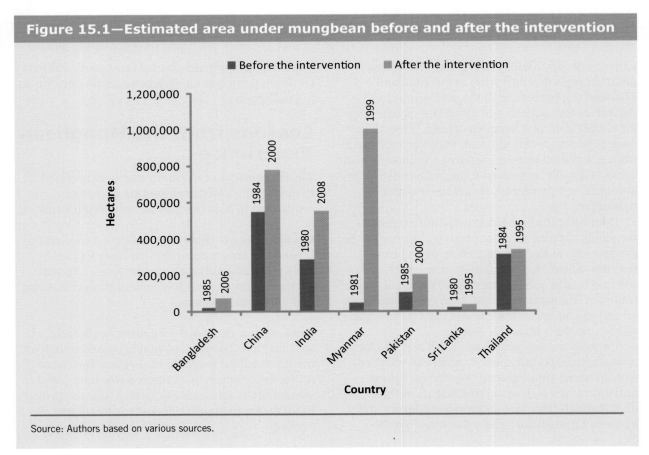

Figure 15.1—Estimated area under mungbean before and after the intervention

Source: Authors based on various sources.

© AVRDC-The World Vegetable Center

Non mildew-resistant mungbean (left) and powdery mildew-resistant mungbean (right)

varieties occupy almost 90 percent of the area under mungbean cultivation in Pakistan and Thailand, 85 percent in China, and around 50 percent in Bangladesh and Myanmar, accounting for almost 3 million hectares of land.[4] Overall in Asia, production of mungbean varieties increased from 2.3 million tons in 1985 to 3.1 million tons in 2000.[5] Globally, improved mungbean constitutes more than 25 percent of worldwide mungbean production.[6]

Moreover, mungbean production is raising the yields of farmers' other crops by improving the productivity of the soil. Including mungbean in the rice–wheat crop rotation system enriches the soil and breaks soil fatigue caused by cereal–cereal rotations. Farmers in Punjab who grow mungbean as well as paddy rice have found their paddy rice yields, and their incomes, rising.

Mungbean also promises health benefits for consumers, especially poor women and children, who are most vulnerable to the effects of poor nutrition and a lack of micronutrients in their diets. Mungbean is rich in protein and iron, and improved mungbean varieties contain 6 milli-

grams of iron per 100 grams of raw seed, whereas traditional mungbean varieties contain only 3.0 to 3.5 milligrams.[7]

Lessons from the Mungbean Experience

The experiences of the many partners involved in developing and disseminating improved mungbean in Asia point to a number of lessons:

Commitment—For the intervention to succeed, it needed a strong commitment from all parties—international research institutes, national partners, donors, nongovernmental organizations, and individual farmers.

Plan with a purpose—Realistic goals and specific plans based on available resources helped the intervention move forward. Deadlines were set for achieving goals. Progress was monitored semiannually and annually, which allowed project participants to make midcourse adjustments as needed.

Focus on farmers—Crop-management practices varied in each country and season. National agricultural research systems developed farmer-friendly technologies to address the farmers' specific constraints in their countries.

Share across boundaries—Progress and success varied between countries and between provinces or states within countries. For instance, Punjab in India was able to make rapid progress in seed production and distribution; Bangladesh was able to adopt and follow the example of Punjab. Within India, Bihar, Haryana, Himachal Pradesh, Jharkhand, and Rajasthan made good progress with assistance from Punjab. Success in one area can serve as a catalyst for success in neighboring states and countries. And sharing resources between countries and between states within a country is the best way to rapidly spread technology and improve productivity, nutrition, and food security.

Welcome all contributions, large and small—China and India are big countries with sufficient resources to maintain large germplasm collections and conduct meaningful research. But smaller countries also made significant contributions: the Philippines developed high-yield, early-maturing, bold-seeded varieties; Pakistan developed lines with a high level of resistance to the mungbean yellow mosaic virus. Even at the community level, the Seed Village Program and other seed exchanges helped rapidly expand mungbean production.

Adapt as needed—Evaluating improved technology, regardless of its source, and determining if it was suitable for local situations returned large dividends in Myanmar, with a small investment.

Train professionals and consumers—Training was essential for researchers, extension staff, farmers, and economists to systematically organize, plan, and implement activities and collect data. In addition, to enhance nutritional security, women received training in mungbean preparation to ensure that valuable nutrients would not be lost during cooking.

Provide visible proof—Demonstration trials, farmers' field trials, and field days proved that "seeing is believing," enabling farmers to see for themselves the performance of the improved varieties compared with local varieties. When farmers actively participated in research and development efforts, they felt they had ownership in the output.

Promote the benefits—The return on investment to the farmer is extremely important for the success of any new crop variety. Farmers need to understand why maintaining pure seed of the improved variety is worthwhile.

It is also important for international agricultural centers to be sensitive to the needs and achievements of the national partners. National agricultural research systems should be properly credited for their efforts, and international agricultural centers should work behind the scenes, providing technology and other support that are unavailable to the national systems. Each country has its own rules and regulations for releasing new varieties, and international scientists should follow them carefully to avoid delays or work closely with national scientists to encourage minor modifications that can speed release.

Conclusion

Only ongoing involvement from all partners will ensure that the mungbean transformation will continue to respond to current and evolving conditions. For instance, for the improved varieties to perform to their full potential, researchers need to refine seasonal and location-specific growing practices. In light of climate change, scien-

Mungbean harvesting

tists will have to develop improved varieties to withstand continuously evolving diseases, insects, and climate conditions. Studies should take the broadest possible view of the intervention's impacts to explain its value to policymakers and donors.

The world population is expected to reach 8 billion within the next 10 years, and more than half of that population will be in Asia. Despite rising incomes in China and India, food and nutrition security continue to be a concern across the continent. Protein, calorie, and micronutrient deficiencies affect almost 2 billion people in the region.[8] In 2000, vegetable sources provided 49.8 grams of protein per capita per day in Asia, compared with 21.2 grams from animal sources.[9] Mungbean—a nitrogen-fixing, protein- and iron-rich legume—will undoubtedly play an ever-growing role in Asian diets as governments seek to enhance food security and sustain their agricultural base. Through continuing research cooperation among local, national, and international partners to improve and share mungbean germplasm and technical expertise, small-scale farmers can increase yields, diversify crop rotations, and increase their incomes by growing this nutritious legume for their families and communities. ■

NOTES

1. Weinberger, K. 2003. *Impact analysis of mungbean research in South and Southeast Asia.* Final Report GTZ Project No. 99.9117.5. Shanhua, Taiwan: Asian Vegetable Research and Development Center.

2. Asian Vegetable Research and Development Center. 1977. *Asian Vegetable Research and Development Center (AVRDC) progress report 1976.* Shanhua, Taiwan.

3. Fernandez, G. C. J., and S. Shanmugasundaram. 1988. The AVRDC mungbean improvement program: The past, present and future. In *Proceedings of the Second International Mungbean Symposium, November 16–20, 1987, Bangkok, Thailand,* ed. S. Shanmugasundaram and B. T. McLean. Shanhua, Taiwan: Asian Vegetable Research and Development Center.

4. Jansen, H. G. P., and S. Charnnarongkul. 1992. *Economic analysis of AVRDC mandate crops through baseline surveys: Mungbean in Thailand.* Working Paper No. 6. Shanhua, Taiwan: Asian Vegetable Research and Development Center; Ali, M., I. A. Malik, H. M. Sahir, and A. Bashir. 1997. *The mungbean green revolution in Pakistan.* Technical Bulletin No. 24. Shanhua, Taiwan: Asian Vegetable Research and Development Center; Huijie, Z., N. H. Li, X. Z. Cheng, and K. Weinberger. 2003. *The impact of mungbean research in China.* Working Paper No. 14. Shanhua, Taiwan: Asian Vegetable Research and Development Center; Weinberger 2003.

5. Weinberger 2003.

6. Shanmugasundaram, S. 2001. New breakthrough with mungbean. *Centerpoint* 19 (2): 1–2.

7. Vijayalakshmi, P. S., S. Amirthaveni, R. P. Devada, K. Weinberger, S. C. S. Tsou, and S. Shanmugasundaram. 2003. *Enhanced bioavailability of iron from mungbean and its effects on health of school children.* Technical Bulletin No. 20. Shanhua, Taiwan: Asian Vegetable Research and Development Center; Gopalan, C., B. V. Rama Sastri, C. V. Balasubramnaian, B. S. Narasinga Rao, Y. G. Deosthale, and K. C. Pant. 1989. *Nutritive value of Indian foods.* Hyderabad, India: Indian Council of Medical Research.

8. Ali et al. 1997.

9. FAO (Food and Agriculture Organization of the United Nations). 2009. FAOSTAT statistical database. Rome.

Conquering the Cattle Plague
The global effort to eradicate rinderpest

Peter Roeder and Karl Rich

Farmers have confronted the scourge of rinderpest, or cattle plague, ever since cattle were domesticated some 10,000 years ago. For centuries, humankind has depended on livestock for draft power, milk, meat, skins, and manure. Rinderpest—which in its severest form can kill 95 percent or more of the animals it infects—has had devastating effects, blighting the lives of farmers throughout Africa, Asia, and Europe. It has been described as "the most dreaded bovine plague known, belonging to a select group of notorious infectious diseases that have changed the course of history."[1]

Rinderpest was detected and confirmed for the last time in 2001 in Kenya. Few veterinarians and even farmers alive today have seen the disease, and its existence is fading from memory. The eradication of rinderpest can be viewed as an achievement on par with the eradication of smallpox from the human population, the only other time an infectious disease has been eradicated. This remarkable feat was accomplished thanks to the efforts of scientists around the world to develop and perfect vaccines and—just as important—to international collaboration and coordination aimed at monitoring the disease and eliminating it wherever it lingered. Rinderpest eradication was the outcome neither of a single project nor the efforts of a single agency; rather, it was the result of a series of periodic, internationally coordinated efforts built on the ongoing national programs of many affected countries during the course of many decades.

History of the Disease

Rinderpest is thought to have had its origins as far back as the domestication of cattle in Asia, possibly in the region of the Indus River in modern-day Pakistan. It has had a severe impact not only on domesticated ruminants and swine, but also on many wild animals such as African buffaloes, giraffes, and warthogs. Related to the human measles virus, rinderpest is a contagious disease characterized by necrosis (cell death) and erosions throughout the digestive tract. Affected animals develop fever, discharges from the eyes and nose, erosions of the mucosa or soft lining in the mouth, diarrhea, dysentery, and death. Animals that recover are debilitated and suffer a long convalescence—although they are thereafter immune to the virus. When the virus is introduced to a formerly unaffected area, it results in high mortality, but in areas where rinderpest is endemic, the morbidity and mortality rates can be low because many animals that survive an earlier exposure (and perhaps received vaccination) are protected.

Warfare was a potent vehicle for spreading rinderpest throughout Europe, Asia, and the Middle East, because of the large cattle herds traveling with marauding armies. The Huns and Mongol invaders brought the disease from Asia into Europe, where it was spread by the movement of livestock meant to feed the populations of the burgeoning cities. For many centuries, no European countries were consistently free from

This chapter is based on Roeder, P. and K. Rich. 2009. *The global effort to eradicate rinderpest.* IFPRI Discussion Paper. Washington, D.C.: International Food Policy Research Institute.

rinderpest. World War II led to a major resurgence of the disease throughout East and Southeast Asia. As late as the early-1990s, the civil disturbance caused by the Gulf War resulted in a major upsurge of infection in Iran, Iraq, and Turkey.

The looting and social disruption of warfare was not alone in spreading rinderpest. Organized trade in cattle, largely from Russia, repeatedly introduced rinderpest into recipient countries in Europe and elsewhere in the 17th, 18th, and 19th centuries. As a result, from 1857 to 1866, Europe was stripped of cattle.

Introduced into eastern Africa in the late 19th century, rinderpest set off what came to be known as the Great African Pandemic. It spread from the Indian to the Atlantic Ocean and moved rapidly down the eastern seaboard of Africa in grazing animals both domestic and wild, reaching Southern Africa in 1896. When the first major African pandemic died down, it left behind pockets of infection from which arose periodic epidemics and pandemics.

An array of sanitary measures—such as the culling of infected animals combined with government compensation for farmers, the safe disposal of carcasses, sanitary cordons around infected farms, and strong legal enforcement—was gradually adopted across Europe in the 18th and 19th centuries, setting the stage for the control and eventual eradication of rinderpest there in 1908. But in much of Africa and Asia, rinderpest remained a persistent scourge throughout the 20th century.[2]

Developing a Vaccine

The eradication of rinderpest in the developing world during the 20th century depended on two factors: first, the discovery of an effective vaccine that worked well in tropical countries, and second, the adoption of a system of mass vaccinations followed by surveillance, and focused vaccinations in case of outbreaks.

In the late-1890s, South African scientists showed that immune serum (serum taken from a recovered animal) and virulent blood (blood taken from an infected animal), when given simultaneously, produced long-term immunity to rinderpest, despite the risk of disease inherent in its use. By 1928, this "serum-simultaneous" method developed independently had eliminated rinderpest from European Russia.

Rinderpest takes its toll on the livestock population in the 1890s, South Africa

Throughout the 20th century, the effort to develop a more effective vaccine continued, with important breakthroughs along the way. Scientists across the globe developed and improved upon attenuated vaccines—that is, vaccines using live but less virulent viruses—in the mid-20th century. Yet the search continued for a vaccine that would provide long-term protection to all types of cattle, would not require the accompaniment of an immune serum, and would not sicken the animals being immunized.

In the late-1950s, Walter Plowright, working at the East African Veterinary Research Organization in Kenya, achieved a breakthrough using tissue culture—in other words, he grew a virus in cells in a lab instead of in animal hosts. His tissue-culture rinderpest vaccine produced neither lesions nor fever and was safe and effective for cattle of all breeds and ages and both sexes. Its only drawback was that it had to be kept at a low temperature—a distinct disadvantage in African climates. However, in the late-1980s, scientists developed a variant of tissue-culture rinderpest vaccine, called Thermovax, that could be kept at ambient temperatures in the tropics for up to four weeks. This vaccine was widely used to great effect in community-based vaccination programs in Africa, particularly in remote areas of Sudan, Somalia, Kenya, Ethiopia, Tanzania, and Uganda, as well as in Afghanistan.

Eliminating Rinderpest

With rinderpest vaccines becoming available, countries and regions began adopting major campaigns aimed at eliminating the disease. In

1948 in western China, for example, rinderpest was killing millions of cattle, buffaloes, and yaks. Recognizing that feeding its millions of citizens required eliminating the disease, the new government made eradicating rinderpest a high priority. The Chinese also undertook heroic measures in this battle. For example, to combat pockets of infection in the Himalayas at a time when there was little or no motorized transport and no refrigeration, the vaccine virus was transported in live, infected sheep on the backs of yaks and horses to sites where the vaccine was produced for immediate use. Success in China came rapidly. No outbreak has occurred there since 1955 and the vaccination process ceased in 1956.

Success in India was slower. In 1954, India initiated its National Rinderpest Eradication Programme. The program aimed to systematically vaccinate 80 percent of cattle and buffaloes in five years, to be succeeded by a follow-up period during which the remaining 20 percent plus the annual calf crop would be vaccinated.[3] Overall, mass vaccinations succeeded in eliminating endemic rinderpest in some states but did not prevent it from being reintroduced. By the mid-1980s, it was clear that the program was failing, and the country shifted course. In the endemic states, mass vaccinations were re-launched with the goal of covering 90 percent of the cattle population within three years. In non-endemic areas, authorities administered focused vaccinations only in the event of an outbreak. Strict controls on the movement of cattle helped reduce the transmission of the disease within India, and rinderpest was eliminated from the country in 1995.

Although China and India managed to eradicate rinderpest within their borders through their own national programs, it took global coordination to wipe out the disease in other parts of the developing world. In the 1960s and 1970s, a number of African countries, coordinated by the Organization of African Unity, joined forces in an effort called Joint Project 15. This project aimed to eliminate rinderpest using intensive, internationally coordinated vaccination campaigns. Although Joint Project 15 was highly successful at first, it failed to eliminate three or four persistent reservoirs of rinderpest, and new pandemics eventually emerged. By the early-1980s, rinderpest pandemics in East and West Africa were converging in Nigeria, in what became known

as the second Great African Pandemic. National emergency control programs, many mounted by the Food and Agriculture Organization of the United Nations (FAO), brought the resurgence under control by 1986. Though devastating, these events did have the beneficial effect of stimulating a continentwide Pan-African Rinderpest Campaign (PARC)—and ultimately the Global Rinderpest Eradication Programme (GREP).

Conceived in 1992 and launched in 1993, GREP operated under the auspices of the FAO, which provided coordination assistance and offered technical guidance. When GREP began, authorities had no clear picture of where rinderpest was occurring or how the virus survived and spread. Once scientists established the geographic extent of rinderpest infection and recognized that hidden reservoirs of infection were giving rise to visible epidemics in normally unaffected populations, it became possible to develop a strategy for its progressive elimination.

GREP set a deadline of 2010 for global freedom from rinderpest, based on internationally coordinated rinderpest-control activities on three fronts: Africa, West Asia, and South Asia. The international

Vaccine preparation in the Pan-African Rinderpest Campaign, Sudan

© Peter Roeder

Rinderpest-free cattle in Omdurman market, Sudan

community would fund these campaigns—often with nominal national contributions—and the regional organizations would implement them. After successfully carrying out rinderpest-control activities, individual countries would undergo an accreditation process to be declared free from rinderpest. The World Organization for Animal Health defined a pathway to accreditation that incorporated a series of verifiable epidemiological objectives, including a requirement that countries cease all vaccinations. Completion of all steps on the pathway to eradication was expected to be far less costly than continuing with endless rounds of mass vaccinations.

As GREP helped spread information on the prevalence and risk of rinderpest, the focus of rinderpest control thus shifted from vaccination to surveillance—but this shift did not always occur quickly or easily. A number of countries in Africa and Asia sought security by continuing to implement annual vaccination campaigns for many years after rinderpest had been eradicated from their territory and the risk of reinvasion had become minimal.

Nonetheless, the shift away from mass vaccinations to surveillance and accreditation did occur over time. The Pan-African Rinderpest Campaign, which was implemented in 20 countries in West Africa and 7 countries in East Africa, combined emergency action to control existing outbreaks with efforts to strengthen veterinary services, for example. It also included a phased vaccination and surveillance program aimed at eradicating remaining pockets of the disease. As noted previously, the last known case of the disease worldwide occurred in Kenya in 2001.

Impact of Rinderpest Eradication

By preventing the illness and death of millions of livestock, rinderpest eradication has generated enormous benefits for people's livelihoods and food security. Eradication has prevented the devastating effects of rinderpest on poor rural households with limited assets or few alternatives to livestock production. Given the many links in the livestock marketing chain, the cessation of rinderpest means increased economic activity among traders, slaughterhouses, brokers, retailers, and other stakeholders. In Pakistan, for instance, rinderpest impeded international trade with the Gulf countries, which sought to keep the disease away from their borders. Cattle exports from Pakistan to the Middle East increased dramatically after those states lifted a ban, imposed because of rinderpest, when Pakistan declared provisional freedom from the disease in 2003 (see Figure 16.1).

Lessons from the Rinderpest Eradication Experience

Obviously, the biology of different diseases and hosts must inform the methods to control and eradicate diseases, but the experiences with rinderpest offer some lessons. The rinderpest-eradication strategy evolved from annual, institutionalized vaccination campaigns to a process of seeking active infection, containing and eliminating it based on a sound understanding of the disease, and then confirming the absence of the rinderpest virus. These lessons learned could act as a model for other endeavors in animal disease control.

A campaign of global eradication requires an international coordinating body. For rinderpest, the FAO was mandated by the ministers of agri-

culture of its member countries to assume this role in 1993, and it provided the basic funding for the GREP. FAO proposed and guided the strategy, monitored progress, and hosted an international forum for exchanging technical information.

At the same time, however, global campaigns are too large to be operated by a central unit only. Regional organizations committed to working closely with the global coordinating body are needed to coordinate regionalized control campaigns and to certify disease freedom. Regional ownership of the accreditation process can help put pressure on intractable countries to undergo the process. Although a number of regional programs were envisioned, in reality only the African regions assumed responsibility for rinderpest eradication through PARC. To safeguard the program, the GREP secretariat ended up promoting rinderpest eradication in parts of the world not covered by regional campaigns.

A global disease eradication program needs a clear and realistic aim supported by a timetable and a step-by-step approach. Before the program starts, planners need to consider such issues as

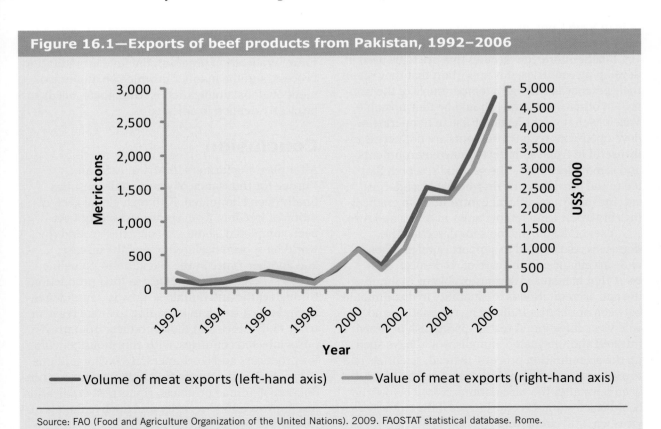

Figure 16.1—Exports of beef products from Pakistan, 1992–2006

Volume of meat exports (left-hand axis) Value of meat exports (right-hand axis)

Source: FAO (Food and Agriculture Organization of the United Nations). 2009. FAOSTAT statistical database. Rome.

vaccine delivery systems, the capacity of targeted countries' veterinary services, legal provisions, and policy issues such as cost recovery.

It is also important to take into account the attitudes of livestock owners by consulting with them beforehand. In Ethiopia, for example, the central planning of vaccination campaigns failed to place vaccination teams at sites amenable to pastoralists and antagonized them by insisting on vaccinating all ages of cattle, which the pastoralists knew to be unnecessary. Rinderpest was quickly eliminated once the program began basing its vaccinations on the preferences of livestock owners, and combining this effort with community-based animal health worker programs in remote areas and the use of a thermostable vaccine.

A disease-eradication campaign also needs appropriate technical tools, such as a clear and evolving understanding of the epidemiology of the targeted disease and safe, effective, affordable, and quality-assured vaccines. The setting of quality-assurance procedures for rinderpest vaccines and the establishment of a facility in Africa where vaccine assessment and certification could be performed made an invaluable contribution, not only to PARC, but also to GREP outside Africa, by offering services to campaigns in other countries.

Furthermore, for vaccines that are to be used in developing countries, it is important that they retain their potency in the warm temperatures of the tropics—in other words, they should be thermostable. Vaccines that might be fit for use in temperate or developed-country environments are not necessarily useful in tropical or developing environments and remote locations. The seminal research that led to the provision of a thermostable rinderpest vaccine made a significant contribution to eradicating rinderpest from remote areas in Africa and Asia.

A set of diagnostic tools for detecting the disease is also needed to support rapid diagnosis and surveillance. In the case of rinderpest, one issue that has caused serious problems in monitoring and accreditation is the inability to discriminate between antibodies induced by vaccination and wild virus infection. A test to distinguish between infected and vaccinated animals would have sped up the accreditation process. Instead, scientists had to wait until a sufficient number of animals had been born after the vaccinations ceased before they could test a suitable cohort to see if the rinderpest virus was still circulating.

Finally, a clearly defined accreditation process for disease freedom is needed. From the start of GREP, it was envisaged that the World Organization for Animal Health would assume responsibility for operating the rinderpest freedom accreditation process. Stringent conditions for accreditation were set, and slow but steady progress was made in accrediting countries as free from the rinderpest disease or infection. Setting a deadline of 2010 for global rinderpest eradication was helpful in guiding countries along the pathway to accreditation. In fact, it is likely that rinderpest stopped circulating in both domesticated and wild animals in 2001—nine years before the deadline—yet no declaration of global freedom has been made because the remaining unaccredited countries are increasingly reluctant to devote any resources to the accreditation process—even though they have eradicated rinderpest. As a result, although no known cases of rinderpest have emerged since 2001, accreditation of all countries individually may not be possible by 2010 (see Figure 16.2). How this will be resolved is unclear. It may be that not every single country needs to be formally accredited as free from rinderpest and intransigent countries do not need to be coerced into undertaking the accreditation process. In any future eradication program, the final accreditation process, and the manner in which an announcement of global eradication is to be made, needs to be clearly defined in advance.

Conclusion

After plaguing farmers in Africa, Asia, and Europe for thousands of years, rinderpest has finally been eliminated. Although global accreditation of freedom from rinderpest has not yet been completed, some 127 countries around the world have been declared free of the disease, and another 11 are in the accreditation pipeline. Besides increasing confidence in food production through cattle and buffaloes, growing confidence in rinderpest freedom is leading to an increase in trade in livestock and their products from previously infected countries, with enormous benefits for producers and consumers. By saving millions of livestock and contributing to the increasing production of animal products, rinderpest eradication has improved food security and the livelihoods of millions of people worldwide.

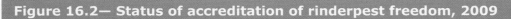

Figure 16.2— Status of accreditation of rinderpest freedom, 2009

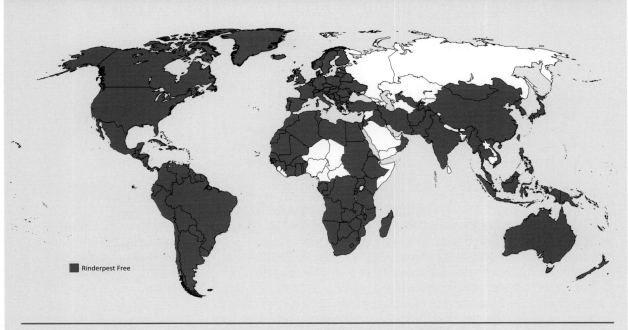

■ Rinderpest Free

Source: World Organization for Animal Health. 2009. www.oie.int/eng/status/Rinderpest/en_RP_free.htm.

Global eradication of an infectious disease has occurred only twice, with smallpox and rinderpest. The experience of rinderpest eradication shows how much a careful combination of scientific expertise and close international cooperation can accomplish. ■

Removing Rinderpest from Remote Areas: The Role of Community-Based Animal Health Workers

Reaching livestock keepers with veterinary services is a perennial challenge, especially where farmers and pastoralists live in remote areas beyond the reach of government service delivery systems. As late as the 1990s, this challenge was seriously hindering efforts to eradicate rinderpest. Outbreaks were still to be found in parts of South Sudan, East Africa, and the Horn of Africa, areas where armed conflict or the remoteness of pastoral communities were hampering eradication efforts.

Two breakthroughs helped wipe out these last pockets of rinderpest. First was the development in the late-1980s of Thermovax, a heat-stable formulation for the rinderpest vaccine that was far less dependent on cold-chain facilities. Second was the realization by international agencies, national governments, and nongovernmental organizations that community-based animal health workers (CAHWs) could be effective in vaccinating cattle in far-flung pastoralist communities.

While the development of the improved vaccine is well documented, less recognized is the role that CAHWs played in combating rinderpest. This novel approach was developed by nongovernmental organizations working with livestock keepers in East Africa and India during the 1980s. It uses community participation to select people from within a rural community to be trained as animal health workers, identify livestock diseases and report outbreaks, and develop locally-acceptable incentives to keep these services running.[a]

Community-based animal health workers were specifically used to combat rinderpest in South Sudan, the Afar region of Ethiopia, Karamoja in Uganda, and Turkana in Kenya, as part of the Pan African Rinderpest Campaign. The effort, directed by the Organization of African Unity/Interafrican Bureau for Animal Resources and implemented in partnership with various nongovernmental organizations working on the ground, quickly achieved dramatic results.

In South Sudan, where armed conflict had disrupted cold chains and brought vaccination efforts to a standstill by 1992, a community animal health worker program using the new vaccine succeeded in vaccinating over 4.3 million cattle between 1993 and 1995; as a result confirmed outbreaks of rinderpest decreased from 11 in 1993 to only one in 1998.[b] In Ethiopia's Afar region, where government teams had been unable to contain the disease through a 15-year campaign dating back to the late-1970s, community animal health workers succeeded in vaccinating 73,000 cattle in just one season in 1994. Because of this success there were no further cases of rinderpest after 1995; the reservoir of infection had been effectively removed.

Prepared by: Andy Catley, Tim Leyland, and Peter Roeder

a. Leyland, T. 1996. The case for a community-based approach with reference to southern Sudan. In *The world without rinderpest*, FAO (Food and Agricultural Organization of the United Nations) Animal Production and Health Paper 129. Rome: FAO.

b. Catley, A., T. Leyland, and S. Bishop. 2008. Policies, practice and participation in protracted crises: The case of livestock interventions in South Sudan. In *Beyond relief: Food security in protracted crises*, ed. L. Alinovi, G. Hemrich, and L. Russo. Rugby, England: Practical Action Publishing and Rome: FAO; Leyland 1996.

NOTES

1. Scott, G. R., and A. Provost. 1992. *Global eradication of rinderpest.* Background paper prepared for the Food and Agriculture Organization of the United Nations expert consultation on the strategy for global rinderpest eradication. Rome: FAO.

2. Roeder, P. L., W. P. Taylor, and M. M. Rweyemamu. 2006. Rinderpest in the 20th and 21st centuries. In *Rinderpest and peste des petits ruminants: Virus plagues of large and small ruminants*, ed. T. Barrett, P. P. Pastoret, and W. Taylor. Amsterdam, The Netherlands: Elsevier.

3. Taylor, W. P., P. L. Roeder, and M. M. Rweyemamu. 2006. Use of rinderpest vaccine in international programmes for the control and eradication of rinderpest. In *Rinderpest and peste des petits ruminants: Virus plagues of large and small ruminants*, ed. T. Barrett, P. P. Pastoret, and W. Taylor. Amsterdam, The Netherlands: Elsevier.

Connecting the Milk Grid

Smallholder dairy in India

Kenda Cunningham

Milk has historically been an important source of protein for Indians, especially for the country's many vegetarians. But India has not always been able to produce enough milk to satisfy consumer demand. In the 1950s and 1960s, India faced severe milk shortages and relied heavily on milk imports. Millions of Indian farmers, most with just a few cows, produced milk, but they had no way of delivering their highly perishable products to the fast-growing cities where demand for milk was high and rising.

Impressed by the success of a dairy cooperative union in Gujarat, the Government of India established the National Dairy Development Board (NDDB) and mandated it to expand the pattern of dairy cooperatives established in the Anand District of Gujarat throughout India. The NDDB conceived and developed the Operation Flood program, which organized dairy farmers into cooperatives, introduced technological advances to help them produce more milk, and transformed the policy environment in support of smallholder dairy. It helped create a national "milk grid," linking India's dairy cooperatives with major cities in a chain of milk production, procurement, processing, and marketing. The beneficiaries have included small-scale dairy farmers, urban and rural consumers, and even landless milk producers. This intervention had a large impact on the evolution of the dairy industry in India and successfully contributed to improving nutrition and reducing poverty.

Today, in the wake of Operation Flood and other development programs targeting the dairy industry, milk production has nearly tripled. India has become the world's largest producer of buffalo and goat milk and the sixth-largest producer of cow milk. Operation Flood contributed to a "white revolution" in India, similar to the Green Revolution in crop production (see Chapter 3).

Flooding India with Milk

India's dairy industry is largely traditional, local, and informal. Milk production is dominated by smallholder farmers, including landless agricultural workers, who rely primarily on family labor to collect and deliver milk to consumers and markets. Eighty percent of milk comes from farms of only two to five cows.[1] These many small farms traditionally lacked access to markets. No system existed for procuring milk produced in rural areas, and the perishable nature of milk made it difficult and expensive to transport.

In response to the limitations of this system, milk producers of the Anand district in the state of Gujarat organized themselves into a private cooperative called Kaira District Cooperative Milk Producers' Union Ltd. in 1946. After a visit to the cooperative, Prime Minister Lal Bahadur Shastri decided that this model should be replicated throughout India. His dream came to fruition in a bold initiative to "flood India with milk" through a sophisticated procurement system using rural production to satisfy urban demand. Operation Flood, a national-scale, federally sponsored intervention, began in 1970 and lasted until 1996.

Operation Flood was designed to increase milk production, ensure that a stable supply reached rural and urban consumers, and raise the incomes

This chapter is based on Cunningham, K. 2009. *Rural and urban linkages: Operation Flood's role in India's dairy development.* IFPRI Discussion Paper. Washington, D.C.: International Food Policy Research Institute.

Smallholder dairy producers test and measure milk, India

of dairy farmers. It replaced the ad hoc production, marketing, and selling of milk with an organized, continuous dairy-supply chain from production to consumption. The intervention was organized in three tiers. At the base, farmer-controlled, village-level cooperatives were responsible for supplying milk to the production and marketing chain, making local dairy sales, and testing samples of dairy products. The middle tier was made up of district-level cooperative unions, which owned and operated processing plants, transported equipment for collecting and processing milk, and managed cattle feed plants. They also provided animal healthcare through livestock centers. At the apex were state federations, which conducted marketing and coordinated interstate sales. This network of village dairy cooperatives, district and regional cooperative unions, and state marketing federations became known as the national milk grid.

The various elements of the dairy industry—production, procurement, processing, and marketing—were, however, carefully scaled up in three phases. Phase one, carried out from 1970 to 1980, targeted just four major urban markets—Mumbai, Kolkata, Delhi, and Chennai (known as Bombay, Calcutta, Delhi, and Madras, respectively, at the time of Operation Flood)—for milk marketing and incorporated 1 million rural milk producers with 1.8 million milk-producing animals. The second phase, from 1981 to 1985, expanded the program to 10 million rural producers with several million head of improved high-quality, crossbred dairy cows. During this phase, the number of milk sheds rose from 18 to 27, and marketing expanded

to cover all 147 major Indian cities. The third phase, lasting through the mid-1990s, focused on consolidating and filling remaining gaps in the grid. It targeted nearly 7 million farm families and 170 milk sheds, and improved veterinary healthcare (see Figure 17.1).

The government of India created the National Dairy Development Board in 1965 and made it responsible for appraising, promoting, and supporting dairy cooperatives. The NDDB was established to direct India's dairy development, by planning and providing farmer extension services, and improving dairy technologies, veterinary services, and nutrition. The founding chair of the NDDB, Dr. Verghese Kurien, the AMUL general manager, transformed cooperatives from an idea into a reality and conceived the overall design for Operation Flood. The Indian Dairy Corporation, established to manage the financial aspects of the intervention, later merged into the NDDB, which continues to oversee dairy development programs throughout India today after the completion of the Operation Flood program.

Financing for Operation Flood came from an innovative source. When the European Economic Community (EEC) donated surplus dairy commodities—skimmed milk powder and butter oil—to India, the architects of Operation Flood incorporated these EEC donations with milk produced by Indian cooperatives and sold the combined products to help pay for development of the dairy industry. In this way, food aid was monetized to support local production. The intervention also drew on loans from the World Bank.

How Operation Flood Reshaped the Dairy Industry

Operation Flood linked rural dairy producers to urban consumers through dairy cooperatives, trucking networks, chilling plants, refrigerated vans, railway wagons, and processing plants. By linking production to consumption, the program created the incentives needed to encourage dairy producers and others involved in the supply chain to invest in order to increase their earnings from dairying. Gradually their confidence in dairying as a stable source of employment and income rose.

Operation Flood aided this process by introducing numerous technological and infrastructural

Figure 17.1—Operation Flood's geographic coverage, 1970–96

Operation Flood	Milksheds	Districts Covered
I (July 70-Mar 81)	39	39
II (Apr 81-Mar 85)	97	161
III (Apr 85-Mar 96)	34	162
Total	170	362

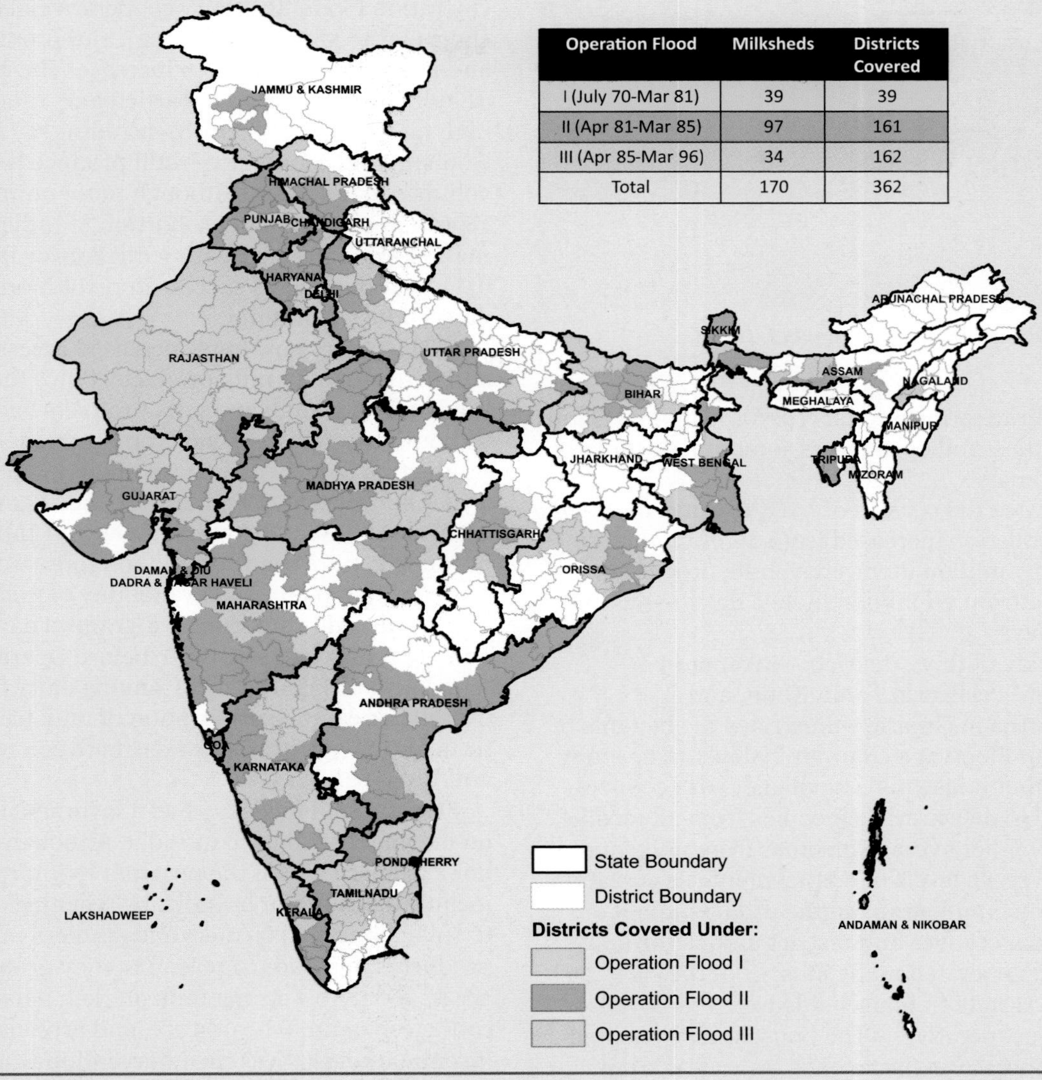

Legend:
- State Boundary
- District Boundary

Districts Covered Under:
- Operation Flood I
- Operation Flood II
- Operation Flood III

Source: National Dairy Development Board. 2009. Personal Communication.

advances in dairying. On the production side, advances included crossing exotic breeds of cows with indigenous breeds to improve production. Estimates show that whereas one indigenous cow provided about 1.5 kilograms of milk a day, a crossbred cow could provide 4 kilograms a day.[2] On the processing side, advances included the introduction of silos, pasteurizers, storage tanks, and refrigerators that conformed to international standards, increasing the nation's capacity to convert milk, a highly perishable commodity, into a

commodity that could be stored and traded nation-wide. And on the marketing side, new technologies were developed to improve the weighing and testing of milk and to improve the capacity to sell it in bulk.

Some critics argued that crossbreeding favored larger farmers, eliminated indigenous Indian animals, and increased reliance on higher-quality feed. In fact, crossbreeding was part of the Indian government's strategy for improving productivity in India without wiping out well-known breeds of Indian cattle. Only a small percentage of Operation

Refrigerated milk goes to market, India

Flood's strategy focused on crossbred animals; and even landless milk producers sometimes acquired these animals.

Between the periods of 1988–89 and 1995–96, milk production increased from 42 million liters a day to 67 million liters a day, milk procurement increased from 28 million liters a day to 35 million liters a day.[3]

A study of three districts—Bikaner in Rajasthan, Periyar in Tamil Nadu, and Sabarkantha in Gujarat—illustrates the benefits of Operation Flood at a community level.[4] The study showed that households in villages with cooperatives had higher average incomes from all income sources, higher average incomes from milk, and higher average levels of employment. The creation of a national milk grid and the establishment of village cooperatives and district unions throughout India generated many jobs; as of the early 21st century, 11 million households were employed by dairy cooperatives.[5] The households benefited from cooperatives they owned, as well as from cooperatives that sold them feed, provided veterinary care, and purchased their milk.

Although India's dairy sector may have grown regardless of Operation Flood and cooperatives set up under Operation Flood accounted for only a small share of the total milk procured and marketed in India, these cooperatives were responsible for a major share of the formal, organized dairy sector. With the help of some other development factors, Operation Flood successfully created an enabling environment for dairy-sector development in India.

A Lasting Impact

More than a decade after the conclusion of Operation Flood, the dairy cooperative network continues to grow (Figure 17.2), and production and marketing continue to increase. The number of individual cooperative participants remains high (at 13 million in 2008, including 3.7 million women), and cooperatives still produce high volumes of milk. And although these numbers represent only a small proportion of India's dairy market from any angle, they still convey the scale of Operation Flood's success in revolutionizing the dairy industry in India.

Consumers now have increased access to more and better-quality milk products. Since the 1970s total output of milk and milk products has continuously risen faster than crop production. Dairy production rose an average of about 4.5 percent a year between 1970 and 2001. Official government statistics for 2007–08 show that India is producing more than 100 million tons of dairy a year and that per capita availability of milk is near 250 grams a day, up from 128 grams a day in 1980 and 113 grams a day in 1968, before Operation Flood began (Figure 17.3).[4] Among dairy farmers, overall per capita consumption of milk increased from 290 to 339 grams per day between 1988-89 and 1995-96.

Operation Flood also had a favorable impact on income distribution in India. Although it was not a primary aim of the program to improve income distribution in India, by reaching out to small, marginal farmers and landless milk producers, it stands to reason that by promoting access for all to a strong milk market, balanced cattle feed, animal healthcare, and artificial insemination services the intervention would have a positive impact on income distribution between the rich and the poor. Studies of Operation Flood showed that the program effectively engaged the rural poor: in 1984, 72 percent of cooperative members were small and marginal farmers (or those who operated fewer than 5 hectares of land) and the majority of these were also from minority castes and tribes.[5] Landless farmers' incomes doubled after the organization of milk collection through cooperatives.[6] Later studies showed that among landless households, milk production made a considerable contribution to income generation and confirmed the potential for poor households to increase their income through milk production.[7]

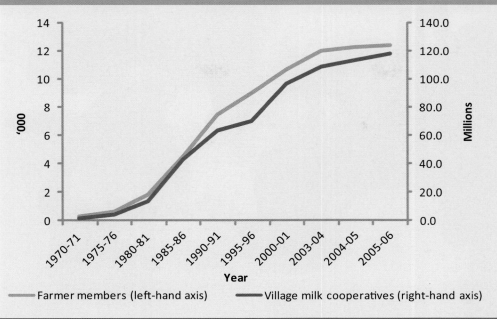

Figure 17.2—Cooperative growth during and after Operation Flood, 1970–2006

Farmer members (left-hand axis)   Village milk cooperatives (right-hand axis)

Sources: Gupta, P. R. 1997. Operation Flood: The third phase. In *Dairy India 1997*, ed. P. R. Gupta. New Delhi: P. R. Gupta; NDDB (National Dairy Development Board). 2006. *Annual report, 2005–2006*. Anand, India; Aneja, R. P. 1994. *Dairying in India: A success story*. APAARI Publication 1994(4). Bangkok, Thailand: Asia-Pacific Association of Agricultural Research Institutions.

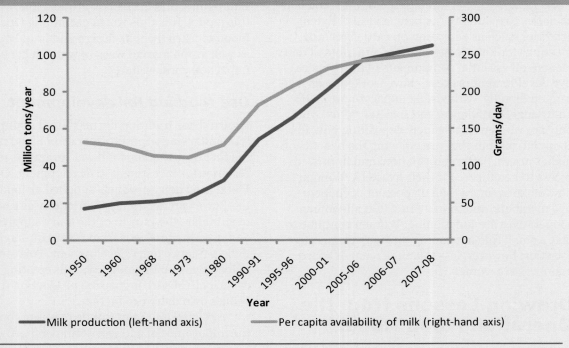

Figure 17.3—Production and per capita availability of milk in India, 1950–2008

Milk production (left-hand axis)   Per capita availability of milk (right-hand axis)

Source: National Dairy Development Board. 2009. National Statistics. < www.nddb.org/statistics/milkproduction.html>; Gupta, P. R. 1997. *Dairy India 1997*. New Delhi: P. R. Gupta; Nair, K. N. 1995. White revolution in India: Facts and issues. *Economic and Political Weekly* 20 (June 22–29): A89–A95.

Providing balanced feed to cattle, India

Operation Flood also benefited women. Employment rates, including those of female workers, were higher among Operation Flood beneficiaries than among nonbeneficiaries.[8] Extension activities, such as education on cattle breeding, meetings for knowledge sharing, and tours of dairy plants—all essential components of the cooperative development process—have worked to engage women directly, with visible impact on women's knowledge, confidence, and societal status. Not only are women increasingly depositing milk in cooperatives, but they are enjoying the benefits of higher prices, better information, and improved access to healthcare for their livestock. Women now make up more than 25 percent of cooperative members, and more than 2,700 all-women cooperatives are functioning. Women continue to play a small role in running the dairy cooperative societies; however, less than 3 percent of board members are women.[9]

Drawing Lessons from the Operation Flood Model

Imitations of Operation Flood have already begun to emerge. In India alone, the Operation Flood model is being replicated for other products, including vegetable oils, fruits, and vegetables. Other Asian countries, such as China, the Philippines, and Sri Lanka, are also following this model. It is thus worth examining Operation Flood to learn from its design and implementation, as well as the myriad ways in which it generated impact on rural welfare.

Use food aid for development

Food aid has traditionally been used mainly for humanitarian purposes. Operation Flood marked the first time that food aid was leveraged as a resource for investment in development. Operation Flood used dairy products supplied as food aid by the European Economic Community as raw inputs to stimulate the growth of the dairy supply chain and used the proceeds from those commodities to help finance dairy development. This strategy helped scale up the industry, thus creating the capacity to absorb increasing production from India's own dairy production.

A related and more subtle message concerns the importance of a longer-term perspective. Several leaders had the foresight to see what could happen if new avenues for dairy development were not pursued: mass quantities of cheap

From Impounding to Empowering: Smallholder Dairy in Kenya

Kenya is the "milkshed" of Africa, with more than 6 million dairy cattle producing roughly 4 billion liters of milk per year, and higher milk consumption (145 liters per person per year) than any other African country. Most dairy cattle are owned by small-scale farmers, and an estimated 86 percent of their milk is supplied in an unprocessed form to consumers through a supply chain dominated by small-scale traders, transporters, and sellers.[a]

Until recently, public policies and business interests controlled the country's dairy supply chain to such an extent that small-scale milk vending of lower-priced raw milk in urban areas was essentially criminalized in the name of food safety and quality. With the support of the Kenya Dairy Board, the government's regulatory agency that oversees the dairy industry, these policies and interests created a market based on unfair competition. The negative repercussions affected both small-scale milk vendors, many of whom are women, and consumers, many of whom prefer to purchase milk from outside the formal industry because of lower prices and preferred taste.[b]

The conflict between the few large businesses on the one hand and the poor, haphazardly organized, and voiceless small-scale milk traders on the other became more apparent in the mid-1990s following the collapse of the dairy market monopoly—the Kenya Cooperative Creameries, a parastatal company—due to poor management, corruption, and weak competitiveness.[c] With the monopoly's collapse, the door was opened for other private-sector dairy processors to enter the market, bringing about a newly vibrant industry for smallholders.

But it quickly became apparent that these new processors were unable to fill the gap left by the monopoly, while the status quo that criminalized raw milk sales in urban areas continued. To address this policy challenge, key stakeholders in the dairy sector redirected the efforts of the collaborative Smallholder Dairy Project, which ran from 1997 to 2005 and brought together the Kenya Agricultural Research Institute and the International Livestock Research Institute with the Ministry of Livestock and various civil society organizations.[d] The project helped set in motion a policy-change process at multiple levels with diverse decisionmakers in both government and industry. The project also developed a pragmatic model for training, supporting, and certifying small-scale traders as a means of assuring milk quality, strengthening their business capabilities, and expanding the market.

In 2004, the project contributed to the introduction and enforcement of new regulations that streamlined license application processes in the dairy trade. This allowed small-scale milk producers, traders, tea shop retailers, and transporters to legally engage in dairy activities and take part in the newly instituted milk quality assurance scheme.

Today, there is evidence that this new legislation, combined with continued growth in Kenya's dairy market and the reorganization of industry players such as the Kenya Dairy Board, has contributed to welfare improvements. Smallholders are able to sell more milk to consumers at a lower cost, consumers are enjoying safe, lower-priced milk, and new jobs are being created throughout the dairy-supply chain. One study suggests that large economic benefits are attributable to the policy change.[e] These benefits have also stimulated wider interest among policymakers in other countries in the East African region, with some already embarking on implementing similar schemes.

Prepared by: Amos Omore and Steve Staal

a. Kaitibie, S, A. Omore, K. Rich, B. Salasya, N. Hooton, D. Mwero, and P. Kristjanson. 2009. *Influence pathways and economic impacts of policy change in the Kenyan dairy sector*. Research Report 15. Nairobi, Kenya: International Livestock Research Institute; Kenya Smallholder Dairy Project. 2005. *The uncertainty of cattle numbers in Kenya*. SDP Policy Brief 10. Nairobi, Kenya: Kenya Smallholder Dairy Project.

b. Staal, S. J., A. N. Pratt, and M. Jabbar. 2008. *Dairy development for the resource poor—a comparison of dairy policies and development in South Asia and East Africa*. Pro-Poor Livestock Policy Initiative (PPLPI) Working Papers. Rome: Food and Agriculture Organization of the United Nations.

c. Owango, M. O., J. S. Staal, M. Kenyanjui, B. Lukuyu, D. Njubi, and W. Thorpe. 1998. Dairy co-operatives and policy reform in Kenya: Effects of livestock service and milk market liberalisation. *Food Policy* 23: 173–185.

d. Kenya Smallholder Dairy Project. 2009. The smallholder dairy project. <www.smallholderdairy.org/objectives.htm>. Nairobi.

e. Kaitibie et al. 2009.

dairy imports could have poured into India and destroyed local markets.

Invest in local markets

Operation Flood focused not only on boosting milk production, but also on developing a strong marketing system for milk. The architects of Operation Flood continuously analyzed the rising demand for livestock products and designed an integrated and comprehensive program to meet this demand, complete with supply-chain management systems and centralized quality control.

Support collective action

Operation Flood demonstrated how collective action can be an effective tool in promoting commercialization among farmers. By bringing dairy producers together in cooperatives, the program provided markets with quantities of milk that would have been too costly to assemble from producers on an individual basis. The cooperatives also played a role in strengthening social cohesion, overcoming rural caste and class hierarchies, and fostering a sense of ownership in the development process.

Envision creative structures

Operation Flood revolutionized how dairy was conceived and organized. Concentrating on a single primary product, it created a vertically integrated value chain encompassing every aspect from primary producer to final consumer. Horizontal integration—bringing inputs, extension, and services all within the same program—also helped ensure that the benefits of economies of scale were available to each producer. The cooperative infrastructure made it easy for producers to use new products and processes.

Conclusion

Operation Flood was a key element in the transformation of India into a self-sufficient milk producer, and even into a milk exporter. By pointing the way to the use of production-enhancing technologies, establishing more effective and efficient supply chains, and orienting producers toward markets, Operation Flood helped promote a more productive Indian dairy industry. Milk is now big business in India. As of 2007 India was the largest milk producer in the world, and milk was a bigger contributor to the country's gross domestic product than rice. At least 20 percent of India's agricultural economy is composed of dairying, and about 70 percent of the rural population is somehow involved in milk production. The growth in production has made milk increasingly available to consumers, providing an important source of nutrition for millions of people. ■

NOTES

1. Perumal, M., P. S. Mohan, and M. Suresh. 2007. *Dairy development and income distribution in India.* Delhi: Abhijeet Publications; Morgan, N. Models and opportunities for smallholder dairy producers in Asia: Lessons learned. In *Smallholder dairy development: Lessons learned in Asia.* RAP Publication. Bangkok, Thailand: Food and Agriculture Organization of the United Nations; Punjabi, M. India: Increasing demand challenges the dairy sector. In *Smallholder dairy development: Lessons learned in Asia.* RAP Publication. Bangkok, Thailand: Food and Agriculture Organization of the United Nations.

2. Guha, H. 1980. Operation Flood II: Some constraints and implications, a comment. *Economic and Political Weekly* 15 (December 7): 2163–70.

3. Shukla, R. K., and S. D. Brahmankar. 1999. *Impact evaluation of Operation Flood on the rural dairy sector.* New Delhi: National Council of Applied Economic Research.

4. Shukla and Brahmankar 1999; Sharma, V., and A. Gulati. 2003. *Trade liberalization, market reforms, and competitiveness of the Indian dairy sector.* Markets, Trade, and Institutions Division Discussion Paper 61. Washington, D.C.: International Food Policy Research Institute; Government of India. 2008. *Annual report 2007–2008, Department of Animal Husbandry, Dairying, and Fisheries, Ministry of Agriculture.* New Delhi.

5. Shah, D. 1993. Replicability, dependency, and equity issues in Operation Flood projects. *Journal of Indian School of Political Economy* 5 (2): 371–78.

6. FAO (Food and Agriculture Organization of the United Nations) Information Division. 1978. *World Food Programme in India: The white revolution.* Rome.

7. Thirunavukkarasu, M., R. Prabaharan, and C. Ramasamy. 1991. Impact of Operation Flood on the income and employment of rural poor: Some micro-level evidence. *Journal of Rural Development* 10 (4): 417–25; Singh, K. S., and V. M. Das. 1984. *Impact of Operation Flood I at the village level.* Anand, India: Institute of Rural Management.

8. Thirunavukkarasu, Prabaharan, and Ramasamy 1991.

9. Nehru, S. 2005. India: Revolutionizing the white revolution. *Women's Feature Service* (September 5).

Chapter 18

© Kevin Fitzsimmons/University of Arizona

Farming the Aquatic Chicken
Improved tilapia in the Philippines

Sivan Yosef

In 2006, there were nearly 9 million farmers in the world who never once tilled soil.[1] They did not tend to livestock or harvest a single plant, yet they are part of one of the world's fastest-growing food-producing sectors: aquaculture. Mainly taking the form of fish farming, aquaculture has skyrocketed in the past three decades. It is growing at 9 percent annually and is projected to contribute 41 percent of world fish production by 2020.[2]

Aquaculture's global popularity has been advanced by a series of innovations in how fish are farmed. One such advance emerged from the Genetic Improvement of Farmed Tilapia (GIFT) project, which began in the Philippines in 1988 and served as a launching point for tropical finfish genetic improvement around the world.

Relying on a coalition of national and international research institutions, governments, donors, and small private actors, the GIFT project produced an affordable and resilient fish that now meets the needs of millions of poor consumers not only in the Philippines, but throughout much of Asia. The project's achievements have generated a lively exchange of ideas, research methodologies, and genetic materials across borders, highlighting the potential of aquaculture to help achieve future food security. If just 5 percent of the area deemed suitable for aquaculture in Africa were put to use, enough extra fish could be produced to feed the growing population on the continent until 2020.[3]

The Long Road to Success

Historically, the world has obtained fish by harvesting them in their natural environments. Capture fisheries comfortably filled this role until the 1970s, when the combination of overuse and a booming global population began to quickly diminish the availability of marine fish. Fifty-two percent of global marine fish stocks are now fully exploited.[4] As a result, aquaculture, or fish culture, has become more attractive. Today, low-income food-deficit countries, mostly in Asia, account for nearly 85 percent of the world's aquaculture production.[5]

Fish are an important part of life in the Philippines. The country's fisheries sector employs 12 percent of the total rural labor force, and the average Filipino consumes 28 kilograms of fish every year, compared with a world average of 16 kilograms.[6] In the face of dwindling fishery stocks, the country has long embraced aquaculture, and the demand for a reliable source of fish drives the development of new aquaculture technologies for raising fish yields in the Philippines.

Ironically, the success of tilapia breeding in the Philippines began with failure. In 1949 the country introduced a batch of Mozambique tilapia from Thailand, publicizing them as "wonder fish" that would ease food-security concerns in the region. Over the next decade, however, farmers encountered major problems related to inbreeding

This chapter is based on Yosef, S. 2009. *Rich food for poor people: Genetically improved tilapia in the Philippines.* IFPRI Discussion Paper. Washington, D.C.: International Food Policy Research Institute.

© WorldFish

Tilapia farming, Philippines

The Emergence of an Aquaculture Superpower

In 1988 the International Center for Living Aquatic Resources Management (ICLARM), now known as the WorldFish Center, and its partners established the Genetic Improvement of Farmed Tilapia (GIFT) project. GIFT scientists were interested in finding the perfect strain of tilapia, but they also knew that the food security of millions of people hinged not just on tilapia, but on fish in general. Thus, the overall aim of the project was to build worldwide capacity to genetically improve all tropical finfish.

Scientists began their research by focusing on Nile tilapia because of its ability to breed and produce new generations rapidly, its tolerance for shallow and turbid waters, its high level of disease resistance, and its flexibility for culture under many different farming systems. Tilapia in general is so versatile and resilient that it has been dubbed the "aquatic chicken." Scientists brought together existing strains of Nile tilapia already being used by Filipino farmers with wild Nile tilapia strains collected from Africa. They conducted a series of experiments in which they bred many different combinations of strains together to create a new strain that could perform extremely well in different environments.

A hybrid between a strain from Egypt and a strain from Kenya outperformed the rest, but the technicalities associated with crossbreeding these two strains were challenging. Thus, ICLARM scientists used selective breeding—the process of choosing and breeding "parents" with favorable traits in order to pass these traits on to the next generation—with the expectation that this approach would improve tilapia performance more than a crossbreeding program within a few generations. So that there would be enough genetic variability, scientists created a synthetic base population using the 25 best-performing fish groups of the 64 tested. This population served as the parents for subsequent generations of GIFT fish.

By 1993, scientists had produced three generations of offspring, which were growing much faster and exhibiting higher survival rates than local tilapia strains. Eventually the GIFT fish showed genetic improvements of 7 percent over nine generations of fish, or a 64-percent cumulative increase in tilapia growth over the original base population—an impressive feat by any standard.[7]

and poor integration with local fish. Additionally, the strain was dark in color and small in size, two traits that consumers largely rejected. Large-scale tilapia culture declined and was not revived until decades later.

In 1974, the Government of the Philippines tried again, this time with a research program on tilapia at the Freshwater Aquaculture Center of the Central Luzon State University. With the discovery that male tilapia grow faster than females, the research focused on ways to produce all-male tilapia cultures. At the same time, a series of commercial technologies were developed, including floating net enclosures for breeding tilapia and floating cages for feeding them. The government transferred these finished products to rural farmers, enticing them with field demonstrations, provincewide workshops, bank credit, and opportunities for collaboration with researchers. The government also encouraged private companies, nongovernmental organizations, and cooperatives to test and adopt many of these new technologies. The Philippines emerged as one of the largest tilapia-producing countries in the world in the 1970s.

Meanwhile, a whole different species of fish was receiving attention in the Philippines. Native to Africa, Nile tilapia was originally introduced to Asia in the 1970s for the purpose of expanding small-scale aquaculture. Even though it showed promise, it soon ran into problems related to the insufficient supply of fish seed (fertilized fish eggs) and poor fish growth. It was not until the late-1980s that this species of fish would change the face of Philippine aquaculture.

Scaling Up

Once the GIFT project had completed its breeding work, it turned to the tasks of distributing the improved fish, building breeding capacity in neighboring countries, and evaluating the positive and negative impacts of its product on the ground. In the project's host country of the Philippines, GIFT fish were initially disseminated to farmers through government agencies. The Freshwater Aquaculture Center of Central Luzon State University and the Bureau of Fisheries and Aquatic Resources took the lead in creating a wide, national distribution network for GIFT and other improved tilapia strains. Using outreach stations and hatcheries, they disseminated more than half a million GIFT seed by the end of 1997, as well as more than 10 million fingerlings (young fish) of improved tilapia by 2003.[8]

To help improve tilapia outside of the Philippines, ICLARM established the International Network on Genetics in Aquaculture (INGA) in 1993 as a forum for exchanging ideas, research methodologies, and genetic materials. Based in Malaysia, INGA brought together developing-country members across Asia and Africa, including scientific institutes, regional and international organizations, and one private-sector institution. ICLARM and INGA started by disseminating improved tilapia strains through trials in five member countries: Bangladesh, China, the Philippines, Thailand, and Vietnam. Results were even better than in the original research in the Philippines: in Bangladesh, for example, GIFT strains showed a 78-percent increase in weight compared with non-GIFT fish.[9] Confident in the performance of the strain, ICLARM and INGA scientists transferred tilapia germplasm, or genetic material, to national agricultural research centers so that the centers could use it in research, breeding, and dissemination to farmers.

To date, 11 countries have received GIFT strains, using them to develop national breeding and dissemination programs. Vietnam, for example, has produced and disseminated nearly 2 million improved tilapia seed. Hatcheries in Thailand produce and circulate 200 million GIFT fry (young fish) annually.[10]

In 1997, the GIFT project had bred nine generations of fish when donor support ended. The project provided genetic material for this ninth generation to all of its institutional partners, mostly for noncommercial use. To continue breeding and outreach efforts, the Philippines established a nonprofit private foundation called GIFT Foundation International (GFII), which signed formal licensing agreements with private-sector hatcheries throughout the country that would allow them to produce GIFT and GIFT-derived strains of tilapia. In 1999, seeking to expand its market and increase its earnings, GFII entered into an agreement with GenoMar, a private Norwegian biotechnology firm. GFII transferred dissemination rights to GenoMar, which in turn rebranded the strain as GenoMar Supreme Tilapia (GST™). GST™ is currently disseminated through GenoMar's private hatcheries in China and the Philippines. According to the company, GST™ has an average genetic gain of 20 percent with every generation, among other enhancements. These results, however, require verification.

Rich Food for Poor People

The impact of GIFT and GIFT-derived tilapia in the Philippines has been enormous. Tilapia production has soared during the past three decades, from 18,540 tons in 1980 to 279,000 tons in 2007 (see Figure 18.1). In 2003, GIFT strain and the GIFT-derived strain GET EXCEL together accounted for 68 percent of total tilapia seed produced in the country, amounting to 624 million fry and fingerlings.[11]

An estimated 280,000 people in the Philippines benefit directly or indirectly from employment in the tilapia industry, with two-thirds of the nation's hatcheries dedicated to producing GIFT and GIFT-derived seed.[12] The net returns to farming improved tilapia are particularly high, primarily because the improvements significantly reduce farmers' production costs. Depending on the production environment, improved strains are 32 to 35 percent cheaper to produce than non-improved strains.[13]

Improved tilapia also serves as a cheap source of highly nutritious food for consumers. Fish contain a substantial amount of protein, as well as a variety of essential minerals, vitamins, and amino acids. In Asia, fish provide an average of 31 percent of the total supply of animal protein. Moreover, as a source of protein in the Philippines, tilapia is generally more affordable than pork, beef, chicken, and even other freshwater fish. From 1990 to 2007, average tilapia prices rose 111

Genetically improved farmed tilapia, Philippines

percent whereas beef prices jumped 148 percent and pork prices 157 percent (see Figure 18.2).

This combination of high nutritional value and high production is good news for food security. From 1997 to 2001, national consumption of fish and fishery products in the Philippines increased 2.2 percent annually.[14] Since 1990, Filipinos have increased their total consumption of tilapia by more than 360 percent.[15] A large percentage of this population consists of poor consumers who buy cheaper fish and rely on fish as their primary source of animal protein.

Murky Issues

GIFT fish will face some obstacles in the future. Although Asia currently caters to a booming global demand for tilapia, the Philippines is still working to strengthen its export competitiveness and performance. The government is currently taking steps to improve the country's export standing by focusing resources on increasing production and building up the country's capacity to package and market tilapia as fillets in response to global market preferences.

Environmentally, the precautions taken by the WorldFish Center and INGA on the responsible movement of fish germplasm across and within borders will need to be sustained. The finite availability of fresh water will require future innovations in fish culture. Tilapia will increasingly need to be produced in systems that improve the circulation of air, filtration and feeding techniques, waste removal, and recycling of water.

As aquaculture booms during the next few decades, sorting out the issue of who exactly owns

fish genetic resources will also be important. GenoMar holds exclusive commercial rights to all subsequent products created from GIFT. Thus, while the WorldFish Center continues to keep the historical 9th generation GIFT fish within the public domain for research and development activities, GenoMar is already working with the 14th generation of GST™ exclusively for commercial purposes and without special consideration for small-scale farmers who were the focus of the original GIFT program. This and other factors have resulted in weak dissemination of GIFT fish to small producers.

Lessons Learned from a Groundbreaking Project

The GIFT project has shown that fish is a viable crop for the developing world. Before the initiative, the Philippines had no systematic way of banking or preserving farmed-fish genetic resources. In fact, fish gene banks are rare, especially in tropical developing countries. GIFT introduced technology and training for gene banking and now maintains an internationally important tilapia gene bank. Tilapia seed producers currently have wider access to high-quality tilapia broodstock.

GIFT also represented the first systematic collection and transfer of Nile tilapia germplasm from Africa to Southeast Asia. Although African fish farmers have yet to benefit from these achievements, introducing GIFT to Africa could improve growth of the current fish stock there by an estimated 64 percent.[16]

The GIFT story also highlights the importance of coordination among key players. A strong commitment on the part of the government and international research institutes to create a favorable policy environment, set up infrastructure, and lead the way in research and development despite past setbacks was key. Regional networks coordinated technology transfers to other countries and initiated projects to monitor and evaluate the development and dissemination of improved tilapia. Public–private partnerships in the dissemination phase influenced the public's access to improved strains. Being able to create win–win partnerships in the future, especially between the public and private sectors, will require paying close attention to such issues as legal protections and ownership of genetic resources.

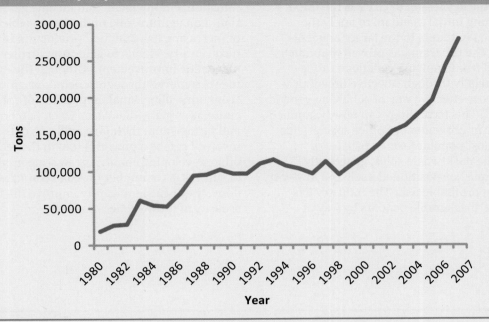

Figure 18.1—Tilapia production in the Philippines, 1980–2007

Source: FAO (Food and Agriculture Organization of the United Nations). 2009. FAOSTAT statistical database. Rome.

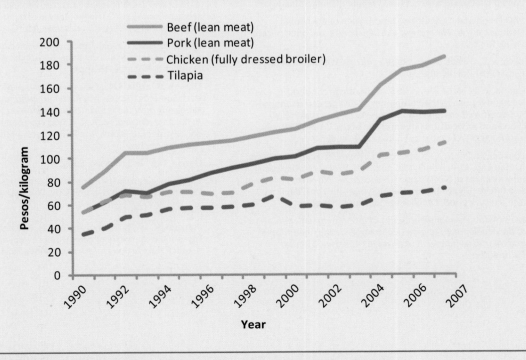

Figure 18.2—Retail prices of tilapia, pork, beef, and chicken in the Philippines, 1990–2007

Source: Philippines' Bureau of Agricultural Statistics. 2009. CountrySTAT tables. Quezon City, Philippines.

Perhaps the key lesson of GIFT is the importance of a strong initial mandate to apply the lessons learned in tilapia to the larger aquaculture picture. The program has proved that much can be gained from applying genetics to aquaculture—especially through selective breeding, a particularly cost-effective way of achieving genetic improvement. This technology can now be applied to the genetic improvement of other species, like the world's most popular farmed fish, carp.

During the past two decades, genetically improved tilapia has positioned itself as a low-cost, high-yielding, profitable fish. The industry has offered direct, measurable benefits by way of nutrition, employment, and income generation. Aquaculture, one of the most viable ways of increasing fish and food production in the next century, stands to gain from further work on genetic improvement. Although the improvements achieved through genetic selection may seem limited in a small population of fish, the cumulative gains that occur when hatcheries and farms—and, therefore, millions of fish—are involved can be a powerful tool in the sector.[17] If other developing countries can scale up this kind of success, as a number of Asian countries have done, they can significantly improve the food security of future generations. ■

NOTES

1. FAO (Food and Agriculture Organization of the United Nations). 2008. *The state of world fisheries and aquaculture 2008*. Rome.

2. Delgado, C. L., N. Wada, M. W. Rosegrant, S. Miejer, and M. Ahmed. 2003. *Fish to 2020*.WorldFish Center Technical Report 62. Penang, Malaysia: WorldFish.

3. WorldFish Center. 2007. *Annual report*. Penang, Malaysia.

4. FAO (Food and Agriculture Organization of the United Nations). 2006. *The state of world fisheries and aquaculture 2006*. Rome.

5. El-Sayed, A–F. M. 2006. *Tilapia culture*. Wallingford, Oxon, U.K.: CABI Publishing.

6. Garcia, Y. T., M. M. Dey, and S. M. M. Navarez. 2005. Demand for fish in the Philippines: A disaggregated analysis. *Aquaculture Economics & Management* 9: 141–168; FAO (Food and Agriculture Organization of the United Nations). 2009. FAOSTAT statistical database. Rome.

7. Ponzoni, R. W., N. H. Nguyen, H. L. Khaw, N. Kamaruzzaman, A. Hamzah, K. R. Abu Bakar, and H. Y. Yee. 2008. Genetic improvement of Nile Tilapia (*Oreochromis Niloticus*)—present and future. Eighth International Symposium on Tilapia in Aquaculture 2008, October 12–14, Cairo, Egypt.

8. ADB (Asian Development Bank). 2006. *An impact evaluation of the development of genetically improved farmed tilapia and their dissemination in selected countries*. Manila, Philippines.

9. Dey, M. M. 2000. The impact of genetically improved farmed Nile tilapia in Asia. *Aquaculture Economics and Management* 4 (1&2): 107–124.

10. Gupta, M. V. and B. O. Acosta. 2004. From drawing board to dining table: The success story of the GIFT project. *NAGA, WorldFish Center Quarterly* 27 (3/4): 4–14.

11. ADB (Asian Development Bank). 2004. *Special evaluation study on small-scale freshwater rural aquaculture development for poverty reduction*. Manila, the Philippines.

12. CGIAR Science Council. 2006. *Improved tilapia benefits Asia*. Science Council/Standing Panel on Impact Assessment Brief Number 6. Rome; ADB 2006.

13. Dey, M. M. 2002. Overview of socioeconomics and environmental issues. In *Tilapia farming in the 21st Century: Proceedings of the International Forum on Tilapia Farming in the 21st century*, ed. R. D. Guerrero and M. R. Guerrero-del Castillo. Los Banos, the Philippines: Philippine Fisheries Association, Inc.

14. Garcia, Dey, and Narvaez 2005.

15. Philippines' Bureau of Agricultural Statistics. 2009. CountrySTAT tables. Quezon City, Philippines.

16. Ponzoni et al. 2008.

17. Ponzoni, R. W., N. H. Nguyen, and H. L. Khaw. 2007. Investment appraisal of genetic improvement programs in Nile tilapia (*Oreochromis niloticus*). *Aquaculture* 269: 187–199.

© Qilai Shen/PANOS

Crossing the River While Feeling the Rocks
Land-tenure reform in China

John W. Bruce and Zongmin Li

In 1977, China's Anhui Province was facing food shortages and flooding that brought the province to the verge of famine. Agricultural productivity was languishing under large-scale, collectivized agriculture, in which farming was managed by communes made up of thousands of people rather than by individual households. In desperation, some communes in the province began secretly allowing farmers to manage their own plots. This small group of farmers achieved stunning improvements in food production, greatly exceeding the productivity of the communes.

The success of these farmers marked the beginning of a massive shift in Chinese agriculture. In 1978, facing up to the weak performance of collective agriculture in many areas of the country, the Chinese Communist Party reluctantly embraced these experiments, giving rise to the Household Responsibility System in which parcels of collective land were allocated to farm households. Once permitted, the system spread throughout China like wildfire. Four years later, more than 90 percent of the country's farmland had been parceled out to more than 160 million farm households.[1]

The shift to household farming, along with other factors (such as reforms in the state's procurement system for agricultural goods, better seeds for rice farmers, and investments in irrigation) led to dramatic increases in food production and reductions in poverty. The per capita incomes of rural people doubled in just five years.[2] Widespread hunger was averted, and hunger and

malnutrition fell dramatically. Although reforms spread across China rapidly, they were generally advanced through careful experimentation— "crossing the river while feeling the rocks," according to Deng Xiaoping, China's paramount leader from 1978 to 1992.[3]

Reform Begins: Desperation and Experimentation

By the late 1970s, China had had more than two decades of experience with collectivized agriculture. When the Chinese Communist Party came to power in 1949, it had launched a brief "land-to-the-tiller" program, but it soon switched to a system of collective agriculture, creating production cooperatives in 1952 and then scaling them up to communes in 1959 (see box next page).

The collectivization of agriculture was expected to benefit from economies of scale and to provide a base for the development of rural industries, but the results were disappointing. Grain production rose by 13 percent during the land-to-the-tiller period (1949-52) and continued to increase less strongly during the agricultural cooperatives period (1952–58). With full collectivization in the Great Leap Forward in 1958, grain production declined and the country suffered serious famine during 1960–63. And during the 20 years that followed (1957–78), the amount of commercial grain contributed by each rural resident fell from 85 to 63 kilograms. Food shortages were rife throughout the country, and food rationing was introduced in urban areas. During the 1970s,

This chapter is based on Bruce, J. W. and Z. Li. 2009. *"Crossing the river while feeling the rocks": Incremental land reform and its impact on rural welfare in China.* IFPRI Discussion Paper. Washington D.C.: International Food Policy Research Institute.

Collective Agriculture and the Shift to Household Responsibility

In the 1950s, the Chinese government adopted a collective system of agriculture in which land was held by the state, and peasant households were reorganized into communes. Each commune was composed of an average of 5,000 households and consisted of several production brigades, themselves further divided into production teams of 20–30 households. The commune might manage as much as 4,000 hectares. Work on private plots was prohibited.[a]

As the shift to household responsibility took place in China beginning in 1978, many communities went through three main stages. In the first stage, the production team was assigned a quota and the whole group was then rewarded or punished according to its performance. In the second stage, a specific plot and output quota were assigned to the household. If the household produced more output than the quota, the excess output would be given to the household or shared between the household and the production team. The third phase—the Household Responsibility System—was identical to the second phase except that there was no unified allocation of income by the production team, so that all excess output went to the household. Not all communities went through all three stages, and many that did moved through them in successive years.

a. Fan, S., and P. G. Pardey. 1995. *Role of inputs, institutions, and technical innovations in stimulating growth in Chinese agriculture.* Environment and Production Technology Division Discussion Paper No. 13. Washington, D.C.: International Food Policy Research Institute.

an estimated one-third of the rural population lacked a stable food supply.[4]

In 1978, driven by famine and the collapse of confidence in collective agriculture, a few production brigades in Fengyang County in Anhui Province—a poor region plagued by flood and famine—secretly distributed land to their member households to farm. These farmers relied on their memories of household farming and their ongoing experience with small household food plots, which many farmers managed even under collectivized agriculture. These small plots—usually smaller than 0.02 hectares—were several times more productive than their collectives' land.[5]

That first year's productivity increases in Anhui were impressive. Some brigades that had returned to household farming had production increases of two to five times those in unconverted brigades.[6] Local officials embraced the reform, which was then carried out under the protection of Wan Li, the provincial governor of Anhui.

The time was right for the Communist Party to consider a change. In 1976, Chairman Mao died and the Cultural Revolution came to an end. China's agricultural sector was in turmoil, with grain failures and famine occurring in parts of the country. Although the Communist Party had expressly forbidden a return to household farming

as late as 1977, the following year it stated that the breakup of communal lands into household holdings was an option.

The return to household farming required party leaders to skillfully manipulate ideological themes in the service of pragmatism. Du Runsheng, director of rural policy of the Chinese Communist Party, described three key points in the reformers' strategy for winning acceptance of the reform within the Party: (1) build the system initially within the communes rather than abolishing them outright, (2) allow the populace to choose from among a number of forms of organization, and (3) allow the reform to spread gradually.[7]

Local communes adopted the new system wholeheartedly. In January 1980, only 1 percent of all production teams in China had converted to household farming, but by December of that year the figure was 14 percent. It reached 28 percent by July 1981, and 45 percent by October 1981. By the time the government recognized that the Household Responsibility System was broadly applicable, 45 percent of the production teams in China had already been dismantled.[8] By the end of 1983, about 98 percent of production teams and 94 percent of farm households in China were farming under the new system.[9]

A Parallel Reform: The State Procurement System

Around the same time that the Household Responsibility System was getting underway on a grassroots level, the Chinese government was formulating another response to the country's food crisis: major changes to the system of state procurement of agricultural products.

In 1977, the government was the only legal purchaser of many key commodities, including rice, wheat, maize, oilseeds, and cotton. Production brigades within communes were assigned quotas, and this quota production had to be sold to the state at prices set by the state. When communes were divided into household farms, meeting these quotas became the responsibility of households. This procurement system gave the government a powerful tool for influencing farmers' production.

After 1977, the government bumped up procurement prices significantly to give farmers an incentive to produce more agricultural goods. In 1979 alone, state procurement prices for major crops rose an average of 22 percent. After 1979, government purchasing prices for grain jumped by 100 percent and those for many other crops increased by 40–50 percent.[10]

Moreover, from 1977 onward, farmers were allowed to trade grain on free markets once they fulfilled their delivery quotas to the state procurement system. Bans that prohibited farmers from growing cash crops were eliminated. Farmers regained the right to grow vegetables or other non-quota cash crops and to sell their products in the open markets.

One of the most distinctive features of the Chinese rural reforms of the 1980s is the manner in which these procurement and market reforms were managed. Whereas most post-communist countries have made a sudden, "big-bang" transition to market prices for agricultural production, China opted for a two-track approach, maintaining quotas and set prices for quota production while at the same time liberalizing markets for non-quota production and allowing markets to control

Planting rice, China

prices for these above-quota crops. This approach provided the state with an assurance of sustained grain production and farmers with an assurance of a predictable if modest farm income during a period of great uncertainty. At the same time, it provided strong incentives for farmers to exceed quotas and to diversify into non-quota crops.

More Food and Higher Incomes for Rural Chinese

Farmers responded to the rural reforms by producing bumper harvests. Crop production grew by 42.2 percent between 1978 and 1984. During those years, the three most important crops—grain, cotton, and oil-bearing crops—grew at annual average rates of 4.8, 17.7, and 13.8 percent, respectively (see Figure 19.1). During the preceding 26 years, these crops had grown at only 2.4, 1.0, and 0.8 percent a year, respectively. Even though farmers were cultivating fewer hectares of grain during this period, the gains in productivity led to more total output. National grain output

rose from about 300 million tons in 1978 to about 407 million tons in 1984.

Although the increases in state procurement prices had some impact on production, the Household Responsibility System reform was the greatest impetus behind the production increases. Given the opportunity to sell part of their output at market prices, farm families responded by investing large amounts of labor and inputs to exceed their quotas, while at the same time diversifying their production into non-quota crops. Technological improvements like hybrid rice (see Chapter 11) and the practice of double cropping (growing two crops a year instead of just one) also helped. China's prior decades of massive government investment in rural infrastructure, especially irrigation, helped lay the groundwork for jumps in productivity as well.

With agriculture growing at breakneck speed in the years following these reforms, the quality of life in rural China improved substantially. In just five years, from 1978 to 1983, rural people doubled their per capita incomes (see Figure 19.2). The rural poverty rate plummeted, falling from

© Mark Henley/PANOS

Harvesting rice in Hunan Province, China

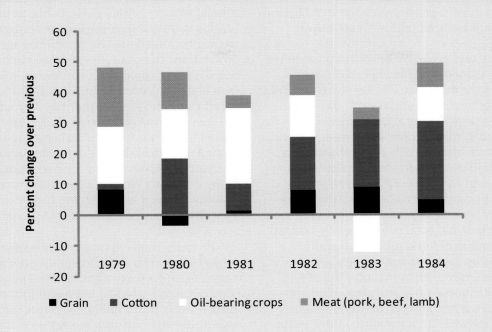

Figure 19.1—Agricultural output in China, 1978–84

Source: Zweig, D. 1997. *Freeing China's farmers: Rural restructuring in the reform era.* Armonk and London: M. E. Sharp.

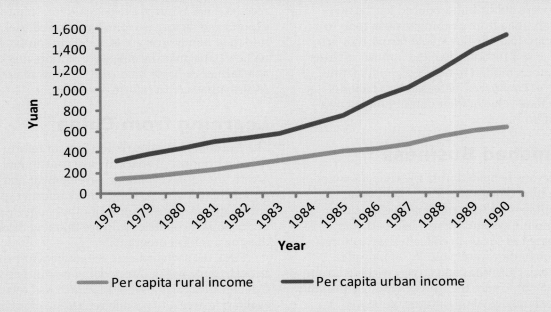

Figure 19.2—Per capita income of rural and urban households, 1978–90

Source: Renwei, Z. 1993. Three features of the distribution of income during the transition to reform. In *The distribution of income in China*, ed. K. Griffin and Z. Renwei. London and New York: The Macmillan Press.

76 percent in 1980 to 23 percent in 1985. The longstanding income gap between rural and urban households was reduced (although not nearly eliminated).

Both rural and urban households also acquired better access to food, and food became more affordable. In the first three years of the Household Responsibility System reforms (1978–81), calorie intake among people in rural China increased by 12 percent. In 1978, rural people were consuming 122 percent of the minimum daily requirement for a healthy life, and by 1979–81 they were consuming between 140 and 143 percent.[11] As farmers began diversifying their crops and growing more non-quota crops, a wider array of foods found their way into markets and rural people rapidly boosted their consumption of foods other than grain.

The transformation of agriculture, large as it was, was just part of an even larger transformation of the Chinese rural economy. Workers who had been underemployed in the commune system were released from the agricultural sector to find other local work. Taking advantage of this abundance of labor, townships and collectives used new revenue earned through the Household Responsibility System to develop township and village enterprises. These enterprises, building on the commune industries and the large public investments in infrastructure during the commune period, were public but produced for the market—everything from clothing to farm tools to electronics. Like the household farms, they grew rapidly. From 1978 to 1994, the number of firms rose from 1.5 million to nearly 25 million, the number of employees increased by a factor of 4.5, and the total value of their output jumped by a factor of 80.[12]

Unfinished Business

Not everyone benefited from the changes sweeping across China. The rural reforms held some disadvantages for women in particular. Under the commune system, women had in theory participated as equals in collective agriculture, even though they were typically employed in more menial positions and largely excluded from management. Under the Household Responsibility System, changing labor patterns, improved economic productivity, and higher living standards resulted in a revival of patriarchal values. The rural industrialization made possible by the shift to

household responsibility also began to change the roles of women in their households, as men took on jobs in township and village enterprises and women became more responsible for agricultural production. The state allocated land to households based on household size, so in theory when a man married, his land allocation should rise, but for efficiency reasons, authorities discouraged too-frequent reallocations of land. Many villages ceased to provide for such reallocations altogether, leaving women at the risk of landlessness in cases of divorce and widowhood. Organizations such as the All-China Women's Federation noted that as women took more and more responsibility in agriculture, they had less and less satisfactory access to land.[13]

Property rights in rural areas remain a broader subject of concern as well. China's extension of more secure property rights to rural people has been not simply gradual but painfully slow. People in rural areas thus find it much more difficult to acquire assets in the new market economy than do their urban counterparts. A consensus within both private and official circles is emerging that rural people in China should be granted fuller and more marketable land-use rights. At the same time, however, land as it is currently distributed serves as an important social safety net. This safety net has come into play recently, as a global economic recession has reduced the demand for China's exports and factory workers have flowed back into their home rural areas. A debate continues on how to balance the efficiency of more marketable farmer rights to land with the losses to social security that such a reform would entail.

Learning from China

The Household Responsibility System reform and the other reforms it sparked have contributed greatly to China's economic development and the welfare of its citizens. The Chinese reform experience suggests some lessons for other policymakers in developing countries who are thinking through their own reform programs.

First, the sequencing of economic reforms is critical. China began by providing new incentives to the mass of rural households—which had relatively egalitarian access to productive assets—thereby achieving broad benefits, gaining support for the reform process, and laying the foundation for an ever-widening reform agenda. During land reforms like this one, it is important to maintain existing structures for input supply and output marketing while the large production units dismantle, and to provide reliable markets for land-reform beneficiaries in the early reform years. As such, in contrast to the beneficiaries of land reforms in many other countries, Chinese beneficiaries of reform faced virtually guaranteed markets for key economic crops during the critical reform years.

Second, where labor costs are low and alternative employment is limited, small household farms can be remarkably productive, provided they have access to input supply and marketing chains.

Third, because rural resources like farmland were so broadly distributed, the poverty-reduction impacts of reform also reached broad swathes of the population, making poverty-reduction reforms in such a rural sector highly strategic.

Fourth, impressive economic growth can take place under public ownership of land if solid land use rights are in place and farmers are operating within a generally supportive and remunerative economic environment. If farmers are confident of their access to land because of a credible social commitment to land access for all families, it may be feasible to phase in stronger property rights gradually, while building new mechanisms to provide social security otherwise provided by universal land access.

Fifth, promoting the development of both agriculture and industry in rural areas can pay off handsomely if labor is plentiful and cheap and if funds are available for substantial public investments in rural infrastructure and facilities to support industry.

Sixth, process is important. Governments need to create space for local experimentation and allow

Harvested rice just separated from its stalks, China

impartial evaluations, the results of which can be conveyed to people at the highest levels of power. Even incremental reform has important benefits: it allows for learning by doing and corrections as needed, as well as the use of existing organizational resources, an avoidance of social turbulence and waste of resources and, finally, a smoother transition to new institutions.

Conclusion

The Household Responsibility System reform, as well as the other reforms that accompanied it, has had a profound positive influence on China's growth and the livelihoods of its people. They have lifted millions of people out of poverty and averted famine. Rural reforms, conducted in a spirit of experimentation, careful evaluation, and adjustment where necessary, have shown the potential for agricultural growth to take off on a massive scale under the right conditions. ■

NOTES

1. Ho, P. 2005. Introduction: The chicken of institutions or the egg of reforms? In *Developmental dilemmas: Land reform and institutional change in China*, ed. P. Ho. New York: Routledge.

2. Fan, S.,. L. Zhang, and X. Zhang. 2004. Reforms, investment, and poverty in rural China. *Economic Development and Cultural Change* 53 (2): 395-415; Gulati, A., S. Fan, and S. Dafali. 2005. *The Dragon and the elephant: Agricultural and rural reforms in China and India*. Markets, Trade, and Institutions Division Discussion Paper No. 87, Development Strategy and Governance Division Discussion Paper No. 22. Washington, D.C.: International Food Policy Research Institute.

3. Chow, C. G. 2002. *China's economic transformation*. Oxford, U.K.: Blackwell.

4. Zhang, H., X. Li, and X. Shao. 2006. Impacts of China's rural land policy and administration on rural economy and grain production. *Review of Policy Research* 23 (2) 607–624.

5. Zhang, Li, and Shao 2006.

6. Lin, J. Y. 1988. The Household Responsibility System in China's agricultural reform: A theoretical and empirical study. *Economic Development and Cultural Change, Supplement: Why does overcrowded, resource-poor East Asia succeed: Lessons for the LDCs?* 36 (3): S199–S224.

7. Du, R. 2006. *The course of China's rural reform*. Washington, D.C.: International Food Policy Research Institute.

8. Lin 1988; Lin, J. Y. 1992. Rural reforms and agricultural growth in China. *American Economic Review* 82 (1): 34–51; Lin, J. Y. 2003. *The China miracle: Development strategy and economic reform*, revised. Hong Kong: Chinese University Press.

9. Lin 1988.

10. Zhu, L. 1991. *Rural reform and peasant income in China: The impact of China's post-Mao rural reforms in selected areas*. New York: St. Martin's Press.

11. Piazza, A. 1983. *Trends in food and nutrient availability in China, 1950-81*. World Bank Staff Working Paper No. 607. Washington, D.C.: World Bank.

12. Oi, J. C. 1999. Two decades of rural reform in China: An overview and assessment. *The China Quarterly, Special Issue: The People's Republic of China after 50 Years* (159): 616-628.

13. All-China Women's Federation. 1999. *Report on violation of women's land rights under the Second Land Adjustment: A Working Paper*. Beijing: Department of Women's Rights and Interests.

Exiting from Collective Agriculture
Land-tenure reform in Vietnam

Michael Kirk and Nguyen Do Anh Tuan

By the mid-1980s, it became painfully clear that Vietnam's system of collective agriculture was not working. In 1987, after several years of slow growth, food production actually declined by 4.4 percent and famine struck parts of the country. Making matters worse, inflation had risen from 92 percent in 1985 to 775 percent in 1986, making food more and more expensive for the country's population of 60 million.

At the Sixth National Party Congress in December 1986, the Vietnamese Communist Party enacted a series of reforms that would ultimately transform Vietnam from a centrally planned economy to a market-oriented one. The reform process, known as *Doi Moi*, did not really take hold until 1988, but once the collectives were dismantled, land-use rights were assigned to farmers, agricultural markets were liberalized, and wider economic reforms were implemented. As a result, Vietnam's economy took off. For about a decade starting in the early 1990s, the country's gross domestic product (GDP) grew at an annual rate of 7.6 percent thanks in large part to the rapid increase in agricultural growth, which grew 4.9 percent annually between 1996 and 2000, when the growth rate reached an all-time high.[1]

The reforms unleashed a new entrepreneurial spirit in Vietnam, both in agriculture and in other sectors. Farmers intensified rice production, diversified into new crops such as coffee and cashews, and improved the quality of the food they produced. By stimulating agricultural and overall economic growth, the reforms helped reduce rural poverty, hunger, and malnutrition. In just five years—from 1993 to 1998—the share of people living in poverty fell by 21 percent. Among children younger than five, the rate of stunting—meaning a low height for age, a symptom of poor nutrition—declined from 53 to 33 percent during the same period.[2]

Collective Agriculture in Vietnam

When Vietnam achieved independence from France in 1954, the Geneva Accords divided it into two countries with opposing ideologies—the Democratic Republic of Vietnam in the north adopted a socialist ideology influenced by China and the Soviet Union, and the Republic of Vietnam in the south pursued a capitalist ideology influenced by the United States. Civil war soon followed.

The rural economies of the two countries were very different. In North Vietnam's collectivized agriculture, groups of households formed production brigades, which were responsible for meeting government quotas for agricultural production. In South Vietnam, agriculture was highly commercialized and more oriented to the export market, and tenant farmers or sharecroppers cultivated land owned by landlords.

Following reunification in 1975, the Vietnamese Communist Party attempted to extend its centrally planned system—in particular, its large-scale agricultural collectivization—to the whole country. In the south, however, collectivization did not take hold. By 1980, only 24.5 percent of farm house-

This chapter is based on Kirk, M., and T. Nguyen. 2009. *Land-tenure policy reforms: Decollectivization and the Doi Moi system in Vietnam*. IFPRI Discussion Paper. Washington, D.C.: International Food Policy Research Institute.

holds belonged to a collective, and in many cases, southern farms were collectives on paper only.[3]

Moreover, collective agriculture was performing poorly. In 1976 and 1977, agricultural production contracted by 0.5 percent and 6.6 percent, respectively. The amount of grain available in the country was falling, forcing the government to increase grain imports sharply. Government procurement of food also dropped, as farmers sought to avoid the state procurement system and instead sold their output through informal private markets, where prices were reported to be 10 times higher.[4]

By the early 1980s, Vietnam faced an economic crisis. Western and Chinese aid to the country was declining, government food procurements were falling, and a food crisis was emerging. The unpopular system of collective agriculture was on the verge of spontaneous breakdown. The Vietnamese Communist Party responded by issuing Directive 100 on January 13, 1981. This directive allowed collectives to contract with individual households to produce a certain amount of agricultural goods and then sell any surplus they produced in the private market or to state trading agencies. In mid-1981, procurement prices of agri-

cultural goods were increased to the same level as market prices.

At first, this partial reform seemed promising—agricultural growth reached 10.6 percent in 1982. Success, however, was short lived. The reforms, designed to make collective agriculture more efficient, were not deep enough to give farmers real incentives to produce more. Agricultural growth started to slow in 1983 and became negative by 1987. Inflation rose sharply, reaching 775 percent in 1986. The gap between free market and official prices was 10 times or more. Per capita food production fell below the minimum needed level of 300 kilograms a year. People were going hungry again.

Overturning Collectivization

Under the *Doi Moi* reform process adopted in December 1986, the collective agriculture system began to be dismantled. The reforms had sweeping goals: they sought to stabilize the economy, develop the private sector, increase and stabilize agricultural output, shift the focus of investment from heavy to light industry, focus on export-led growth, and attract foreign investment.

It was not until 1988, however, that the Communist Party issued Resolution 10, which

© Jeremy Horner/PANOS

Selling rice in the market, Vietnam

shifted the focus of rural development from collectives to household production. Resolution 10 obliged the agricultural collectives to contract land to households for 15 years for annual crops and 40 years for perennial crops. Households were allowed to buy and sell animals, equipment, and machinery. They still had to meet production quotas, but the production amounts and prices were fixed for five years, giving households a degree of certainty that they had previously lacked. The private sector was allowed to engage in food marketing.

Further reforms followed. From 1987 to 1991, the government relinquished control over prices and opened markets for both domestic and international trade. In 1989, it sharply devalued the country's currency, making Vietnamese exports much more competitive on international markets.

The reforms unleashed a surge of entrepreneurship and productivity. Agricultural growth jumped, reaching 3.8 percent a year from 1989 to 1992. As the government retreated from controlling markets and prices, farm households had new incentives to produce more and sell their surpluses. Vietnam, which had imported more than 460,000 tons of food in 1987 and again in 1988 to meet shortfalls in national production, became the world's third-largest exporter of rice in 1989, alleviating national food shortages and generating large amounts of foreign exchange for the country.

Success in agriculture became a key driver of overall economic growth. Inflation plummeted to 36 percent in 1989. Growth in the agricultural sector in turn increased demand for construction and services. Although Vietnam experienced cuts in foreign aid owing to the collapse of the Eastern European socialist system during 1990–91, economic growth in the country remained strong. By 1992, Vietnam had fully recovered from the shock caused by the collapse of the socialist system, and the economy's growth rate climbed to 8.7 percent.

Still, it was difficult for farmers to grow commercial crops such as coffee, rubber, cashew nut, and pepper, in large part because they still did not have complete, long-term rights to their land. Financial institutions refused to accept existing land-use rights as collateral, preventing households from acquiring loan funds for agricultural investment. And local governments still played a dominant role in deciding crop patterns for specific types of land, requiring most land to be used for food production and discouraging agricultural diversification and further commercialization. In

Figure 20.1—Compounded annual agricultural growth rates in Vietnam, 1976–2005

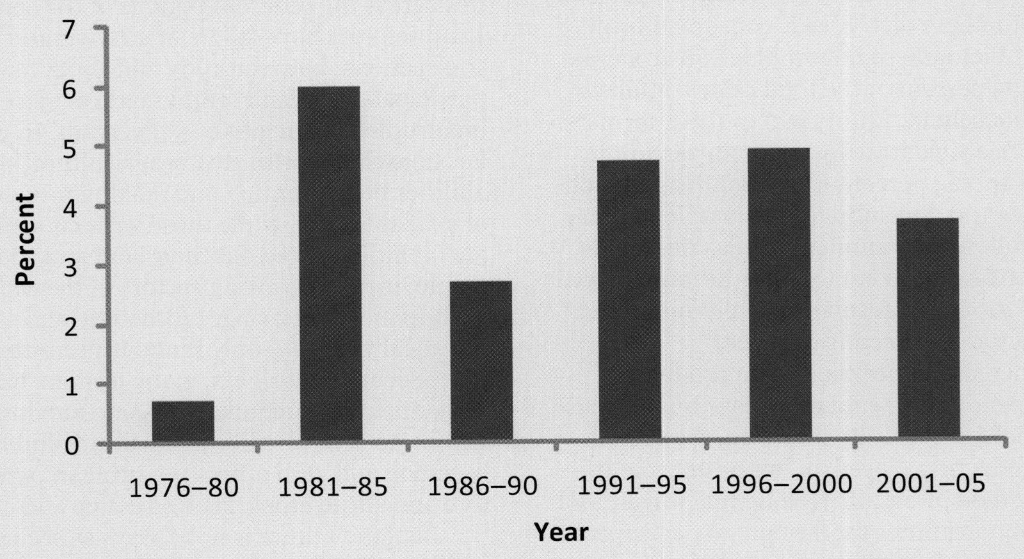

Source: Authors, based on data from the General Statistics Office of Vietnam, various years.

addition, many rural households, especially poor and smallholding ones, had difficulty obtaining access to production technologies, inputs, and capital for production. In 1993, Vietnam passed a Land Law that extended land tenure to 20 years for annual crops and 50 years for perennial crops such as coffee and rubber.

The period from 1993 to 2000 was the "golden age" of the market economy in Vietnam. The agricultural sector grew at 4.6 percent annually, and the nonagricultural sector grew by more than 8 percent, thanks in large part to heavy foreign investment in Vietnamese industries. Even during the Asian financial crisis during 1997–2001, Vietnam maintained strong economic performance and the agricultural growth averaged 3.9 percent per year.

Dramatic Effects for Agriculture, Incomes, and Nutrition

Since the late 1980s, Vietnam's economic reforms have generated powerful incentives to invest in agriculture. The resulting rural growth has raised households' incomes and standards of living. Agricultural growth peaked at an average of 4.9 percent per year during 1996–2000 (see Figure 20.1).[5]

Reforms have led to greater food security and better nutrition, partly by increasing the production of rice, by far the most important staple food in the Vietnamese diet. Rice is consumed by 99.9 percent of Vietnamese households and accounts for about 75 percent of the total caloric intake of a typical household. From 1980 to 1984, farmers saw their rice yields rise by about 32 percent in the North and 24 percent in the South as a result of Directive 100 and subsequent complementary reforms, followed by similar gains as rice yields increased from 3.2 to 4.9 tons per hectare between 1990 and 2006, as a result of Resolution 10 and other policy and economic changes.[6]

The increase in per capita rice production provided people with enough to eat, thus increasing national food security. Later on, the growth of food production played an important role in stabilizing food prices, increasing real wages, and creating opportunities for farmers to participate in more profitable, higher-value farming and nonfarm activities.[7] Increased food production and higher incomes have also led to more diversi-

fied diets, with measurable benefits for nutrition. Between 1993 and 1998, the rates of underweight in children younger than age five fell slowly, but rates of stunting in children dropped dramatically, from 53 to 33 percent.[8]

The economic changes launched by the *Doi Moi* reforms also pulled many Vietnamese out of poverty. From 1993 to 2002, the incidence of poverty in Vietnam fell from 58 to 29 percent.[9] The number of people living in absolute poverty (regardless of how it is defined) is still high, but the poverty that persists today reflects the fact that some households still have poor access to land or have access only to poor-quality land.

During the 1990s, rice prices increased substantially. Nearly three-quarters of Vietnamese households both produced and consumed rice, but households that produced more rice than they consumed benefited from the higher prices. On average, higher rice prices thus helped households in rural areas, where most of the poor live, at the expense of households in urban areas.

Land Issues Remain Complicated

Vietnamese farmers now have much more secure rights to land than they did in the 1970s and 1980s. From the 1990s on, land transactions increased considerably as a consequence of the tenure reforms, although with different intensities across the different regions of the country. Land reforms have led to an active market in land transactions: between 1993 and 1998, household participation in land rental markets more than quadrupled, from 3.8 to 15.5 percent. In particular, households with strong agricultural skills and abilities began renting and making productive use of available land, while those without such skills and abilities rented out their land and sought employment in growing sectors of the economy such as manufacturing.[10] Although land sales are technically illegal—only rental is permitted—with more secure land rights, many farmers have diversified their production, with some moving even more into activities like aquaculture and livestock breeding and with others investing in perennial tree and shrub crops, such as coffee and cashews.

But land tenure is not always as secure as it might seem. From the beginning of the reforms, local authorities frequently reassigned land. In rural northern Vietnam, although households were supposed to retain rights to their assigned land for 20 years, authorities reallocated land twice in a period of five years to accommodate new settlers in the villages, thus undermining incentives for long-term investment.

Moreover, the new system does not necessarily work to everyone's benefit. When poor rural households experience an emergency, they may lease or sell their land to wealthier households, losing control of their land temporarily or permanently and raising the specter of a growing group of landless people in rural areas. In addition, land-use certificates have space for only one name per family, and women's names are normally left off. Women's access to land thus often depends on their marital status, and unmarried and divorced women who devote large amounts of labor to the land are rarely named on titles. A revision of the Land Law in 2004 made an important contribution to gender balance by including the names of both the husband and the wife on land-use certificates, thus creating incentives for women to invest in land and reap its benefits in case of divorce or widowhood.

Land-tenure arrangements have not increased rural people's access to credit as much as may have been expected. Although having a land-use certificate should improve a rural household's access to credit, in particular from formal banking institutions like commercial or rural cooperative banks, banks seem reluctant to accept such certificates as collateral, believing that the land will be hard to seize in case of credit default.

Finally, the reforms have had mixed results for the environment. On the one hand, more secure property rights have led many farmers to adopt agroforestry and rice terraces—practices that help maintain soil fertility and prevent erosion. On the other hand, strengthening people's individual rights to land can put fragile lands at risk. When land reform allocates a rural wetland to a household, for example, the household tends to convert the land to agricultural use or aquaculture.

Lessons on Land and Market Reforms

Land-tenure reforms designed to enable a smooth transition from a centrally planned economy to a market economy will achieve their objectives only if they are linked to reforms in markets for agricultural commodities (such as rice and coffee), inputs (such as fertilizer), and services (such as

Loading sacks of rice, Vietnam

credit). Generating strong economic incentives for rural producers is crucial, and markets play an important role in every dimension of this process.

Secure and long-term rights to land on which to grow annual and perennial crops are essential. Farmers are much more likely to invest in sustainable agricultural practices, such as soil conservation and agroforestry, if they have long-term, inheritable tenure rights. Vietnam's process of trial and error, with several adjustments made to the leasehold periods, is understandable politically, but it may have delayed the implementation of reforms in some places.

Nonetheless, a flexible, incremental approach in carrying out reforms has advantages over a "big-bang" approach because all steps must be legitimized not only at the national level, but also at the local level. A great deal of information and communication is needed to break resistance against reforms and to convince different stakeholders of the benefits.

Conclusion

Through its *Doi Moi* reforms, Vietnam has achieved stunning success. After spending decades mired in civil war, poverty, and food insecurity,

Vietnam used policy reforms to build a vibrant and dynamic economy that plays a major role in global markets for rice and coffee, among other things. Economic growth, led by agricultural growth, has drastically reduced poverty and led to improved diets, with measurable results in child nutrition. To be sure, concerns remain. The income gap between rural and urban areas has widened, and more than 70 percent of the poor are concentrated in rural areas. Rules and regulations on land tenure and land markets could be improved to clarify and strengthen farmers' rights. Yet Vietnam's success proves just how powerful policy changes can be in stimulating food production and economic growth, thus improving the lives and livelihoods of millions. ▪

NOTES

1. Fritzen, S. 2002. Growth, inequality, and the future of poverty reduction in Vietnam. *Journal of Asian Economics* 13 (5): 635–57; Minot, N., B. Baulch, and M. Epprecht. 2006. *Poverty and inequality in Vietnam: Spatial patterns and geographic determinants*. Research Report 148. Washington, D.C.: International Food Policy Research Institute; Minot, N. 2003. Income diversification and poverty reduction in the northern uplands of Vietnam. Paper presented at the American Agricultural Economics Association annual meeting, July 27–30, 2003, Montreal, Canada.

2. Fritzen 2002.

3. Kerkvliet, B. J. T. 1995. Rural society and state relations. In *Vietnam's rural transformation*, ed. B. J. T. Kerkvliet and D. J. Porter. Boulder: Westview Press; Que, T. T. 1998. *Vietnam's agriculture: The challenges and achievements*. Singapore: Institute of Southeast Asian Studies.

4. Fforde, A., and S. de Vylder. 1996. *From plan to market: The economic transition in Vietnam*. Boulder: Westview Press.

5. Macaulay, T. G., S. P. Marsh, and P. V. Hung. 2006. Agricultural development and land policy in Vietnam: An overview and theoretical perspective. In *Agricultural development and land policy in Vietnam*, ed. S. P. Marsh, T. G. MacAuley, and P. V. Hung. Canberra, Australia: Australian Centre for International Agricultural Research.

6. Pingali, P. L., and V.-T. Xuan. 1992. Vietnam: Decollectivization and rice productivity growth. *Economic Development and Cultural Change* 40 (4): 697–718.

7. Minot, N., and F. Goletti. 2000. *Rice market liberalization and poverty in Vietnam*. Research Report 114. Washington, D.C.: International Food Policy Research Institute.

8. Fritzen 2002.

9. World Bank. 2003. *Vietnam development report 2004: Poverty*. Hanoi, Vietnam.

10. Deininger, K., and S. Jin. 2008. Land sales and rental markets in transition: Evidence from rural Vietnam. *Oxford Bulletin of Economics and Statistics* 70 (1): 67–101.

Chapter 21

© Helen Keller International

Diversifying into Healthy Diets
Homestead food production in Bangladesh

Lora Iannotti, Kenda Cunningham, and Marie Ruel

The health and lives of billions of people around the world are threatened by micronutrient deficiencies—a lack of essential vitamins and minerals such as iron, zinc, and vitamin A—resulting from poor dietary quality. Vitamin A deficiency, identified as a public health problem in nearly 80 developing countries, is one of the most serious. An estimated 127 million preschool children in developing countries are vitamin A deficient, and nearly 5 million preschoolers suffer from xerophthalmia, which causes irreversible eye damage and blindness in extreme cases. Vitamin A deficiency alone is responsible for 6 percent of all deaths among children under five years of age.

In the early-1980s, Bangladesh had a severe problem with vitamin A deficiency. At the beginning of the decade, more than 1 million children in Bangladesh showed visible signs of the condition. More than 3 percent of the rural population, including half a million children, suffered from night blindness, a condition in which one cannot see in dim lighting. Even worse, 30,000 children were going completely blind each year.[1] However, evidence indicated that children from homes with homestead gardens were less likely to suffer night blindness; it appeared that access to homegrown fruits and vegetables rich in certain forms of vitamin A could help combat vitamin A deficiency and prevent its dire health consequences.

Helen Keller International, a nongovernmental organization that combats malnutrition and blindness around the world, seized on this finding to launch a comprehensive intervention promoting home gardening, small livestock production, and nutrition education. This homestead food production program, implemented by more than 70 local nongovernmental organizations (NGOs) and the government of Bangladesh, succeeded in increasing participants' production and consumption of micronutrient-rich foods, empowering women, and promoting community development. In two decades of operation, homestead food production in Bangladesh has improved food security for nearly 5 million vulnerable people—nearly 4 percent of the population—in diverse agroecological zones across much of the country.[2]

Starting Small and Scaling Up

The homestead food production program in Bangladesh started small. The effort began in 1990 with a pilot program, targeting 1,000 households with a combination of home gardening and nutrition education. The pilot succeeded; results showed that participating women and children were consuming more vegetables and eating a more nutritious and varied diet. The next step was to scale it up, and in 1993, Helen Keller International and partnering organizations launched the NGO Gardening and Nutrition Education Surveillance Project (NGNESP), which broadened the reach of the package of home gardening, nutrition education, and other community-development activities across Bangladesh. By 2003, the project covered more than 4.7 million

This chapter is based on Iannotti, L., K. Cunningham, and M. Ruel. 2009. *Improving diet quality and micronutrient nutrition: Homestead food production in Bangladesh.* IFPRI Discussion Paper. Washington D.C.: International Food Policy Research Institute.

Homestead food production beneficiary with home garden, Bangladesh

individuals in 870,000 households, residing in 210 of the country's 460 subdistricts.[3]

To encourage households to grow fruits and vegetables and eat more nutritiously, Helen Keller International and local NGOs provide households with the materials needed to get started, such as seeds and seedlings. Home gardens alone, however, do not necessarily improve nutrition: nutrition education is needed to translate greater food availability at the household level into healthier diets, particularly for vulnerable household members such as women and children. Homestead food production projects thus also supply nutrition information. For instance, project group leaders may hold meetings to discuss the need for regular consumption of foods rich in iron, zinc, and vitamin A, or they may conduct cooking demonstrations to show the importance of washing vegetables before preparing them, or adding meat or eggs to dishes to increase their nutritional value.

The original model focused primarily on increasing consumption of vitamin A-rich vegetables and fruits, such as sweet gourd, black arum leaves, and bottle gourd leaves, from home gardens. New research in the 1990s, however, showed that pro-vitamin A or carotenoids from vegetables and fruits are less bioavailable (less easily absorbed and used by the body) than previously thought and significantly less bioavailable than vitamin A

from animal sources. Animal-source foods, such as chicken meat, are also a more efficient and bioavailable source of other essential micronutrients, including iron and zinc.

Given this new evidence, a pilot animal-production program was introduced to find out if the home gardening model could accommodate animal husbandry. The successful pilot project resulted in the integration of home gardening and animal husbandry into a broader homestead food production model. Other homestead food production projects and programs have followed, focusing on different populations within Bangladesh and different agroecological regions, such as hilly terrains where tea estates are located, flood-prone areas, peri-urban and urban slums, and areas with high-salinity soil. For instance, homestead food production programs have been implemented in the chars (islands of silt within rivers) and other low-lying floodplain areas in Bangladesh to help the food-insecure population in these areas prevent and mitigate agricultural losses from flooding.

A Chain of Impacts

Homestead food production programming launches a chain of impacts that ultimately leads to improved food security (see Table 21.1). This

Table 21.1—Select impacts of homestead food production programs in Bangladesh

Impact category	Example of impact
Production	
More home gardens	Year-round gardening increased from 3 percent to 33 percent
Increased varieties of foods	Vegetable varieties increased by more than two-fold
Increased quantities of foods	135 kg instead of 46 kg of vegetables in 3 months
Consumption	
Increased consumption of home grown vitamin A-rich foods	Egg consumption increased by 48 percentage points
Increased expenditures on non-cereal foods	Lentils and animal products bought with income earned
Economic status	
Employment opportunities	More than 60,000 rural jobs
Women's status	
Garden management	73 percent of gardens are managed by women, and these women are the main decisionmakers for garden practices and use of the income earned from selling garden produce
Income decisionmakers	At least 90 percent of target households are represented by women

Note: All impact data are for the NGNESP program, except for the data on egg consumption, which comes from another HFP program known as Char II.

Source: Compiled by the authors with information drawn from the following: World Bank. 2007. *Agriculture to nutrition: Pathways, synergies, and outcomes.* Washington, D.C.: World Bank; Sifri, Z. 2007. *Large-scale home gardening programs: The Helen Keller International experience in Bangladesh.* Washington, D.C.: International Food Policy Research Institute; Helen Keller International, Asia-Pacific. 2001. *Homestead food production: a strategy to combat malnutrition and poverty.* Jakarta, Indonesia; Bushamuka, V. N., S. de Pee, A. Talukder, L. Kiess, D. Panagides, A. Taher, and M. Bloem. 2005. Impact of a homestead gardening program on household food security and empowerment of women in Bangladesh. *Food and Nutrition Bulletin* 26 (1): 17–25; Taludker, A., L. Kiess, N. Huq, S. de Pee, I. Darnton-Hill, and M. W. Bloem. 2000. Increasing the production and consumption of vitamin A-rich fruits and vegetables: Lessons learned in taking the Bangladesh Homestead Gardening Programme to a national scale. *Food and Nutrition Bulletin* 21 (2): 165–72; Taher, A., D. Panagides, R. A. Karim, A. Habib, A. Baten, A. Uddin, N. Sultana, G. Stallkamp, and A. Talukder. 2004. Homestead food production in the Chars. Slide presentation. Bangladesh: Helen Keller International.

chain begins with people's adoption of improved or developed homestead gardens. Helen Keller International classifies gardens into three types—traditional, improved, and developed. Traditional gardens are seasonal, found in scattered plots, and involve the production of gourds and traditional vegetables. Improved gardens are typically fixed plots involving the production of a wider variety of vegetables, but are not utilized year round. Developed gardens offer a wider range of vegetables produced in fixed plots all year long. In 2002, a study showed that among active participants in the NGNESP, 78 percent were cultivating developed gardens—that is, growing fruits and vegetables year round—compared with 15 percent of nonparticipants.[4]

Households participating in homestead food production also grew a greater quantity and variety of foods than nonparticipants. During a three-month period, the participants produced 135 kilograms of fruits and vegetables, whereas the nonparticipants produced just 46 kilograms.[5] Homestead food production interventions have also succeeded in raising the production of animal-source foods. An evaluation of the animal production pilot in 2003 revealed that program participants produced 200 eggs during a three-month period, compared with 21 eggs produced by nonparticipants.[6]

By combining greater food availability and access with nutrition education, homestead food production has led to increased consumption of higher-quality foods. What is more, homestead gardening programs in Bangladesh increased vitamin A intake, especially among women and children. One study shows that the percentage of children aged 6-59 months and mothers eating dark-green leafy vegetables containing carotenoids, for example, increased from approximately one-third to three-quarters (see Figure 21.1). Research also shows that children living in households with developed gardens consume 1.6 times more vegetables than children without such gardens. Homestead food production has also led to a 48-percent increase in the consumption of eggs, a rich source of bioavailable, pre-formed vitamin A. Although vitamin A consumption was the initial focus of home gardening and animal pro-

duction programs, it is likely that participants also consumed higher levels of other nutrients, given their increased consumption of vegetables, fruits, and animal-source foods. More research is needed, however, to test whether these improvements in diet quality led to a better nutritional status of individuals, especially among women and children.

Homestead food production also empowers women by giving them greater decisionmaking power within the household and providing new opportunities for them. The program was designed to target households represented by women. Women perceive themselves as making greater contributions to household income because of home gardens, and greater proportions of women participants have reported full decision-making power on a range of issues compared with women who are not participating in the project. Moreover, when programs target women, the vegetables are more likely to be consumed (rather than sold), particularly by children. Also, in intervention areas in the chars, women participating in the program earn a greater income and use these funds to invest in their children's education.

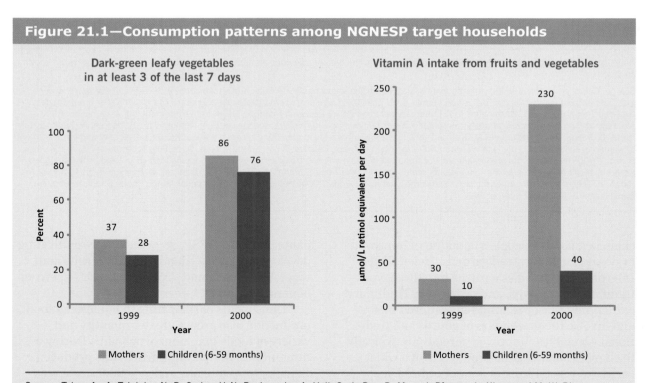

Figure 21.1—Consumption patterns among NGNESP target households

Source: Taher, A., A. Talukder, N. R. Sarkar, V. N. Bushamuka, A. Hall, S. de Pee, R. Moench-Pfanner, L. Kiess, and M. W. Bloem. 2004. Homestead gardening for combating vitamin A deficiency: The Helen Keller International, Bangladesh, experience. In *Alleviating malnutrition through agriculture in Bangladesh: Biofortification and diversification as sustainable solutions*, ed. N. Roos, H. E. Bouis, N. Hassan, and K. A. Kabir. Washington, D.C.: International Food Policy Research Institute.

Overcoming Challenges and Promoting Sustainability

Homestead food production programming in Bangladesh faces several challenges. Changing people's preferences for producing and consuming food can be quite difficult. Bangladeshi farmers, for example, are accustomed to growing rice, and have sometimes hesitated to devote greater time and attention to the production of fruits and vegetables because this new practice appears risky. Another challenge is to ensure that homestead food production not only increases the quantity of foods produced, but also improves the diets of vulnerable household members. Advancing sustainable changes in people's dietary patterns requires an understanding of the potential barriers to change and effective communications to promote food choices, child-feeding practices, and the beneficial ways of allocating food and other resources among household members.

The apparent low bioavailability of micronutrients in fruits and vegetables has raised other challenges. Skepticism about the potential of home gardens alone to reduce micronutrient deficiencies grew. This led to the expansion of homestead food production programs to include animal production. While this shift can greatly increase the potential for homestead food production to improve micronutrient nutrition, it also has added enormous complexity to the programs. For example, model poultry farms must be established in villages and the poultry require immunization and caging. Cows must be dewormed and fed better fodder. In addition, animal production may increase the risk of zoonotic diseases and may reduce the cost effectiveness of programs by requiring more labor and capital.

Despite these challenges, homestead gardening programs combined with nutrition education have proven to be a sustainable approach. In Bangladesh, less than 3 percent of participants drop out of homestead food production projects annually.[7] Homestead gardening is environmentally sustainable as well. Programs embrace environmentally friendly agricultural practices like tree planting, organic fertilizer and pesticide use, safe use of pesticides more generally, and live fencing (using trees and shrubs as fence lines) to enrich the soil with nitrogen.

Homestead food production has also proven to be financially sustainable. Costs of homestead

Homestead animal production, Bangladesh

© Helen Keller International

food production programs are shared among participating households, partner organizations, and Helen Keller International; this joint ownership of homestead food production has ensured local buy in, which has played a role in the program's financial sustainability. In addition, locally available materials (like fencing, home-generated manure, and indigenous pest control) can be used, and the multiple uses of garden products present many opportunities for households to earn returns.[8]

Finally, social and political sustainability impact homestead food production. The government continues to invest in the programs, and each year hundreds of local NGOs voice their desire to participate. Planning workshops and information-sharing practices offer regular opportunities for collaboration and capacity strengthening for NGOs. Homestead gardening is flexibly integrated into each local NGO's existing community-based health and development programs.

Lessons for the Future

Homestead food production in Bangladesh began with the initial goal of increasing consumption of vitamin A-rich foods to reduce the health threats associated with vitamin A deficiency. However, by promoting the production of more and healthier foods, educating people on how to improve their diets and nutrition, and raising people's incomes, the large-scale intervention has improved food security for millions of people. And while it has increased the production and consumption of foods rich in vitamin A, further research is needed on the role of homestead food produc-

© Helen Keller International

Learning about nutrition, Bangladesh

tion in addressing the health conditions resulting from micronutrient deficiencies. Nonetheless, the experience of homestead food production in Bangladesh points to various lessons for future projects in the country and elsewhere.

First, translating food production into improved dietary intakes involves making nutrition education and behavior-change communication a high priority—including messages about allocation of resources among household members and optimal feeding and care practices for infants, young children, and women. Education raises participants' awareness and helps ensure that they choose to grow foods rich in micronutrients all year long. Homestead food production in Bangladesh has shown that dialogue and negotiation with caregivers, households, and communities are more effective at changing behavior than lectures and top-down transfers of knowledge.

Second, homestead food production programming has also benefited from adopting a multifaceted, multidisciplinary approach that links agricultural activities to other health and development activities in the community. These linkages between the agricultural sector and the health sector are particularly needed to help ensure that preventative and curative healthcare is available for mothers and children to address the well-known interactions between nutrition and disease.

Third, building on local practices and existing organizations also helps advance the adoption of homestead gardening and avoids paternalistic programming. Rooted in local values, customs, and practices, homestead food production inherently emphasizes community participation at all stages of the program. Local NGOs have been instrumental in funding, designing, and implementing the programs. Helen Keller International collaborates with these local NGOs on strategic planning, developing proposals and work plans, monitoring programs, managing finances, and organizing the involvement of government and other local authorities.

Fourth, a standard but flexible design allows implementing organizations to maintain quality control while also ensuring that programs are responsive to their context. For each program, Helen Keller International is involved for an initial three-year period, and local NGOs continue to support beneficiaries for an additional two years. Another advantage of using a standardized approach is the ease of replication and scaling up, as shown by the broad reach of homestead food production within Bangladesh.

Finally, Helen Keller International and others involved with homestead food production projects have invested in information systems that provide feedback and enable improvements in the interventions. The history of homestead food production in Bangladesh shows an active feedback process between information collected and programming interventions. Information sources include national (or sometimes local) surveys that help determine where to locate the project; monitoring surveys every four months to identify problems; and longer-term evaluations to inform and improve programming and motivate greater investment and commitment of donors, governments, and other partners.

At the end of the day, homestead food production programming has gone well beyond its original objective to take on a range of goals designed to improve lives and livelihoods in rural Bangladesh. In addition to improving diet quality, this holistic package of interventions empowers women, households, and communities through economic and social development. It respects local customs and practices and gains longevity in return. It leaves a legacy of knowledge, awareness, and understanding with its many partners and beneficiaries. If homestead food production continues to be responsive to new information and receptive to changes in the environment and sociopolitical landscape, it will continue to enhance food security for vulnerable populations for years to come. ■

NOTES

1. Taludker, A., R. K. Nael Islam, R. Klemm, and M. Bloem. 1993. *Home gardening in South Asia: The complete handbook.* Dhaka: Helen Keller International.

2. Helen Keller International. 2006. Homestead food production: The potential and opportunity to improve the food security and rural livelihood in Barisal division. *Homestead Food Production Bulletin* 3. New York; Helen Keller International. 2006. Homestead food production: An effective integrated approach to improve food security among the vulnerable char dwellers in Northern Bangladesh. *Homestead Food Production Bulletin* 4. New York.

3. Bushamuka, V. N. , S. de Pee, A. Talukder, L. Kiess, D. Panagides, A. Taher, and M. Bloem. 2005. Impact of a homestead gardening program on household food security and empowerment of women in Bangladesh. *Food and Nutrition Bulletin* 26 (1): 17–25.

4. Bushamuka, de Pee, Talukder, Kiess, Panagides, Taher, and Bloem 2005.

5. Helen Keller International. 2004. Homestead food production improves household food and nutrition security. *Homestead Food Production Bulletin* 2. New York.

6. Helen Keller International 2004.

8. Helen Keller International Asia-Pacific. 2001. Asia-Pacific. *Homestead food production: A strategy to combat malnutrition and poverty.* Jakarta, Indonesia.

9. Bushamuka, de Pee, Talukder, Kiess, Panagides, Taher, and Bloem 2005; de Pee, S., A. Talukder, M. Bloem. 2008. Homestead food production for improving nutritional status and health. In *Nutrition and health in developing countries*, ed. R. D. Semba and M. W. Bloem. Totowa: Humana Press.

MillionsFed

PROVEN SUCCESSES IN AGRICULTURAL DEVELOPMENT

www.ifpri.org/millionsfed

South America

Innovating in the Pampas
Zero-tillage soybean cultivation in Argentina

Africa

- **Resisting Viruses and Bugs**
  Cassava in Sub-Saharan Africa

- **Re-Greening the Sahel**
  Farmer-led innovation in Burkina Faso and Niger

Navigating through Reforms
Cotton reforms in Burkina Faso

Unlocking the Market
Fertilizer and maize in Kenya

Breeding an "Amaizing" Crop
Improved maize in Kenya, Malawi, Zambia, and Zimbabwe

Global

- **Fighting a "Shifty Enemy"**
  The international collaboration to contain wheat rusts

- **Conquering the Cattle Plague**
  The global effort to eradicate rinderpest

Asia

- **Transforming Agriculture**
  The Green Revolution in Asia

- **Counting on Beans**
  Mungbean improvement in Asia

- **Leaving the Plow Behind**
  Zero-tillage rice–wheat cultivation in the Indo-Gangetic Plains

- **Seeing the Forest Through the Trees**
  Community forestry in Nepal

- **Pushing the Yield Frontier**
  Hybrid rice in China

- **Crossing the River while Feeling the Rocks**
  Land-tenure reform in China

- **Improving Crops for Arid Lands**
  Pearl millet and sorghum in India

- **Exiting from Collective Agriculture**
  Land-tenure reform in Vietnam

- **Connecting the Milk Grid**
  Smallholder dairy in India

- **Pumping up Production**
  Shallow tubewells and rice in Bangladesh

- **Diversifying into Healthy Diets**
  Homestead food production in Bangladesh

- **Farming the Aquatic Chicken**
  Improved tilapia in the Philippines

ANNEX B
Methodology

David J. Spielman, Rajul Pandya-Lorch, Kenda Cunningham, and Sivan Yosef

A study such as this one cannot be an exhaustive review of all policies, investments, and programs in agricultural development—five decades of rich and diverse experiences simply cannot be summed up in a single volume. So instead, this book focuses on relatively large-scale and long-term successes that were backed by strong evidence of positive impact.

The methodology used to identify and analyze these successes is detailed below. This methodology draws on several previous efforts to document successes in development, including studies by Gabre-Madhin and Haggblade (2004) and Levine (2004).[1] Additional insights were extracted from studies by the World Bank (2008, 2006), Uphoff, Esman, and Krishna (1998), Krishna, Uphoff, and Esman (1997), and the Asia-Pacific Association of Agricultural Research Institutions (2009).[2]

The method for arriving at the 20 case studies of success found in this book involved four steps: (1) throwing the net out, (2) sorting the catch, (3) selecting the most appropriate cases, and (4) synthesizing the evidence.

1. Throwing the net out. A first step in identifying these successes was to seek input from those who participate in or study agricultural policies, investments, and programs that aim to improve food security and reduce hunger—practitioners, scholars, policymakers, and many others. To this end, the project team circulated a global "Call for Nominations" on successes in agricultural development in late 2008 while it simultaneously compiled suggestions from experts in the field and from information garnered from scholarly literature, project documents, websites, and other sources. By early 2009, about 250 potential successes were identified.

2. Sorting the catch. The project team sorted through these potential successes using two qualifying criteria that had to be met in order for a case to be considered further, and five evaluative criteria that focused on the specific attributes and impacts of the intervention.

The first qualifying criterion was that the intervention must have been operational in at least one developing country. For the purposes of this project, developing countries are those classified as low-income, lower-middle-income, or higher-middle-income countries according to the World Bank-defined income groups or the equivalent classification that was current when the intervention was being implemented.[3] Note that this criterion does not imply that interventions were chosen because they only benefited developing countries—if an intervention generates benefits that also accrue to high-income industrialized countries, it was still considered.

The second qualifying criterion was that the intervention must have engaged agriculture directly—that is, it must have operated on constraints that are specific to agriculture. This criterion excludes certain types of interventions that operate on agriculture indirectly. For example, although there is strong evidence indicating that basic education, health, and sanitation programs targeting the rural poor contribute to increasing their labor productivity, and thus their incomes and nutritional status, these interventions were not considered here because their point of entry is not directly related to the production, distribution, or marketing of agricultural goods and services. Similarly, while rural school feeding programs, rural conditional cash transfer programs, rural safety net programs, and food aid are often viewed as important to increasing rural incomes, building rural assets, and improving nutrition, their indirect impact on agriculture means that they were ruled out from consideration here.[4]

Once these criteria were met, the potential success had to meet five evaluative criteria:

- Importance—the intervention should have tackled an important food-security problem by addressing the needs of a vulnerable group;

- Scale— the intervention should have operated at scale, measured in terms of whether the number of beneficiaries exceeded several hundred thousand individuals or whether the intervention was, at a minimum, national in coverage;

- Time and Duration—the intervention should have been (1) fully operational at scale long enough to generate significant reductions in hunger or improvements in food security and (2) implemented in the past 50 years;

- Proven Impact—the intervention should have been supported by documented and rigorous evidence of a clear and measurable impact on individual or household hunger or nutritional status; and

- Sustainability—the intervention should have been sustainable, whether in financial terms (cost-effectiveness) or in broader social, political or environmental terms.

3. Selecting the most appropriate cases. While efforts were initially made to apply each criterion as a necessary (but not sufficient) condition for selection, it was recognized that no case study could meet all criteria. As such, the criteria were relaxed somewhat, although the qualifying criteria were maintained as necessary conditions, along with the following evaluative criteria: importance, scale, and time/duration.

With respect to the proven impact and sustainability criteria, very few case studies were supported by what may be termed "state-of-the-art" impact assessments that documented the effects of an intervention through randomized experiments that establish attribution by combining before-and-after comparisons with treatment-and-control comparisons. In many cases, such experiments did not exist when the intervention was in operation; in other cases, neither the resources nor the expertise were available to undertake such data-intensive assessments. Relaxing these criteria meant that alternative forms of evidence were accepted. These alternative forms of evidence include: geospatial imagery documenting changes in agroecological landscapes over time; quantitative evidence using estimation techniques that were not necessarily the most up-to-date methods; and qualitative evidence gleaned from policy analyses and from surveys conducted among direct beneficiaries.

As a result of these criteria, this book does not feature several types of successes. First, the book does not cover nonagricultural interventions, such as rural health, rural education, or rural social protection programs, for example. These programs undoubtedly comprise an important class of intervention, but they do not directly address agriculture in its strictest sense. However, one success case that was included—improving micronutrient consumption in Bangladesh—does feature a rural nutrition program that promotes home-based production of fruits, vegetables, and livestock to improve nutrition and health among the poor.

Second, this book does not examine programs that integrate agriculture with health, education, microfinance, microenterprise, governance, and other development priorities. These too represent an important class of intervention, but because of the complex synergies between these many activities, it is hard to disentangle the evidence. However, several successes featured in this book, while primarily defined as agricultural development programs, do examine the importance of integrated approaches. The study of community forestry in Nepal, which highlights the importance of integrating agricultural development with local governance, is one such success.

Third, this book does not cover cases of failure. Often, learning lessons is as much about observing the failures as it is about observing the successes. But while there are many failures in agricultural development from which to learn—and many studies that highlight the causes of their failure—this book chooses to focus on the successes only, primarily because it is the absence of successes in agricultural development that has marginalized its importance in discussions of how to improve food security and reduce hunger in developing countries.

4. Synthesizing the evidence. Each success highlighted in this book is based on a synthesis of evidence from multiple sources that range from first-hand accounts by individual participants and beneficiaries to large-scale impact-evaluation studies that combine both quantitative and qualitative evidence at the highest levels of academic rigor.

But few successes are evidenced by a common set of impact-assessment methodologies, indicators, or conclusions—there is no one indicator that can appropriately describe the numbers of millions fed, or the quantitative improvement in food security, resulting from an intervention.

This may not be a disadvantage to the present analysis when considered more closely. A glance at the chapters in this book indicates that the interventions vary so greatly—in terms of what they aim to achieve, how they do so, and what they actually end up accomplishing—that a single indicator runs the risk of reducing an intervention's impacts to something entirely impractical.

Moreover, the casual reader should not conclude that only those interventions that are backed by rigorous impact-assessment materials and definitive indicators are successes. For example, a program that was not rigorously evaluated by teams of independent scholars conducting lengthy household surveys may nonetheless be a success. Or a program that was initially seen as a success may nonetheless fail in the long term.

In fact, there are many successes in agricul-

tural development that are not covered by this volume but that may have equal merit. Examples include smallholder cultivation of high-value export crops in Kenya and Guatemala; systems of rice intensification (SRI) that have become popular in several countries during the past two decades; New Rice for Africa (NERICA), which is being developed and disseminated for farmers in several Sub-Saharan African countries; or the Greenbelt Movement in Kenya that has encouraged community-based tree planting on a massive scale.

But even with these caveats in mind, we know that there are clearly discernible pathways—interventions that seek to improve crops, livestock, forestry, and fisheries, conserve natural resources, and strengthen the markets, institutions, and policies that relate to these social and economic activities— that link agricultural development with improvements in food security. These pathways, and the stepping stones along them, are the main focus of impact assessments, and thus the main focus in proving success. ■

NOTES

1. Gabre-Madhin, E. Z. and S. Haggblade. 2004. Successes in African agriculture: Results of an expert survey. *World Development* 32 (5): 745-766; Levine, R. 2004. *Millions saved: Proven successes in global health.* Washington, D.C.: Center for Global Development.

2. World Bank. 2008. *World development report 2008: Agriculture for development.* Washington, D.C.; World Bank. 2006. Agriculture investment sourcebook. Washington, D.C.; Uphoff, N., M. J. Esman, and A. Krishna. 1998. *Reasons for success: Learning from instructive experiences in rural development.* West Hartford: Kumarian Press; Krishna, A., N. Uphoff, and M. J. Esman. 1997. *Reasons for hope: Instructive experiences in rural development.* West Hartford: Kumarian Press; APAARI (Asia-Pacific Association of Agricultural Research Institutions). 2009. APAARI success stories. www.apaari.org/publications/apaari-success-stories/.

3. World Bank. 2009. Data and statistics: Country groups. go.worldbank.org/K2CKM78CC0.

4. Conditional cash transfer programs such as the Programa de Educación, Salud y Alimentación (Progresa) in Mexico were, in fact, treated as health (rather than agricultural) interventions by Levine (2004) in the predecessor to this project entitled *Millions saved: Proven successes in global health.*

ANNEX C
Improving the Proof: Impact Assessment in Agricultural Development

Mywish K. Maredia

Whether, what, and how agricultural development has had an impact on people's lives have long been topics of inquiry by researchers, development practitioners, investors, and beneficiaries of development interventions. As long as there have been interventions, people have formally or informally, systematically or haphazardly, scientifically or unscientifically assessed, analyzed, measured, estimated, and evaluated their impacts. The motivation to assess impacts arises from the need for accountability (whether and what impacts development efforts have on people and their environment) and interest in institutional learning (how impacts are achieved or not achieved, and what lessons can be derived to improve programs). Assessment of impacts provides the "proof" that development does or does not work, in what contexts, and why.

There are several concepts and terminologies that are closely associated with the field of monitoring, evaluation, and impact assessment. Broadly speaking, these can be grouped into two categories: (1) assessments that occur before or during the project implementation, such as ex ante impact assessment, project appraisal, and monitoring and (2) those that occur retrospectively after an intervention ends or once project outputs have been scaled up. Each has evolved dramatically over the last 50 years in response to changing themes in development, methodological advancements, and demand for documenting rigorous evidence of impacts. The evolution and emerging trends in methodologies offer lessons for best practices to enhance the culture of impact assessment in agricultural development.

Ex Ante Impact Assessment, Project Appraisal, and Monitoring

Ex ante impact assessments are used to predict the likely consequences of an intervention. The original approach, beginning in the 1950s, was primarily driven by multilateral and bilateral donors who used ex ante analyses of the social and economic costs and benefits to quantify the projected impacts of a project. These analyses were often used as a condition to approve, adjust, or reject funding for development projects. In agriculture, these assessments are still routine (and mandatory, in some instances) for large investments such as irrigation systems, dams, and rural roads. Over time, as a result of rapid increases in computing technologies, modeling tools have joined the ex ante impact assessment family. These models have the capacity to simulate a wide range of market conditions, technology scenarios, likely spillover effects, and alternative trade regimes in order to project the economic benefits of a proposed investment.[1]

In the 1970s, the toolkit for ex ante assessments was augmented by the introduction of logical framework analysis, a planning and appraising tool for development projects. Logical framework analysis provides a clear hierarchy of inputs, activities, and objectives alongside assumptions about the external environment in an effort to more effectively map out how an intervention will have an impact on its intended target population. This addition resulted from rising criticism that investments in large projects were neither involving nor benefitting the poor in any substantial way.

Continued concerns about the involvement and engagement of the poor in development, particularly rural development, acquired more attention in the 1980s with the introduction of new participatory development methods. Tools such as participatory rural appraisal, rapid rural appraisal, participatory action research, participatory impact assessment, and participatory impact pathways analysis sought to make people and communities active participants in development, rather than mere objects of it.[2] Similar participatory tools applied to organizations and sectors known as institutional learning and change have added a further dimension to these types of assessments.[3]

Retrospective Assessments

The focus of retrospective assessments is to document realized outputs, outcomes, and impacts of an intervention. These types of assessments come closest to providing the proof of development effectiveness. Project evaluation, a type of retrospective assessment, usually occurs at the end of an intervention or soon after its conclusion. Its main objective is to track project inputs, outputs, and immediate outcomes, and to document the processes that led to these effects. These are often distinguished from retrospective assessments that focus on outcomes and impacts. The latter type of retrospective assessment, commonly referred to as simply "impact assessment," is defined as the systematic analysis of the significant or lasting changes in people's lives brought about by a given action or series of actions in relation to a counterfactual, or what may have occurred had an intervention not been taken.

Three types of retrospective impact assessments are distinguishable in the agricultural development literature: macro-level assessments that focus on the contribution of developmental efforts to an impact goal aggregated at the sector or system level; micro-level impact evaluations that focus on estimating the average effect of an intervention on outcomes at the beneficiary level; and micro-level ex post impact analysis and assessment that focus on the total effects of a development effort after the outputs are scaled up. In the context of programs that affect large

numbers of people, it is the micro-level impact assessments that are particularly vital to demonstrating what works and why.

Micro-level ex post impact analysis and assessment have evolved and expanded over the decades in both breadth and depth in response to evolving development themes and methodological advancements. In the area of agricultural development, the field of ex post impact assessments was pioneered by Zvi Griliches, who examined the social benefits of investing in hybrid corn technology in the United States.[4] This approach flourished during the Green Revolution (see Chapter 3) in the 1970s, and, over the past five decades, hundreds of studies have documented economic returns on investment in agricultural research.[5] In essence, the approach is to estimate returns on investments in an intervention, expressed as a ratio between the total values of the inputs and the effects generated from those inputs, which are based on a variety of methods and sources of data. In subsequent decades, these methods expanded from their primary focus on assessing the impacts of crop-technology adoption to assessing the impact of interventions in areas such as gender, health, natural-resource management, policy research, and poverty reduction.

Since the 1990s, retrospective assessments (namely, micro-level impact evaluations) that focused on estimating a program's effects have benefited from two mutually reinforcing developments: the introduction of qualitative methods and the improvement of quantitative methods. In qualitative assessments, the focus is on understanding processes, behaviors, and conditions as they are perceived by the individuals or groups being studied.[6] Qualitative approaches use relatively open-ended data collection and analysis tools, often rely on an evaluation of participants' knowledge of the conditions surrounding the project or program, and bring participants into the assessment itself by having them determine the objectives of the study and participate in data collection and analysis.

Improvements in quantitative assessments revolve around efforts to improve the rigor with which impacts are identified and measured in relation to a counterfactual. Natural scientists have a long tradition of assessing impact through the use of experiments that are typically performed under strictly controlled conditions in the laboratory or field, for example, treating one plant with fertilizer and comparing the results against another plant that did not receive fertilizer treatment. But social scientists can rarely apply similar protocols to the study of people, technologies, and policies in a real-world setting. Recent applications in the development field of methods known as experimental and quasi-experimental designs, however, are helping researchers to better establish the causal link between an intervention and its impact in ways that are conceptually similar to those used by natural scientists.[7] There is still debate over these designs, including issues of whether they are relevant beyond the immediate individuals and locations of the investigation. Practical challenges of implementing the field experiments, their high costs, and ethical concerns over withholding an intervention from a control group prohibit the widespread use of these designs as an assessment tool.[8]

Conclusion

The portfolio of impact assessment has expanded over the last 50 years from measuring the proof of development effectiveness in terms of economic rates of return to measuring it across a range of dimensions using a wide array of tools. This broadening agenda is a result of not only methodological advancements but also the evolution of development ideas that have shifted away from a one-dimensional (that is, economic), top-down view of development to a multi-dimensional, participatory, people-focused development that also addresses the demand for donor, government, and beneficiary accountability. Despite these developments, it is rare for impact assessments to include an explicit indicator called "food security" that measures the impact of an intervention on this goal. Most studies measure food-security impacts through changes in outcome indicators related to consumption or imply this impact through changes in outcomes related to production, income, and prices.

The emerging concern is that despite billions of dollars being spent on development programs, there is relatively little knowledge about the net impact of most of these programs.[9] The generation of robust knowledge that feeds into making developmental policies requires a hierarchical and cumulative approach to "improving the proof" through rigorous, varied impact assessment methods applied at the project, program, and system level. A good practice guideline is to subject as many ongoing and new development interventions as resources allow to rigorous impact evaluation based on a common framework. This can help build a critical body of evidence on impacts of development interventions and help build a knowledge base on what works and what does not. Until such a critical body of knowledge is developed, however, one way to move closer to both understanding and achieving impact on challenges such as food security, malnutrition, and poverty is to learn from past proven successes in agricultural development. By examining impact assessments of what worked and why, decision-makers can equip themselves with the knowledge to make wise choices about where, when, and how to invest. ▪

NOTES

1. Alston, J. M., G. W. Norton, and P. G. Pardey. 1998. *Science under scarcity: Principles and practice for agricultural research evaluation and priority setting.* Wallingford, UK: CAB International.

2. Chambers, R. 1994. The origins and practice of participatory rural appraisal. *World Development* 27 (7): 953–969; Chambers, R. 2007. Poverty research: Methodologies, mindsets and multidimensionality. IDS Working Paper 293. Brighton, UK: Institute of Development Studies, University of Sussex; Catley, A., J. Burns, D. Abebe, and O. Suji. 2007. *Participatory impact assessment: A guide for practitioners.* Medford: Feinstein International Center, Tufts University; Douthwaite, B., B. S. Alvarez, S. Cook, R. Davies, P. George, J. Howell, R. Mackay, and J. Rubiano. 2007. The impact pathways approach: A practical application of program theory in research-for-development. *Canadian Journal of Program Evaluation* 22 (2): 127–159.

3. Guijt, I. 2007. *Assessing and learning for social change: A discussion paper.* Brighton, UK: Institute of Development Studies, University of Sussex; Watts, J., R. MacKay, D. Horton, A. Hall, B. Douthwaite, R. Chambers, and A. Acosta. 2003. *Institutional learning and change: An introduction.* ISNAR Discussion Paper 3. The Hague, The Netherlands: International Service for National Agricultural Research.

4. Griliches, Z. 1958. Research costs and social returns: Hybrid corn and related innovations. *Journal of Political Economy* 66: 419–431.

5. Alston, J. M., C. Chan-Kang, M. C. Marra, P. G. Pardey, and T. J. Wyatt. 2000. *A meta-analysis of rates of return to agricultural R&D: Ex pede Herculem?* IFPRI Research Report 113. Washington, D.C.: International Food Policy Research Institute; Evenson, R. E. 2001. Economic impacts of agricultural research and extension. *Handbook of agricultural economics*, Vol. 1a, ed. B. L. Gardner and G. C. Rausser. Amsterdam, The Netherlands: Elsevier.

6. Mohr, L. B. 1999. The qualitative method of impact analysis. *American Journal of Evaluation* 20: 69-84.

7. Baker, J. L. 2000. *Evaluating the impact of development projects on poverty: A handbook for practitioners.* Washington, D.C.: World Bank; Ravallion, M. 2008. Evaluating anti-poverty programs. In *Handbook of Development Economics*, vol. 4, ed. T. P. Schultz and J. Strauss. Amsterdam, The Netherlands: Elsevier.

8. Deaton, A. 2009. *Instruments of development: Randomization in the tropics, and the search for the elusive keys to economic development.* NBER Working Paper no. 14690. Cambridge: National Bureau for Economic Research.

9. Center for Global Development. 2006. *When will we ever learn? Improving lives through impact evaluation.* Washington, D.C.: Center for Global Development.

ANNEX D
Advisory Committee and IFPRI Project Team

Advisory Committee

Harris Mule, Committee Co-Chair, Former Permanent Secretary, Ministry of Finance, Kenya

Raul Montemayor, Committee Co-Chair, General Secretary, Federation of Free Farmers Cooperatives Inc., Philippines

Chris Dowswell, Executive Director, Sasakawa Africa Association, Mexico

Mahabub Hossain, Executive Director, Bangladesh Rural Advancement Committee, Bangladesh

Isatou Jallow, Chief, Women, Children and Gender Policy, World Food Programme, Italy

Marina Joubert, Science Communication Editor, Southern Science, South Africa

Ruth Levine, Vice President, Programs and Operations, Center for Global Development, USA

Xiaopeng Luo, Professor, China Academy for Rural Development, Zhejiang University, China

Stephen Muliokela, Executive Director, Golden Valley Agricultural Research Trust, Zambia

Raj Paroda, Executive Secretary, Asia-Pacific Association of Agricultural Research Institutions, Thailand

Christie Peacock, Chief Executive, Farm Africa, United Kingdom

Prabhu Pingali, Deputy Director, Agricultural Development, The Bill & Melinda Gates Foundation, USA

Martín Piñeiro, Director, GrupoCeo, Argentina

Papa Seck, Director General, Africa Rice Center, Benin

Camila Toulmin, Director, International Institute for Environment and Development, United Kingdom

Ajay Vashee, President, International Federation of Agricultural Producers, Zambia

Joachim von Braun, Ex-Officio Member, Director General, International Food Policy Research Institute, USA

IFPRI Project Team

Rajul Pandya-Lorch, Project Leader—Chief of Staff, Director General's Office, and Head, 2020 Vision Initiative

David J. Spielman, Project Research Lead—Research Fellow, Knowledge, Capacity, and Innovation Division

Klaus von Grebmer, Project Communications Lead—Director, Communications Division

Kenda Cunningham, Research Support—Senior Research Assistant, Director General's Office

Sivan Yosef, Research Support—Senior Research Assistant, Director General's Office

161

ANNEX E
List of Contributors

Chapter Contributors

Joshua Ariga (arigajos@msu.edu) is a research fellow with Tegemeo Institute of Agricultural Policy and Development, Egerton University, Kenya, and is currently a PhD candidate at Michigan State University, USA.

Tanguy Bernard (bernardt@afd.fr) is a research fellow with Agence Française de Développement, France.

John P. Brennan (jpjkbrennan@gmail.com) is an economist at Coolamaine Economic Research, Australia.

John W. Bruce (jwbruce@ladsiinc.com) is president of Land and Development Solutions International, Inc., USA.

Eugenio J. Cap (ecap@correo.inta.gov.ar) is director of the Institute of Economics and Sociology (INTA), Argentina.

Ashwini Chhatre (achhatre@illinois.edu) is an assistant professor in the Department of Geography at the University of Illinois at Urbana-Champaign, USA.

Kenda Cunningham (k.cunningham@cgiar.org) is a senior research assistant in the Director General's Office at the International Food Policy Research Institute, USA.

H. J. Dubin (hjdubin@comcast.net) is a consultant and was formerly the associate director of the Wheat Program, International Maize and Wheat Improvement Center (CIMMYT), Mexico.

Olaf Erenstein (o.erenstein@cgiar.org) is a senior scientist with the International Maize and Wheat Improvement Center, Mexico, and is currently outposted in Ethiopia.

Peter Hazell (p.hazell@cgiar.org) was formerly director of the Development Strategy and Governance division at the International Food Policy Research Institute and is now retired and living in the United Kingdom.

Derek Headey (D.Headey@cgiar.org) is a research fellow in the Development Strategy and Governance Division at the International Food Policy Research Institute, USA.

Mahabub Hossain (hossain.mahabub@brac.net) is the Executive Director of the Bangladesh Rural Advancement Committee, Dhaka, and the former head of the Social Sciences Division at the International Rice Research Institute, Philippines.

Jacqueline d'Arros Hughes (jackie.hughes@worldveg.org) is deputy director general of research at the AVRDC – The World Vegetable Center, Taiwan.

Lora Iannotti (liannotti@wustl.edu) is an assistant professor at Washington University in St. Louis, USA, and formerly a postdoctoral research fellow in the Poverty, Health, and Nutrition Division at the International Food Policy Research Institute, USA.

T. S. Jayne (jayne@msu.edu) is a professor of international development in the Department of Agricultural, Food, and Resource Economics at Michigan State University, USA.

Jonathan Kaminski (kaminski.jonathan@gmail.com) is a research fellow at the Hebrew University of Jerusalem, Israel.

J. D. H. Keatinge (dyno.keatinge@worldveg.org) is director general of the AVRDC – The World Vegetable Center, Taiwan.

Michael Kirk (kirk@wiwi.uni-marburg.de) is a professor of development economics at Marburg University, Germany.

Jiming Li (jiming.li@pioneer.com) is a senior research manager at Pioneer Hi-Bred International, Philippines.

Zongmin Li (zli@ladsiinc.com) is vice-president of Land and Development Solutions International, Inc., USA.

Valeria N. Malach (vmalach@correo.inta.gov.ar) is a researcher at the Institute of Economics and Sociology (INTA), Argentina.

Mywish K. Maredia (maredia@msu.edu) is an associate professor in the Department of Agricultural, Food, and Resource Economics at Michigan State University, USA.

Latha Nagarajan (nagarajan@aesop.rutgers.edu) is a research associate at the Department of Agriculture, Food, and Resource Economics at Rutgers, The State University of New Jersey, USA.

Nguyen Do Anh Tuan (ndatuan@gmail.com) is director of the Southern Office of the Institute of Policy and Strategy for Agriculture and Rural Development, Vietnam.

Felix I. Nweke (nwekefel@yahoo.com) is a visiting professor at Michigan State University, USA.

Hemant R. Ojha (ojhahemant1@gmail.com) is editor of *Journal of Forest and Livelihoods* and a natural resource governance specialist at ForestAction Nepal.

Rajul Pandya-Lorch (r.pandya-lorch@cgiar.org) is chief of staff in the Director General's Office and head of the 2020 Vision Initiative at the International Food Policy Research Institute, USA.

Lauren Persha (lpersha@umich.edu) is a research fellow in the School of Natural Resources and Environment at the University of Michigan, USA.

Carl E. Pray (pray@aesop.rutgers.edu) is a professor in the Department of Agriculture, Food, and Resource Economics at Rutgers, The State University of New Jersey, USA.

Chris Reij (c.reij@chello.nl) is a natural resource management specialist with the Center for International Cooperation of Vrije Universiteit Amsterdam, Netherlands.

Karl M. Rich (k.rich@cgiar.org) is an assistant professor of economics at the American University in Cairo, Egypt, and an agricultural economist at the International Livestock Research Institute, Kenya.

Peter Roeder (peter.roeder@taurusah.com) is an independent veterinary consultant specializing in control of transboundary animal diseases, United Kingdom.

Marie T. Ruel (m.ruel@cgiar.org) is director of the Poverty, Health, and Nutrition Division at the International Food Policy Research Institute, USA.

Subramanyam Shanmugasundaram (sundar19392004@yahoo.com) was formerly deputy director general of research, AVRDC – The World Vegetable Center, Taiwan, and is currently an agricultural consultant in the United States.

Melinda Smale (msmale@oxfamamerica.org) is a senior researcher, agriculture and trade, Oxfam America, and formerly a senior research fellow in the Environment and Production Technology Division at the International Food Policy Research Institute, USA.

David J. Spielman (d.spielman@cgiar.org) is a research fellow with the Knowledge, Capacity, and Innovation Division of the International Food Policy Research Institute and is currently outposted in Ethiopia.

Gray Tappan (tappan@usgs.gov) is a physical geographer with the U.S. Geological Survey at the EROS Center in Sioux Falls, USA.

Eduardo J. Trigo (etrigo@grupoceo.com.ar) is director of Grupo CEO, Argentina.

Federico Villareal (fedevillarreal78@gmail.com) is a research associate at Grupo CEO, Argentina.

Sivan Yosef (s.yosef@cgiar.org) is a senior research assistant in the Director General's Office at the International Food Policy Research Institute, USA.

Yeyun Xin (xinyeyun@hotmail.com) is a research professor at the China National Hybrid Rice Research and Development Center, China.

Longping Yuan (lpyuan@hhrrc.ac.cn) is the Director General of the China National Hybrid Rice Research and Development Center, China.

Box Contributors

Andy Catley (andrew.catley@tufts.edu) is a research director with Tufts University, USA and is based in Ethiopia.

Ashwini Chhatre (achhatre@illinois.edu) is an assistant professor in the Department of Geography at the University of Illinois at Urbana-Champaign, USA.

Antônio Flavio Dias Ávila (flavio.avila@embrapa.br) is coordinator, research evaluation at the Brazilian Agricultural Research Corporation (Embrapa), Brazil.

Tim Leyland (tjleyland@yahoo.com) is livestock sector adviser to the U.K. Government's Department for International Development (DFID).

Hemant R. Ojha (ojhahemant1@gmail.com) is editor of *Journal of Forest and Livelihoods* and a natural resource governance specialist at ForestAction Nepal.

Amos Omore (a.omore@cgiar.org) is a scientist with the International Livestock Research Institute, Kenya.

Lauren Persha (lpersha@umich.edu) is a research fellow in the School of Natural Resources and Environment at the University of Michigan, USA.

Peter Roeder (peter.roeder@taurusah.com) is an independent veterinary consultant specializing in control of transboundary animal diseases, United Kingdom.

David J. Spielman (d.spielman@cgiar.org) is a research fellow with the Knowledge, Capacity, and Innovation Division at the International Food Policy Research Institute, USA and is currently outposted in Ethiopia.

Steve Staal (s.staal@cgiar.org) is director of the Market Opportunities Research Theme at the International Livestock Research Institute, Kenya.

Levon Yeganiantz (levon.yeganiantz@embrapa.br) is a consultant to the Brazilian Agricultural Research Corporation (Embrapa), Brazil.

Patricia Zambrano (p.zambrano@cgiar.org) is a senior research analyst in the Environment and Production Technology Division at the International Food Policy Research Institute, USA.

ANNEX F
Discussion Papers

These papers can be downloaded at **www.ifpri.org/millionsfed**

Combating stem and leaf rust of wheat: Historical perspective, impacts, and lessons learned
H. J. Dubin and John P. Brennan

The Asian Green Revolution
Peter B. R. Hazell

Controlling cassava mosaic virus and cassava mealybug in Sub-Saharan Africa
Felix Nweke

Community forestry in Nepal: A policy innovation for local livelihoods
Hemant Ojha, Lauren Persha, and Ashwini Chhatre

Agroenvironmental transformation in the Sahel: Another kind of "Green Revolution"
Chris Reij, Gray Tappan, and Melinda Smale

The case of zero-tillage technology in Argentina
Eduardo Trigo, Eugenio Cap, Valeria Malach, and Federico Villarreal

Zero tillage in the rice-wheat systems of the Indo-Gangetic plains: A review of impacts and sustainability implications
Olaf Erenstein

The impact of shallow tubewells and boro rice on food security in Bangladesh
Mahabub Hossain

Hybrid rice technology development: Ensuring China's food security
Jiming Li, Yeyun Xin, and Longping Yuan

Pearl millet and sorghum improvement in India
Carl E. Pray and Latha Nagarajan

Institutional reform in the Burkinabè cotton sector and its impacts on incomes and food security: 1996–2006
Jonathan Kaminski, Derek Headey, and Tanguy Bernard

Private sector responses to public investments and policy reforms: The case of fertilizer and maize market development in Kenya
Joshua Ariga and T. S. Jayne

The mungbean transformation: Diversifying crops, defeating malnutrition
Subramanyan Shanmugasundaram, J. D. H. Keatinge, and Jacqueline d'Arros Hughes

The global effort to eradicate rinderpest
Peter Roeder and Karl Rich

Rural and urban linkages: Operation Flood's role in India's dairy development
Kenda Cunningham

Rich food for poor people: Genetically improved tilapia in the Philippines
Sivan Yosef

"Crossing the river while feeling the rocks": Incremental land reform and its impact on rural welfare in China
John W. Bruce and Zongmin Li

Land-tenure policy reforms: Decollectivization and the Doi Moi System in Vietnam
Michael Kirk and Nguyen Do Anh Tuan

Improving diet quality and micronutrient nutrition: Homestead food production in Bangladesh
Lora Iannotti, Kenda Cunningham, and Marie Ruel

Improving the proof: Evolution of and emerging trends in impact assessment methods and approaches in agricultural development
Mywish K. Maredia